ACS SYMPOSIUM SERIES 382

Biological Monitoring for Pesticide Exposure

Measurement, Estimation, and Risk Reduction

Rhoda G. M. Wang, EDITOR
State of California, Department of Food and Agriculture

Claire A. Franklin, EDITOR
Department of National Health and Welfare, Ottawa

Richard C. Honeycutt, EDITOR
Ciba-Geigy

Joseph C. Reinert, EDITOR
U.S. Environmental Protection Agency

Developed from a symposium sponsored
by the Division of Agrochemicals
at the 194th Meeting
of the American Chemical Society,
New Orleans, Louisiana,
August 30–September 4, 1987

American Chemical Society, Washington, DC 1989

CHEM
SEP/ae

Library of Congress Cataloging-in-Publication Data

Biological monitoring for pesticide exposure : measurement, estimation, and risk reduction
  Rhoda G. M. Wang, editor ... [et al.].

    p.   cm.—(ACS Symposium Series; 382)
Includes bibliographies and index.

    ISBN 0–8412–1559–6
    1. Pesticides—Toxicology—Congresses. 2. Biological monitoring—Congresses. 3. Agricultural workers—Health risk assessment—Congresses.

I. Wang, Rhoda G. M., date. II. Series.

    [DNLM: 1. Environmental Exposure–congresses. 2. Environmental Monitoring–congresses. 3. Pesticides–toxicity–congresses. 4. Risk–congresses. WA 465 B61615 1988]

RA1270.P4B53 1988
632′.95042—dc19
DNLM/DLC
for Library of Congress   88–39189
                                            CIP

Copyright © 1989

American Chemical Society

All Rights Reserved. The appearance of the code at the bottom of the first page of each chapter in this volume indicates the copyright owner's consent that reprographic copies of the chapter may be made for personal or internal use or for the personal or internal use of specific clients. This consent is given on the condition, however, that the copier pay the stated per-copy fee through the Copyright Clearance Center, Inc., 27 Congress Street, Salem, MA 01970, for copying beyond that permitted by Sections 107 or 108 of the U.S. Copyright Law. This consent does not extend to copying or transmission by any means—graphic or electronic—for any other purpose, such as for general distribution, for advertising or promotional purposes, for creating a new collective work, for resale, or for information storage and retrieval systems. The copying fee for each chapter is indicated in the code at the bottom of the first page of the chapter.

The citation of trade names and/or names of manufacturers in this publication is not to be construed as an endorsement or as approval by ACS of the commercial products or services referenced herein; nor should the mere reference herein to any drawing, specification, chemical process, or other data be regarded as a license or as a conveyance of any right or permission to the holder, reader, or any other person or corporation, to manufacture, reproduce, use, or sell any patented invention or copyrighted work that may in any way be related thereto. Registered names, trademarks, etc., used in this publication, even without specific indication thereof, are not to be considered unprotected by law.

PRINTED IN THE UNITED STATES OF AMERICA

SD 2/21/89 ƏẮ

ACS Symposium Series

RA 1270
P4B 531
1989
CHEM

M. Joan Comstock, *Series Editor*

1988 ACS Books Advisory Board

Paul S. Anderson
Merck Sharp & Dohme Research
Laboratories

Harvey W. Blanch
University of California—Berkeley

Malcolm H. Chisholm
Indiana University

Alan Elzerman
Clemson University

John W. Finley
Nabisco Brands, Inc.

Natalie Foster
Lehigh University

Marye Anne Fox
The University of Texas—Austin

Roland F. Hirsch
U.S. Department of Energy

G. Wayne Ivie
USDA, Agricultural Research Service

Michael R. Ladisch
Purdue University

Vincent D. McGinniss
Battelle Columbus Laboratories

Daniel M. Quinn
University of Iowa

James C. Randall
Exxon Chemical Company

E. Reichmanis
AT&T Bell Laboratories

C. M. Roland
U.S. Naval Research Laboratory

W. D. Shults
Oak Ridge National Laboratory

Geoffrey K. Smith
Rohm & Haas Co.

Douglas B. Walters
National Institute of
Environmental Health

Wendy A. Warr
Imperial Chemical Industries

Foreword

The ACS SYMPOSIUM SERIES was founded in 1974 to provide a medium for publishing symposia quickly in book form. The format of the Series parallels that of the continuing ADVANCES IN CHEMISTRY SERIES except that, in order to save time, the papers are not typeset but are reproduced as they are submitted by the authors in camera-ready form. Papers are reviewed under the supervision of the Editors with the assistance of the Series Advisory Board and are selected to maintain the integrity of the symposia; however, verbatim reproductions of previously published papers are not accepted. Both reviews and reports of research are acceptable, because symposia may embrace both types of presentation.

Contents

Preface

Assessing worker exposure to pesticides through biological monitoring is the main thrust of this book. Historically, in the absence of dermal absorption data in humans and animals, regulatory agencies often assumed that pesticides were 100% absorbed by dermally exposed workers. However, 100% absorption may not actually occur. Accurate measurement of the dose absorbed is necessary in order to estimate the health risk to exposed workers.

In recent years, pesticide regulatory agencies have made progress in effectively communicating the need to develop dermal pesticide absorption data. However, despite the improved quality and availability of exposure and dermal absorption data generated in rodents and other species, current methods are not accurate for estimating total pesticide uptake during exposure. Poor estimates result from attempting to measure the amount of pesticide found on limited areas of dermal pads and to extrapolate this information to a much greater body surface area (which magnifies or reduces any inherent errors) and from assuming that percutaneous absorption in animals approximates or equals that in humans. Interspecies differences affect individual dermal absorption rates, and humans tend to have a lower dermal absorption rate than many common test animals.

The kinetics of absorption, biotransformation, and excretion cannot be addressed by passive dosimetry, even when the percent of absorption has been factored in. The critical dose of a toxicant must be transported dermally, reach plasma concentration, and be distributed to the target organs and tissues before it can evoke a toxicological effect. Therefore, without this vital information, the assessment of exposure health risk is at best a presumptuous estimation. Nevertheless, the combined use of dermal pad and absorption data remains a valid choice.

In conjunction with sensitive biomarkers, biological monitoring can offer a distinct advantage over conventional methods. However, biological monitoring methods have intrinsic limitations and barriers. For instance, unless the pharmacokinetic behavior of a pesticide in humans is well understood, it could be difficult to relate the urinary excretion of a pesticide to the internal dosage. Obtaining full cooperation of field workers to provide 24-hour urine samples during and after exposure can be difficult. Isolation and identification of unlabeled metabolites in biological fluids is a complex procedure, even with modern analytical chemical techniques.

I hope this book marks the beginning of a long journey devoted to improved estimation of pesticide or other chemical exposure.

RHODA G. M. WANG
California Department of Food and Agriculture
Sacramento, CA 95814

April 19, 1988

BIOLOGICAL MONITORING

Biological Monitoring for Pesticide Exposure

In many countries, pesticides are subject to premarket review to determine their efficacy and safety in use. Data obtained from toxicity tests conducted in animals are required as well as food residue data. Only recently has attention been given to user and bystander (people inadvertently exposed when pesticides are used by others) exposure. From these data, a risk assessment can be made to ensure that there is an adequate margin of safety between human exposure levels and the level at which effects were observed in the test animals.

In occupational hygiene, it has been stated that the first and foremost purpose of monitoring is "to determine adherence to an established legal standard or consensus guideline for the quality of the air breathed by the employee" (1). A broader purpose of monitoring is to determine the average exposure of workers to toxic chemicals. For many years, reliance was placed on ambient (environmental) monitoring where the concentration of the chemical in air was measured using stationary monitors (2). The data collected could be used in a plant situation to ensure effectiveness of control measures, to indicate trends in air quality of the work environment, to provide a historical record of the workplace, to evaluate needs for site specific emission controls and even to verify validity of worker complaints (1). In a broader sense, detection of a chemical in air, food or water would suggest that exposure to humans could occur. However, these types of ambient monitoring do not provide any quantitative estimate of exposure unless there is additional information on how much air was breathed, water consumed or food eaten (3).

Historically, pesticide exposure has been estimated using ambient monitoring. Inhalation exposure is measured using personal sampler pumps with the absorbent filter approximating the breathing zone of the worker. A new technique for estimating inhalation exposure through measurement of the level of the chemical in exhaled breath is presented in the paper in this section by Morgan (4). Dermal contact exposure is estimated using absorbent patches placed on the workers' body or clothing or by extraction of clothing worn during application. In his paper, Fenske (5) discusses the limitations of the patch technique and points out that "dermal exposure assessment methods in current use have never been validated in terms of absolute accuracy". They have focussed on "relative accuracy by comparing environmental monitoring data to a relative index of exposure". He presents new data on the use of fluorescent tracers coupled with video imaging as an alternative approach.

A significant deficiency in exposure estimates obtained from ambient monitoring (personal samplers, patches, clothing, tracers) is that they estimate the amount of pesticide that impinges on the surface of the body (contact exposure) and not the dose (amount absorbed into the body). Unfortunately most of the animals studies are conducted using the gastrointestinal (G.I.) route of exposure

2

whereas most of the exposure to workers is dermal. The significant differences between uptake from the G.I. tract and dermal absorption preclude using the dermal contact exposure as an estimator of dose.

Increased emphasis on occupational health, hygiene and safety led to further development of human monitoring to supplement or replace ambient monitoring (6). Biological monitoring involves the analysis of the chemical, its metabolites or biotransformation products in body tissues such as urine, blood, fat, hair, nails, sweat, saliva and expired air. However, to be used effectively, the relationship between the concentration of a chemical and a specific health effect must be known (7). Such a correlation is difficult to establish in most instances and emphasis must be placed on increasing our capability to do so. The major advantage of biological monitoring is that it provides an integrated estimate of exposure from all sources and routes.

Several approaches have been used. The first is to determine how much pesticide is absorbed through the skin and then use the percent absorbed to correct the contact dermal exposure, thus providing an estimate of internal dose. In the section on Percutaneous Absorption of Pesticides this approach is discussed.

A second approach is to estimate dermal contact exposure by doing controlled studies in which increasing amounts of the pesticide are applied dermally and the urinary metabolite levels determined. This allows a curve to be set up from which an estimate of dermal exposure can be extrapolated from the urine metabolite levels (8, 9).

The third approach is to measure the concentration of the pesticide and its metabolites in body tissues and relate this to dose. More recently, some authors refer to these measurements in body fluids as biological markers of exposure (10). As Nigg et al. (11) point out in their paper in this section not all biological monitoring studies done on pesticide workers were designed to quantitatively estimate exposure. Many of these studies merely provide evidence that the worker was exposed and a relationship between these urinary metabolite levels and toxic effects cannot be drawn. However, these studies have been useful in a more general sense to assess the reliability of patch data.

The relationship between dose and toxic effect is dependent upon many factors; uptake, distribution, metabolism, and excretion all have a role in determining blood levels and concentration at the target tissue. To try to use urinary metabolite levels by simply correcting for molecular weight would ignore all of these factors. It may be feasible that, if urinary metabolite levels were measured in the animal studies, a metabolite/response curve could be drawn. This method would be analogous to the use of a dose/response curve. The next step would be to determine whether the metabolism and excretion in humans were similar to the test animals. If they were, then the metabolite levels could be related to toxic effects directly. A distinct advantage to using biological monitoring and metabolite levels is that an integrated measure of exposure from all sources and all routes is made, allowing a more meaningful risk assessment to be done.

Not all biological monitoring is aimed at providing a quanti- tative estimate of exposure. A more classical utilization of biological monitoring is presented in the paper in this section by Balu (12) where urinary levels of the metabolites of chlordimeform were measured to ensure that workers were not being overexposed.

Biological monitoring can also be used to measure the effects on health related to exposure. An effect has been defined as "an actual health impairment or (by general consensus) recognized disease; an early precursor of a disease process that indicates a potential for impairment of health; or an event peripheral to any disease process but correlated with it and thus predictive of development of impaired health" (10). A biological marker of an effect or response would measure changes in function or even changes in organs or tissues not directly affected but merely acting as surrogates. An example of this is given in the paper by Lotti (13) outlining a method which measures depression of NTE enzyme in circulating human blood lymphocytes as a surrogate for NTE activity in the central nervous system. Decreases in activity of this enzyme are related to exposure to organophosphorus pesticides capable of inducing delayed neurotoxicity.

If the mechanism of action of the pesticide is understood, more specific markers can be utilized. Such an example is given in the paper by San et al. (14) where human exposure to potential carcinogens was assessed by measuring the mutagenic activity of urine from pesticide applicators in in vitro genotoxicity tests. Another way of estimating exposure to genotoxic compounds is to measure the DNA adducts formed following exposure (15).

The paper by Cowell et al. (16) shows how biological monitoring can be used to evaluate the effectiveness of procedures designed to reduce worker exposure. Blair et al. (17) focus our attention on the need to have good estimates of exposure. He challenges scientists working in this field to assist in developing better methods to estimate exposure particularly for use in epidemiology studies. In these studies, the exposure of interest generally has occurred many years previously and sometimes it is difficult to identify which products were used. Estimates of actual exposure are almost impossible.

Further directions for research include continuing on the quest to obtain more accurate estimates of contact exposure, validation of the use of generic data to estimate exposure (18, 19), validation of the method used to calculate absorbed dose by correcting contact exposure with the dermal penetration and development of data on several selected pesticides to determine the relationship between metabolite levels in urine and toxic effects to more fully evaluate the usefulness of this approach.

Literature Cited

1.   Corn, M. In Assessment of Toxic Agents at the Workplace: Roles of Ambient and Biological Monitoring; Berlin, A.; Yodaiken, R.E.; Henman, B.A. Eds. Martinus Nijhoff Publishers for the EEC, 1984; pp. 54-70.
2.   Bernard, A.; Lauwerys, R. In Biological Monitoring of Exposure to Chemicals, Organic Compounds; Ho, M.H.; Dillon, H.K. Eds.; Wiley & Sons, N.Y. 1987, pp. 1-16.

3. Zeilhuis, R.L. In <u>Assessment of Toxic Agents at the Workplace:</u>
    <u>Roles of Ambient and Biological Monitoring</u>; Berlin, A.;
    Yodaiken, R.E.; Henman, B.A. Eds.; Martinus Nijhoff Publishers
    for the EEC, 1984, pp. 84-94.

4. Morgan, M. In Biological Monitoring of Pesticide Exposure,
    Wang, R.G.M.; Franklin, C.A.; Honeycutt, R.C.; Reinert, J.C.
    Eds.; ACS Symposium Series, Chpt. 5, This book.

5. Fenske, R. op. cit. Chpt. 6.

6. Ashford, N.A.; Spadafor, C.J.; Caldart, C.C. <u>Harvard Environ.</u>
    <u>Law Rev.</u> 1984, 8, 263-363.

7. <u>Berlin</u>, A.; Wolff, A.H.; Hasegawa, Y. In <u>The Use of Biological</u>
    <u>Specimens for the Assessment of Human Exposure to Environmental</u>
    <u>Pollutants</u>, Martinus Nijhoff Publishers for the EEC, 1979; p.
    3.

8. Franklin, C.A.; Greenhalgh, R.; Maibach, H.I. In <u>IUPAC</u>
    <u>Pesticide Chemistry: Human Welfare and the Environment</u>;
    <u>Pergamon Press</u> 1983; pp. 221-226.

9. Franklin, C.A.; Muir, N.I.; Moody, R.P. <u>Toxicol. Lett.</u> 1986,
    33, 127-136.

10. Goldstein, B., Chairman, Environ. Hlth Pers., 1987, 74, 3-9.

11. Nigg, H.; Stamper, J.H. <u>In Biological Monitoring of Pesticide</u>
    <u>Exposure</u>. Wang, R.G.M.; <u>Franklin</u>, C.A.; <u>Honeycutt</u>, R.C.;
    <u>Reinert</u>, J.C. Eds.; ACS Symposium Series, Chpt. 1, This book.

12. Balu, K. op. cit. Chpt. 4.

13. Lotti, M. op. cit. Chpt. 9.

14. San, R.H.C.; Rosin, M.P.; Lee, R.H.; Dunn, B.P.; Stich, H.F.
    op. cit. Chpt. 8.

15. Shugart, L.R.; Adams, S.M.; Jimenez, B.D.; Talmage, S.S.;
    McCarthy, J.F. op. cit. Chpt. 7.

16. Cowell, J.E.; Dubelman, S.; Klein, A.J.; Ohta, K. op. cit.
    Chpt. 2.

17. Blair, A.; Zahm, S.H.; Cantor, K.; Stewart, P. op. cit. Chpt.
    3.

18. Hackathorn, D.R. and Eberhart, D.C. In <u>Dermal Exposure Related</u>
    <u>to Pesticide Use</u>; Honeycutt, R.C.; <u>Zweig, G.; Ragsdale, N.N.;</u>
    <u>Eds.; ACS</u> Symposium Series No. 273; American Chemical Society:
    Washington D.C.; 1985; pp. 341-355.

19. Honeycutt, R.C. <u>Toxicol. Lett.</u>, 1986, <u>33</u>, 175-182.

Claire A. Franklin
Environmental and Occupational Toxicology Division
Environmental Health Directorate
Tunney's Pasture
Ottawa, Ontario K1A 0L2
Canada

RECEIVED June 1, 1988

Chapter 1

Biological Monitoring
for Pesticide Dose Determination
Historical Perspectives, Current Practices, and New Approaches

H. N. Nigg and J. H. Stamper

Citrus Research and Education Center, University of Florida, Lake Alfred, FL 33850

The rationales governing biological monitoring experiments are presented, together with a review of past studies and results. Purposes and shortcomings are covered. Deficiencies in blood and urine monitoring are reviewed. Sampling procedures and statistical considerations are discussed. New approaches are outlined, including vagal tone monitoring, saliva and perspiration assays and erythrocyte adducts.

There are various ways of estimating pesticide exposure. Environmental monitoring includes measurement of ambient levels of pesticide in the worker's environment and passive dosimetry to estimate the quantity which comes into contact with the worker. Dermal patches and personal air samplers have been used to estimate dermal and inhalation exposure in pesticide workers. Biological monitoring includes the measurement of parent compounds, their metabolites, or an indicator of response (e.g. acetylcholinesterase inhibition) in a biological sample such as urine, blood, sweat, saliva, exhaled breath, hair or nails.

The use of biological samples as indicators of pesticide dose is a new research area and there is not yet agreement on the meaning of even the most commonly used terms. By "exposure" to pesticide, we mean here the deposit of compound onto the clothing or skin of the worker, the latter being "dermal exposure". "Dose" is that amount which enters the body, including skin sequestration. The majority of the dose to an agricultural worker arises through transdermal absorption, but other routes such as respiratory or oral ingestion also play a role. A "biological indicator" is any biological sample taken from the worker which contains reliable evidence that a pesticide dose has been received.

General Rationale

Our purposes here are to describe current and prospective biological monitoring methods and to raise questions. The kinds of questions we ask the reader to consider throughout this article are

0097–6156/89/0382–0006$06.50/0
© 1989 American Chemical Society

the following. If human biological samples are negative for a
given pesticide, what can be concluded about dose? On the other
hand, if they are positive, can dose be reliably quantified? Many
of the biological methods we review here have been combined with
non-biological methods for measuring exposure. References 1-5
provide reviews of non-biological methods.

Factors Affecting Exposure of Agricultural Workers

For applicator/mixer-loader groups, the type of equipment used, the
number of tanks applied per unit time, the concentration of the
tank mix, the loading method, and the protective clothing worn
affect the dermal exposure process. Especially important are
personal work habits. This has been known for years and is
described in many published reports (1, 6).
   Regardless of crop type, the production rate of harvesters
appears to be related to their exposure. The worker's production
rate is related to the amount of contact with the plant, a subject
which has been studied using movies and time analysis (7) and
estimated with surveys (8). The production rate can be quantified
as the number of boxes picked, crates loaded, tassels removed,
etc., but is confounded with residue levels in affecting exposure.

Estimation of Dose

One of the reasons for measuring worker pesticide exposure is to
aid in determining the safety of the product. To do this, it must
be known whether the amount of pesticide to which the worker is
exposed may lead to a toxic effect. The toxic effect of a
pesticide is evaluated through testing in animals by establishing
its relationship with dose (generally gastrointestinal). In order
to extrapolate the animal data to humans, there must be an
equivalent estimate of dose. Two approaches have been used to do
this in pesticide workers. One involves the measurement of dermal
exposure (most prevalent route) with a correction for the estimated
percentage of percutaneous penetration. The other approach relates
the urinary metabolite level(s) to dose. Most biological studies
in the literature were never designed to quantitatively estimate
exposure and care must be exercised in using such studies to draw
conclusions about the utility of biological monitoring.

Biological Indicators of Pesticide Exposure—Prevalently Used Methods

Blood. One of the earlier biological monitoring studies was
undertaken by Quinby et al. (9). Cholinesterase activity was
measured in aerial applicators, together with residues on worker
clothing and in respirator filters. In spite of physical
complaints by the pilots, either normal or only slightly depressed
cholinesterase values were reported. Cholinesterase values were
compared with the 'normal' range for the U.S. population rather
than the pilots' own individual 'normal' values. In 1952, Kay et
al. (10) measured cholinesterase levels in orchard parathion
applicators. These were compared with cholinesterase levels taken
from the same workers during non-spray periods. Plasma

cholinesterase for workers reporting physical symptoms was 16%
lower during the spray period. The corresponding reduction for
symptomless workers was about 13%. Red blood cell (RBC)
cholinesterase was depressed 27% for the symptom group vs. 17% for
the non-symptom group, but these means were not statistically
different. Roan et al. (11) measured plasma and erythrocyte
cholinesterase and serum levels of ethyl and methyl parathion in
aerial applicators. Serum levels of the parathions could not be
correlated with cholinesterase levels. However, serum levels did
correlate with the urine concentration of p-nitrophenol. Drevenkar
et al. (12) measured plasma and erythrocyte cholinesterase levels
and urine concentrations of organophosphorus and carbamate
pesticides in plant workers who formulate these materials. No
correlation existed between urinary metabolites and cholinesterase
depression. Bradway et al. (13) studied cholinesterase, blood
residues, and urinary metabolites in rats. Eight organophosphorus
compounds were included in this experiment. Even under controlled
conditions and known doses, correlations of cholinesterase activity
with blood residues and urine metabolite levels were poor. The
overriding general conclusion from these data is that
cholinesterase inhibition contains too many variables, known and
unknown, to be useful for estimating dose.

   Whole blood has rarely been used to monitor dose in humans
despite pleas from pesticide chemists, toxicologists, and
pharmacologists (14). Very nice studies of 2,4,5-T and 2,4-D in
human blood and urine are references 15, 16 and 17. An oral dose
of 2,4,5-T was excreted in the urine of five human volunteers with
a half-life of 23 h wherein 88.5 + 5.1% of the administered dose
was recovered. Its half-life in plasma was also 23 h (15). 2,4-D
was taken orally and also excreted unchanged in urine (75%
recovered in 96 h) (16). There was marked individual variation in
when the peak of 2,4-D occurred in plasma. Sauerhoff et al. (17)
administered a single 5 mg/kg oral dose to five male human
volunteers. 2,4-D disappeared from plasma with an average
half-life of 11.6 h and from urine with an average half-life of
17.7 h. From 88-106% of the dose was recovered in urine over 144
h; over 50% was recovered in 24 h. 2-(2,4,5-trichlorophenoxy)
propionic acid (silvex) was administered to seven men and one woman
at 1 mg/kg. Biphasic disappearance from plasma and urine with
half-lives of 4.0 + 1.9/16.5 + 7.3 h and 5.0 + 1.8/25.9 + 6.3 h,
respectively were determined (18) and 65% of the dose was excreted
in urine in 24 h. Human exposure to phenoxy herbicides has been
reviewed by Lavy (19).

   There are several problems with blood monitoring. It is
difficult (probably even impossible with the present human subject
committee oversight) to conduct human experiments as in 15, 16 and
17. Also, workers are averse to blood testing; noninvasive methods
are much preferred. Blood has been used in epidemiological studies
(1, 20, 21), but an original dose can probably never be inferred.
For the future, the rapid clearance of newer, biodegradable
pesticides from blood may eliminate blood as an exposure monitoring
tool for pesticide dose and may also eliminate blood as an
epidemiological monitoring tool. However, Lewalter and Korallus
(22) reviewed erythrocyte protein conjugates as a monitoring
technique for pesticide exposure. Though not validated, this blood

monitoring technique appears promising for estimating dose for some
pesticides which form erythrocyte adducts. The erythrocyte is
extracted for adducts of pesticide parent and/or metabolites.
Dose-concentration-effect relationships may be possible with this
technique. Readers are encouraged to consult reference (22) and
references therein.

Urine. The first problem in monitoring urine is the variability in
urinary output. Newborn infants may excrete 17-34 mL/d, 6-10 year
old boys 459 $\pm$ 175 mL/d, 10-14 year old boys 605 $\pm$ 294 mL/d, 6-10
year old girls 274 $\pm$ 125 mL/d, 10-14 year old girls 441 $\pm$ 305 mL/d,
men 1360 $\pm$ 443 mL/d, and women 1000 $\pm$ 430 mL/d (23). Men working
in heat excrete about 900 mL/d (Nigg amd Stamper, unpublished). In
one study, long distance runners excreted only 600 mL/d whereas
controls excreted 1300 mL/d (24).
    Some authors propose the use of creatinine to normalize
differences in the urinary excretion of a compound. These
differences can arise from changes in fluid intake, pathology, or
physiological changes such as sweating. In order to be useful,
creatinine in urine should show a constant day-to-day excretion
rate regardless of the volume of urine output, food intake, or
physical activity, and should reflect only small interindividual
variation. In a large study of creatinine excretion, Alessio et
al. (25) found that men excreted more creatinine than women,
younger subjects more than old, and individuals varied in their 24
h creatinine output from 9.2 to 79.4%, perhaps due to fluid intake.
It appears that great care must be taken if creatinine is to be
used to normalize urine samples.
    Perhaps the best study of adjusting urine concentrations of
excreted substances is by Araki et al. (26). These authors studied
the excretion of lead, inorganic mercury, zinc, and copper in
urine. They concluded that urinary flow-adjusted concentration is
applicable to monitoring all substances in urine, creatinine
included. Creatinine, urinary specific gravity, and timed
excretion plus urinary flow had limited uses.
    Consequently, it is necessary to use 24 h, total urine
collection when urine will be used to estimate the pesticide dose.
    Urine monitoring to determine dose necessarily depends on
certain assumptions and disparate pieces of available data. The
excretion kinetics of the pesticide employed must be known for both
dermal and oral administration. If the total dose is excreted by
small animals in 24-48 h, the same may also be true of humans. If
the dose is excreted over a period of a week, a simple test
correlating dermal exposure with an immediate effect on urine
pesticide levels will not work. However, the use of prolonged
sampling periods over which mean values of urinary pesticide
excretion rates are calculated presents problems also. It is
common to see a 100% coefficient of variation among urinary
excretion samples. As a consequence, a major change in urinary
pesticide levels would have to occur before a significant
difference could be confirmed statistically. Part of this
unfortunate variation no doubt results from reckless work
practices. Workers spill concentrated materials. They service
contaminated machinery with bare hands. We have observed one
worker remove his gloves, roll up his protective suit sleeve, and

retrieve a crescent wrench from a mixed tank of pesticide.
However, if the dermal dose excretion kinetics are known, if urine
is reflective of dose, if 24 h urines are collected and if sample
numbers are based on expected variation, then urine could be used
to monitor dose and also the efficacy of protective devices.

Many pesticides in common use are not excreted in urine in
proportion to dose. Organochlorines are usually excreted more in
feces than in urine. Significant storage in body tissue may occur.
An example of current interest is dicofol. With multiple oral
doses, this organochlorine rapidly reached a plateau in urine,
while excretion levels steadily increased in the feces (27).
The excretion kinetics available for most compounds have resulted
from studies using only one, or a very few oral doses. Workers,
however, receive daily dermal and respiratory doses. There are no
animal data reflecting these continuous and multiple routes of
exposure. There are kinetic models which could represent
pesticides recycled into the bile (28). These models do not
account for the differences in the exposure route for workers, the
frequency of dose, or the subsequent excretion differences in
workers compared to small animals.

Urinary metabolites of pesticides have been used for
indicating absorption and excretion. Swan (29) measured paraquat
in the urine of spraymen, Gollop and Glass (30) and Wagner and
Weswig (31) measured arsenic in timber applicators, and Lieben et
al. (32) measured paranitrophenol in urine after parathion exposure
as did Durham et al. (33). Chlorobenzilate metabolite
(dichlorobenzilic acid) was detected in citrus workers (34),
phenoxy acid herbicides in farmers (35), and organophosphorus
metabolites in the urine of mosquito treatment applicators (36).
Davies et al. (37) used urinary metabolites of organophosphorus
compounds and carbamates to confirm poisoning cases. These studies
document exposure, but no quantitative estimate of dose can be made
from urinary metabolite levels alone.

Other studies have used air sampling and monitored hand
exposure in combination with urine levels (38), and air sampling
plus cholinesterase inhibition plus urine levels (39).
Non-biological methods, combined with measurement of urinary
metabolites, have also been used to compare worker exposure for
different pesticide application methods (40, 41) as well as to
monitor formulating plant worker exposure (42) and homeowner
exposure (43).

Several studies have used non-biological methods in an attempt
to correlate urine levels with an exposure estimate (40, 43-48).
Lavy et al. (47, 48) found no such correlation with 2,4-D or
2,4,5-T. Wojeck et al. (40) found no paraquat in urine and
consequently no relationship between dose and urine levels.
However, the group daily mean concentration of urinary metabolites
of ethion and the group mean total estimated dermal dose to ethion
on that day correlated positively, with significance at the 97%
confidence level (46). For arsenic, the cumulative total estimated
dose and daily urinary arsenic concentration correlated positively,
with significance at the 99% confidence level (45). Franklin et
al. (43) found a positive correlation between 48 h excretion of
azinphosmethyl metabolites and the amount of active ingredient
sprayed. A significant correlation could not be made, however,

between 48 h excretion and an exposure estimate using dosimeters. In the Franklin et al. (43) experiment, a fluorescent tracer had been added to the spray mixture. Qualitatively, unmonitored areas (face, hands, neck) also received significant exposure, perhaps leading to a weak correlation between the exposure estimate and urinary metabolites. Franklin et al. (49) also studied excretion of DMTP in orchard workers in two other areas in Canada and again found that urine data more closely reflected the amount of pesticide applied. Grover et al. (50) also obtained a correlation (R = 0.82) between the amount of 2,4-D applied and urinary excretion. Total deposition of 2,4-D estimated with dosimeters and urinary excretion correlated at only R = 0.47. Winterlin et al. (51) monitored the dermal exposure of applicators, mixer-loaders, and strawberry harvesters to captan using exposure pads. Although the applicator, mixer-loader group showed higher estimated dermal exposure, no metabolite was detected in their urine; harvester urine had detectable levels, perhaps because urine samples were not properly collected. Contamination of dermal patches by splashes, etc., could have led to an overestimated exposure in the applicator, mixer-loader group. Leng et al. (52) reviewed the excretion of 2,4,5-T in humans exposed in the field. Excretion was slower with dermal field exposure than with oral doses of 2,4,5-T in humans. Kinetic excretion models of 2,4,5-T indicated that the absorbed daily dose did not exceed 0.1 mg/kg/day. This dose estimation did not agree with exposure estimates made from dermal collection patches.

Part of the problem appears to be the excretion kinetics and excretion routes of pesticides, the complexity of which may render useless any search for a simple linear correlation between exposure and urinary metabolites. Funckes et al. (53) exposed the hand and forearm of human volunteers to 2% parathion dust. During exposure, the volunteers breathed pure air and placed their forearm and hand into a plastic bag which contained the parathion. This exposure lasted 2 h and was conducted at various temperatures. There was an increased excretion of paranitrophenol with increasing exposure temperature. Importantly, paranitrophenol could still be detected in the urine 40 h post exposure after this dermal exposure. Feldmann and Maibach (54) dosed human volunteers with radiolabeled ^{14}C-pesticides intravenously and followed urinary excretion for 5 days using total urine collection. The same volunteers were subsequently exposed dermally on the forearm with the same ^{14}C-pesticides, and urinary metabolites were again followed for 5 days. The % pesticide excreted after forearm (dermal) dosing was then corrected for incomplete i.v. excretion. For instance, the dermal excretion (absorption) of a pesticide was doubled if the i.v. dose was only 50% excreted in urine. ^{14}C-azodrin, ethion, guthion, malathion, parathion, baygon, carbaryl, aldrin, dieldrin, lindane, 2,4-D and diquat were the compounds applied. Wester et al. (55) applied ^{14}C-paraquat dichloride to the legs, hands and forearms in a similar experiment. Urinary excretion of ^{14}C was followed over 5 days. The highest corrected urinary recovery in these two studies was for carbaryl at approximately 74% of the dermally applied compound (forearm); the lowest was for paraquat at 0.23% (hand). The rest of these dermally-applied ^{14}C-pesticides were recovered in urine from 0.3% (diquat) to 19.6% (baygon) of the

dermally applied dose. Individuals vary in their absorption of
chemicals; also, different anatomic sites absorb chemicals at
different rates in both humans and animals (56, 57). Occlusion of
the anatomic site may also increase absorption of chemicals (54,
58, 59). In another human experiment, Kolmodin-Hedman et al. (60)
applied methylchlorophenoxy acetic acid (MCPA) to the thigh.
Plasma MCPA reached a maximum in 12 h and MCPA appeared in the
urine for 5 days with a maximum in about 48 h. Given orally,
urinary MCPA peaked in urine in 1 h with about 40% of the dose
excreted in 24 h. Using three male and two female volunteers,
Akerblom et al. (61) performed three experiments with MCPA. In one
experiment, the hands and forearms were dipped into a 2% solution.
The dried solution was washed off after 30 min. In a second
experiment, oral MCPA (15 μg/kg) was given. In a third experiment,
10 mL of a 10% aqueous solution of commercial MCPA formulation was
placed on a 10 cm^2 pad which was affixed to the thigh for 2 h.
Urine and blood were monitored. MCPA was not detected in blood or
urine with the hand and forearm dip. With oral MCPA, the peak
concentration occurred at about 6 h in urine and 1 h in plasma. In
the MCPA thigh absorption study, the urine peak occurred at 24-48
h. Nolan et al. (62) dosed six male volunteers orally with
4-amino-3,5,6-trichloropicolinic acid (picloram). They were
exposed dermally in a separate experiment. In 72 h, over 90% of
the oral dose was excreted in the urine. The dermal application
was poorly absorbed (0.2%) and was still being excreted in urine at
72 h. Nolan et al. (63) studied the excretion of chlorpyrifos in
human urine after an oral or a dermal application. Total urine was
collected from 24-48 h prior to administration through 120 h after
administration. 70 $\pm$ 11% (n = 6) of the oral dose was recovered in
urine. 1.28 $\pm$ 0.83% (n = 6) of the dermal dose was recovered in
urine. Blood levels peaked in 6 h after the oral dose and in 24 h
after the 5 mg/kg dermal dose. The urine elimination half-life was
about 27 h for both oral and dermal doses.

In a rat experiment, seven different organophosphorus
coupounds at two different doses were fed to rats (13). Rats were
removed from exposure after the third day and blood and urine
collected for the next 10 days. The average percents of the total
dose excreted in urine over the 10 days were: dimethoate, 12%;
dichlorvos, 10%; ronnel, 11%; dichlofenthion, 57%; carbophenothion,
66%; parathion, 40%; and leptophos, 50%. Very little of this
excretion occurred beyond the third day post exposure. Intact
residues of ronnel, dichlofenthion, carbophenothion, and leptophos
were found in fat on day 3 and day 8 post exposure.

Morgan et al. (64) dosed humans orally with methyl and ethyl
parathion. Paranitrophenol, which appears in urine after exposure
to either pesticide, was excreted at 37% of theoretical while the
alkyl phosphates were excreted at 50%+ of theoretical in 24 h.
Thus, about 50% of the oral dose administered to humans was not
recovered in urine in 24 h. In another rat experiment, animals
were administered azinphosmethyl dermally and intramuscularly (65).
The purpose of the experiment was to determine whether a linear
response existed between the amount of azinphosmethyl applied
dermally and the excretion of DMTP. If it did, it is possible that
the DMTP levels might be useful to predict dermal exposure. A
similar linear relationship appears to exist in humans. This

suggests that DMTP levels can be multiplied by the ratio
(azinphosmethyl exposure)/(DMTP level in urine). This is a 10 to 1
ratio. Using data from several field applications, it appears that
the DMTP-times-10 result is more closely related to the amount
sprayed than the dermal exposure estimated from patches (49).
Franklin et al. (49) concluded that without adequate
pharmacokinetic information for the parent compound, urine is
useful only as a screening tool for indicating exposure or as a
predictor of overexposure.

These experiments illustrate the excretion differences between
dermal, intramuscular, and oral administration, the excretion
differences between compounds, and also problems about which
urinary metabolite to monitor (65). Consequently, a very
discriminating experimental design would be necessary to model
dermal exposure and absorption vs. urinary metabolite levels.
Statistical problems, centered on replicate variation and the
resulting necessity for large numbers of replications, make the
cost of either a human or small animal experiment very expensive.

A small animal excretion study with multiple applications
could be done. However, which administration method should be
used? Should it be dermal, since the human worker receives mostly
dermal exposure, or should it be a mixture of oral, dermal, and
respiratory? What if the compound has associated data suggesting
skin penetration is low? Wester and Noonan (66) have reviewed the
relevance of animal models for percutaneous absorption. The pig
and the monkey were the most nearly like humans in this respect.
These authors warn that a clear understanding of the species and
methods used is a prerequisite to extrapolation to humans. Dedek
(67) presents an interesting case for the effect of solubility of
pesticides in solvents and skin penetration. Polar compounds
penetrated better when applied in nonpolar solvents and nonpolar
compounds penetrated better in polar solvents. The effect of
solvent and concentration should be included in dermal penetration
experiments. Since regulations are designed to protect humans,
real world estimates, relevance to work exposure, and accuracy in
the preliminary small animal studies are extremely important.

Another possibility is to perform an actual human excretion
study. At the end of the spray season, with the workers removed
from further exposure, a series of 24 h urine samples might yield
the necessary kinetic data. We suggest splitting the daily
sampling periods into two 12 h or four 6 h segments. For compounds
which are very rapidly excreted, this division into timed segments
will help to obtain the necessary data points. Removal of workers
from exposure is paramount, even if the experimenter must closely
monitor their work activities and wash the workers' clothing over
this period. We have discovered, to our surprise, that workers
have interpreted 'removal from exposure' as 'stop spraying,' and
then proceeded to clean and maintain heavily contaminated equipment
over our sampling period. Spittler et al. (68) discussed a variety
of 'extraneous' pesticide exposure possibilities. Even if all of
these factors are controlled, the chemical type, its metabolism and
variability among subjects, may prohibit the drawing of
statistically valid inferences.

Biological Indicators of Pesticide Exposure--New Methods

Vagal Tone. Vagal tone monitoring refers to the
respiratory-cardiac neural reflex and is measured by quantifying
the amplitude of the respiratory sinus arrhythmia. Respiratory
sinus arrhythmia is described as a decrease in heart period with
inspiration and an increase with expiration (69, 70). This is a
complex physiological function, but it can be measured. Its
measurement illustrates a delayed effect from organophosphorus
compounds (69, 70, 71). The exposure of military personnel to
neurotoxic agents has generated interest in this method. In
dichlovos treated dogs, vagal tone was not altered 90 min after
treatment. Plasma CHE was 47% of normal; RBC cholinesterase 56% of
normal. Ninety min after 2-PAM and atropine administration, vagal
tone was less disrupted in treatment dogs vs. control dogs. Plasma
CHE was inhibited at 47%, i.e., not reactivated; RBC CHE was 83% of
normal. Three weeks later, neither RBC nor plasma enzyme
activities were inhibited in the treatment dogs. Challenged with
atropine, the vagal tone response of experimental dogs was
attenuated compared to control dogs. The delayed effect on vagal
tone by OP compounds may signal delayed human performance changes.
A similar experiment was conducted with Rhesus monkeys treated with
pyridostigmine. Although a delayed effect was not investigated,
the same attenuated vagal tone response to atropine was
demonstrated in the short term (72). The atropine response,
itself, is also important. Since atropine impairs the performance
of aviators (71) and monkeys (69), the implications for self-dosing
military personnel are obvious. It may be possible to measure
vagal tone response to dose and this might be possible over a long
period of time. If so, a (qualitative) dose of an organophosphorus
compound might be inferred from a noninvasive physiological
measurement long after the event.
        These experiments illustrate an innovative and attractive
approach to biological monitoring. Perhaps we have overlooked
other physiological responses for monitoring exposure to
pesticides.

Saliva. Saliva has never been popular as a monitoring medium for
pesticides. Perhaps suspicion that oral contamination is too
likely or that daily total saliva production is too difficult to
quantify has led to this situation. It also may be that all
salivary pesticide, once swallowed, will ultimately appear as
urinary pesticide, but this has not been established. Nonetheless,
saliva has been used to indicate exposure for a wide variety of
other environmental contaminants.
        Saliva would seem to offer advantages for monitoring
pesticides. We produce about 1000 mL of saliva per day (23).
Saliva collection is relatively easy and procedures such as
pre-rinses may be used to avoid contamination. Saliva secretion is
variable with time; therefore, samples may have to be taken at the
same time each day (73). Its use for monitoring drugs, metals,
hormones, immunoglobulins, testosterone, stress, phosphate,
progesterones, estriols and pesticides has been shown. Stowe and
Plaa (74) in their review of the literature through June 1967 on
extrarenal secretion cited references which demonstrated the

excretion in saliva of sulfa drugs, barbiturates, penicillin, dihydrostreptomycin and tetracyclines. Drugs such as digitalis (75, 76), nefopam (77), caffeine, theophylline and theobromine (78), cannabis (79), and phenylcyclidine (80) have been isolated in saliva and paired with determinations in urine or plasma. Saliva has been used with psychiatric patients undergoing lithium therapy as an indicator for lithium (81) and as a systemic indicator for zinc during pregnancy (82) as well as for potassium and calcium (83, 84, 85) and magnesium (86). Metals in the environment, e.g., lead (87), cadmium (88), copper, silver, tin, mercury, and zinc (89) have been found in the analysis of salivary samples. Salivary phosphate has been used as an indicator of ovulation (83). IgA levels in saliva increase during pregnancy (90) and decrease in cases of academic stress (91). IgA and IgM changes are reflected in rheumatoid arthritis (92). Salivary hormones may be used in the diagnosis of some forms of cancer (93, 94, 95). Testosterone in saliva has been used as a determinant of testicular function (96) and cortisol as a determinant of adrenocortical function (97). Salivary progesterones and estriols have been used in the assessment of ovarian function (97, 98, 99) and during pregnancy as indicators of fetal viability (100-105). Secretion of pesticides in saliva has been demonstrated (83, 106, 107, 108).

Skalsky et al. (106) studied the effects of parathion and carbofuran on cholinesterase activity in plasma, erythrocytes and saliva. Rats were dosed orally by direct intubation. A correlation between cholinesterase activities was obtained. Skalsky et al. (107) also studied the effect of carbaryl on salivary and serum cholinesterase and carbaryl distribution in tears, urine, saliva, and blood of rats. The abdominal wall was opened and ^{14}C-carbaryl was injected directly into the stomach at doses of 0, 50, 100 or 200 mg/kg. At a 200 mg/kg dose, carbaryl secretion in saliva peaked in about 60 min. The plasma peak occurred in about 75 min. Maximum plasma concentration was 35 ppm, saliva about 28 ppm. By thin layer chromatography (at the 200 mg/kg dose) the same three compounds, including carbaryl, appeared in saliva, plasma, and RBC. Tears contained carbaryl and α-naphthol. Urine contained 9 compounds, the major being α-naphthol. At the 100 and 50 mg/kg doses, saliva showed only two compounds: carbaryl and another metabolite which did not appear at the 200 mg/kg dose. Saliva, plasma, and RBC cholinesterases were inhibited at 50 mg/kg.

Borzelleca and Skalsky (108) studied salivary secretion of chlordecone in rats. Dosing was by stomach injection as in 107 at 50 mg/kg. Salivary flow was stimulated by pilocarpine. Chlordecone peaked in saliva in 6-24 h. ^{14}C-chlordecone appeared in saliva at less than 1/2 the plasma level; however, chlordecone excretion was monitored for only 48 h.

There are problems with using saliva as in these experiments. Human salivary esterases are carboxylesterases (109) and much of this "human" enzyme activity may be contributed by oral bacterial enzymes (110). It is unknown how these results with pesticides relate to humans. There was no mass balance work done with these animals, so we have no idea of the relationship between the pesticide in saliva and the total pesticide excreted or dose received. These were stomach, or essentially oral, doses. What

might the results have been with dermal applications? Mass balance
experiments in small animals and semi-mass balance experiments in
humans would be required for determining the relationship to dose.

Saliva appears to present less analytical complexity compared
to urine. At least in rats, no carbaryl was detected in saliva
after 24 h. If this were true for humans, saliva might be used to
predict when an exposure had occurred, i.e., if a compound were
present, exposure might have occurred within 24 h. For workers
exposed to pesticides on a daily basis, saliva might be an
estimator of dose. As for urine, excretion kinetics would have to
be known. Excretion patterns of parent and metabolite in relation
to dose would have to be known. Unfortunately, we cannot collect
the total daily excretion of saliva as we can for urine. These
problems, speculations and suppositions await experimental
resolution.

Sweat. Feldmann and Maibach suggested in 1974 that the effect of
sweating on dermal penetration should be documented (54), and this
was perhaps the first suggestion that sweat might be important to
the human pesticide absorption/excretion process. Let us assume
that all problems associated with monitoring urine for pesticides
and metabolites have been solved. Further, assume that the dermal
exposure of several workers is exactly the same in each of two
weeks. Can we then expect the mean level of urinary metabolites
during the second week to equal that during the first week?
Rosenberg et al. (111) used sweat patches to collect
dichlorobenzilic acid (a metabolite of chlorobenzilate) from the
backs of chlorobenzilate applicators. Urine analyses were also
performed. The proportion found in sweat and urine was
approximately 1:1. Sell et al. (112) conducted a human exposure
experiment with 2,4-D and monitored urine and sweat. Of the total
2,4-D excreted over one week after a single dermal application to
the hand, 15% was excreted in urine and 85% was found in sweat
(average for three workers). There are, however, many questions
about just how the 2,4-D experiment was performed based on the
2,4-D human excretion data referenced here in the urine section,
validation of analytical sensitivity and the continued wearing of
contaminated personal articles. Although the sweat monitoring data
for pesticides is preliminary, we have overlooked sweat excretion
in our design. Unfortunately, rats do not sweat, so rat urinary
excretion data may not be applicable to humans. If a pesticide
and/or metabolite is excreted in sweat, the sweat/urine excretion
ratio may change with the human physiological response to heat.
Consider how little we know about this process. Could a dermal
exposure, subsequently manifested in sweat, simply be pesticide
recycled at the skin level? Is this then an "internal" dose? Does
a sweat collection device also collect interstitial fluid? If it
collected only interstitial fluid, we could quickly estimate an
internal dose. Peck et al. (113, 114) have studied the transdermal
collection of drugs and parathion in small animals. A model for
chemical disposition in skin is available (115). The experiments
with humans are waiting to be run.

There is the problem of quantifying sweat which makes it a
less attractive medium to monitor. However, cystic fibrosis is
diagnosed with a sweat test which depends on quantification and

Webster (116) has reviewed the problems of sweat quantification.
Quantification may not be a serious problem locally, but the rate
of sweating and total daily production would have to be estimated.
There are estimates of fluid loss due to sweating available. A
nationally ranked 47 kg runner sweated at 1.2-1.3 L/h (reduction in
body wt = 5%+) over 10 miles and 82 min (117). Twelve,
unacclimatized males were tested at 30.0 $\pm$ 0.7°C WBGT, 1.0 $\pm$ 1 m/s
wind velocity on a treadmill (118). Subjects walked/climbed for 30
min and rested sitting for 30 min over 6 h. They sweated at a rate
of about 425 mL/h while walking. This rate decreased to 125 mL/h
while sitting. Their cumulative sweat loss over 6 h averaged about
3300 mL. This loss was offset by water intake over the 6 h. Seven
men exercising at 50% of maximum oxygen uptake averaged 2.19 L
water loss through sweat in 2 h (119). Marathoners in a warm
environment may lose 2.8 L/h through sweat and incur 8% loss of
body weight through sweat, resulting in a 13-14% loss of body water
(24). In spite of quantification difficulties, the study of this
route of pesticide excretion and its inclusion in exposure
estimates is warranted.

When the excretion of pesticide metabolites and parent
compounds in human sweat is understood, we may be able to determine
our possible underestimation of exposure or dose through the use of
urine only. For comments on the future of dermal monitoring
technology, we refer the reader to Peck et al. (120).

If urinary excretion kinetics following dermal exposure are
ignored, the interpretation of the results of a urine experiment
might be 100% wrong. If, in addition, sweat excretion is ignored,
additional 100% mistakes appear possible.

Table I presents a hypothetical case of pesticide excretion in
a worker in a hot environment. Typical adult daily fluid
elimination rates were assigned to urine, sweat, and sebum. From
typical pesticide concentrations within those fluids following a
single dermal exposure, daily pesticide excretion rates were
estimated for each of the three elimination pathways. A total
internal dose was then inferred under the assumption that 100% of
the dose was executed during the day. If the internal dose were
estimated from urine data alone, the result would have been roughly
one-half of that calculated.

Do the rough calculations of Table I suggest a real problem?
If we return to the data of Feldmann and Maibach (54), 100% of an
i.v. dose of 2,4-D was excreted in urine in 120 h. In 24 h, about
70% was recovered. The range for recovery over 120 h of i.v. doses
of biodegradable (metabolizable) pesticides was 7.4% (carbaryl)-
90.2% (malathion). In 24 h, i.v. malathion appeared in urine at
about 88% and carbaryl at about 5% of the i.v. dose. An i.v.
administration is the ideal case since it represents a known
internal dose. The average total dose recovered in urine for
azodrin, ethion, guthion, malathion and parathion, all considered
biodegradable, was 62.3% over 5 days of total urine collection
after an i.v. dose. We should, as scientists, account for the rest
of the dose. Do Feldmann and Maibach's data suggest other routes
of excretion? Are some of these compounds or their metabolites
excreted in sweat? Are some excreted in saliva either as parent or
metabolite(s) and only partially reabsorbed and excreted in urine

Table I. Typical Excretion Rates* of Noninvasive Biological
          Fluids and an Estimated Internal Dose
          after a Single Dermal Exposure

Fluid	Fluid excretion rate	Ref. No.	Estimated pesticide conc.	Pesticide excretion rate	% of total
Urine + swallowed saliva (excreted in urine)	900 mL/d	**	50 ng/mL	45 µg/d	47
Sweat***	6,400 mL/d	23	8 ng/mL	51 µg/d	53
Sebum	3.8 mg/d	23	8 pg/mg	3×10^{-5} µg/d	--
			Total	96 µg/d	

Total Dose = 96 µg, or 0.0014 mg/kg

*Light, steady work by a 70 hg adult, temperatures above 32°C
**Nigg and Stamper, unpublished
***8h, 0.6 L/h; 16 h, 0.1 L/h, reference 23, 117-119

or stored in adipose tissue or metabolized and excreted as CO_2?
Only for 2,4-D does it appear that urine monitoring would be
adequate.
        The first problem of modeling the excretion process as in
Table I lies with the oral (stomach) dosing of the rats in most
kinetic studies. The kinetics of excretion are different for oral
vs. dermal administrations. Since rats do not sweat, rat data,
even following a dermal exposure, may not be applicable. We do not
presently have the data to make an estimate as in Table I. We have
failed to collect the basic information on human excretion of
organic molecules, i.e., the rat and mouse models really apply only
to rats and mice.
        Table II presents the i.v. data of Feldmann and Maibach (ref.
54, p. 129, Table I) in a different form. Since the original
half-lives were excretion rate half-lives, we transformed the
original data to percent-dose-unaccounted-for by multiplying
excretion rate by hours, producing a cumulative total for each of
the 8 time periods monitored and subtracting this value from 100.
These decreasing percent values were then subjected to a
first-order linear regression analysis. Correlation coefficients
from that analysis are presented. The linear regression lines
allowed us to predict statistically the times at which 50% (and
also 90%) of the i.v. dose would be eliminated in urine.
Ninety-five % confidence internals were calculated for each of the
two times. Except for 2,4-D, the projections of Table II had to be

extended beyond the range of the data. This procedure adds to the uncertainty in the projections, as evidenced by some of the larger confidence intervals. Because of the necessity in this experiment to extend the model beyond experimental data, Maibach et al. extend urinary excretion experiments to non-detection (H. Maibach, personal communication). We encourage other investigators in this area to conduct urinary excretion experiments to non-detection.

Elimination or excretion rate half-lives are virtually useless for predicting dose if only a small percentage of the dose is accounted for with data. The same rate half-life could result, regardless of whether 10 or 100% of the dose was excreted. Mathematical representation might present problems with urinary excretion of oral doses and will certainly be a problem with

Table II.   Projected Urinary Excretion of Pesticides Using Data of Feldmann and Maibach (54)*

| Pesticide | Projected period for 50% and 90% excretion of total i.v. dose | | first-order correlation coefficient (n = 8) |
	50% excretion period (h)	90% excretion period (h)	
Azodrin	76 [60, 104]*	253 [200, 345]*	0.966
Ethion	187 [129, 337]	620 [429, 1120]	0.913
Guthion	68 [58, 83]	226 [192, 276]	0.984
Malathion	73 [37, 1284]	241 [124, 4264]	0.727
Parathion	134 [90, 258]	445 [300, 857]	0.901
Baygon	99 [51, 1263]	329 [171, 4194]	0.735
Carbaryl	1670 [1063, 3894]	5548 [3532, 12936]	0.868
2,4-D	17 [16, 19]	58 [53, 64]	0.997
Diquat	204 [129, 493]	679 [429, 1637]	0.863

*95% confidence interval (h)

dermally-applied pesticides which penetrate human skin poorly and are excreted in a non-first-order manner. Problems which have not been resolved with any human excretion of pesticides include whether the excretion rate or route is dose dependent. We encourage, in any event, mass-balance or near mass-balance experiments.

Combination of Nonbiological and Biological Estimation Methods

Here, we discuss in greater detail the statistical considerations in experimental design for the field estimation of dose by combining biological and non-biological methods. Data analysis for current experiments usually necessitates comparing two mean values, each from about the same number of replications. For examples, we might wish to compare the mean urinary level of a pesticide metabolite in a week when coveralls were worn vs. a week when they were not worn or to compare the mean pesticide concentration on one collection device with that on another collection device. The

number of replications per mean is typically the product of the
number of sampling periods (sampling days) and the number of
participating subjects, but this is contingent upon validation, by
an analysis of variance of the obtained data, that exposure levels
do not vary significantly day-to-day or subject-to-subject. This
may be the case if all subjects performed the same tasks each day.

The question must be addressed as to how many replicates
(subjects X days) will be necessary to confirm statistically a
difference between means. Two parameters must be estimated first.
What difference in means is expected to arise from the data and
what variation among replicates is expected? A large estimate for
the first expectation or a small estimate for the second
expectation would reduce the number of replicates necessary per
mean. Our experience has shown that protective clothing reduces
mean pad exposure by about 90% (121). Similarly, the use of gloves
may reduce handwash residues by about 85%, according to a recent
study of dicofol exposure by Nigg et al. (122). As for variation
among replicates, the coefficient of variation is typically about
100% for exposure pad and handwash residues (6, 121). This
variation could also subsequently affect the variation in
parent/metabolite quantities in biological samples.

Standard statistical procedures then show (123) that, on the basis
of the above estimates, two means may be judged significantly
different at the 95% confidence level by taking at least ten
replications per mean. The (approximate) calculation is $n > 8$
$(100\% \div 90\%)^2$, or $n > 10$ replications. For gloves, the
corresponding calculation would be $n > 8$ $(100\% \div 85\%)^2$, or $n > 11$
replications. These numbers represent an absolute minimum based on
the above two expected values. An increase in n of 50% to provide
some margin for error, in the above cases to $n > 15$ and $n > 17$, is
certainly warranted in view of the guesswork involved about sample
means and variances.

If more than two means are to be compared concurrently, as
with comparing residues at various body locations, the situation
becomes somewhat more complicated. While it is now harder to
generalize, the optimum number of replications per mean can be
roughly adduced by the same calculation, with the final result that
the means are grouped into significantly different categories, at
some confidence level.

Whether to utilize, e.g., three subjects for six sampling
periods each, or six subjects for three sampling periods each, to
obtain, say, 18 replications is usually dictated by factors other
than statistical ones. A good rule to follow is not to overload
the design too heavily in favor of either variable. If many
subjects are used for a very few sampling days, and the data
indicate large differences from subject to subject the available
number of replicates now decreases to the number of sampling days
alone. This experiment makes a very unreliable statement about
each of many subjects; no valid overall conclusion may emerge.

Remember that these statistical calculations show significant
differences between means, but do not estimate the difference.
Suppose one mean is 90% less than the other, as above, but that one
wishes to validate the claim that 50 of that 90% is statistically
significant. The approximate calculation for the requisite number

of replications per mean is now n $>$ 8 $[100\% \div (90\% - 50\%)]^2$ = 50, or n $>$ 75 with the safety factor.

From another perspective, suppose 24 h urines were collected from 20 workers during two different periods: one where workers wore protective clothing and one where they did not. The urine excretion means for the two periods would have to differ by 48% to be statistically different at the 95% level, assuming a coefficient of variation of 75%. For field studies using fewer than 20 subjects (replicates), differences in urinary excretion means would have to exceed 48% for a statistical difference to be validated.

Another consideration is the amount of chemical removed by a collection device which subsequently is not excreted in urine because it never became an internal dose. If twenty 103 cm^2 (4 in. x 4 in.) pads are used for monitoring a worker, about 2000 cm^2 of body surface area would be covered. The average human has a surface area of ca. 20,000 cm^2. Since 10% of the body surface area is covered, will this reduce the urinary metabolite by 10%? Hardly. First, the pads are worn no longer than four hours, usually only one or two hours, over the eight hour workday. The maximum percentage reduction is thus 5%. This 5% difference could be reduced by incomplete percutaneous absorption. We challenge any researcher to show a statistically valid 5% difference in urinary excretion in any field experiment.

The use of a hand rinse or cotton gloves to monitor hand exposure may invalidate urine results. Suppose workers who normally work ungloved and do not customarily wash their hands participate in an exposure study. Requiring that they wear gloves in order to monitor hand exposure might reduce their total dermal exposure, and, hence, their urinary metabolite level, by 21%. This is on the assumption that hand exposure originally constituted 50% of the total dermal exposure and that the gloves, worn for 1/2 of the workday, gave 85% protection. Requiring handwashes might lead to a similar reduction. However, for workers who normally wear gloves or who regularly wash their hands, hand rinses or cotton glove monitors may not affect the experimental outcome.

Properly designed biological monitoring studies are a future possibility and probability. As previously stated, the excretion kinetics of pesticides and pesticide metabolites in sweat and urine and perhaps saliva after a dermal exposure must be understood before any biological fluid can be validated as a dose estimator. When we understand human exposure route absorption and excretion route kinetics and their interrelationships, biological fluid monitoring will allow an accurate calculation of pesticide exposure and internal dose.

Research Needs

There are specific questions future research should answer before biological monitoring can be reliably used to estimate dose and risk.

1. What are the routes and kinetics of excretion in humans following dermal exposure to a chemical?
2. What is the relationship between internal dose and the routes and kinetics of excretion in humans?
3. What physiological changes does a human undergo in

response to a pesticide and can these changes be related to dose?

4. How do the interrelationships between routes of excretion change with changes in human physiology, i.e., heat stress, work load, etc.?

5. What are the ranges in total daily output volumes of the various human routes of pesticide excretion in relation to different working conditions? Can we use these ranges to estimate a dose from grab samples?

6. Can we collect interstitial fluid in humans and measure parent and metabolite molecules to estimate dose?

7. Do we see changes in excretion patterns and excreted metabolites in human workers exposed to a pesticide day after day?

General Conclusions

Much of our present data associated with dose estimation using human urine, blood, saliva, and other biological fluids preclude their use for determining internal dose. A notable exception to this statement are the phenoxy herbicides. We should remember, however, that few biological monitoring experiments in the literature were designed to monitor dose. The uncertainty in a dose estimate based on biological monitoring generally results from the lack of basic information on relevant human biochemistry and physiology. We must proceed with new biological monitoring experiments designed to estimate dose and we must be cognizant of the possible application of data never collected. Biological monitoring for pesticide dose estimation is a viable technological frontier, one which could simplify regulatory problems. Science can and should provide this technology.

Acknowledgments

We appreciate the excellent reviews of this manuscript by Dr. Marguerite Leng, Dow Chemical, Dr. Claire Franklin, Health and Welfare, Canada, and an anonymous reviewer. Their suggestions improved this review in very positive ways.

Literature Cited

1. Davis, J. E. Residue Rev. 1980, 75, 33-50.
2. Nigg, H. N.; Stamper, J. H., in Dermal Exposure Related to Pesticide Use, R. C. Honeycutt, G. Zweig, N. Ragsdale, Eds., ACS Symposium Series 273, 1985. Washington DC, Chapter 7, pp. 95-8.
3. Popendorf, W. J.; Leffingwell, J. T. Residue Rev. 1982, 82, 125-201.
4. Nigg, H. N.; Stamper, J. H., in Pesticide Residues and Exposure, J. Plimmer, Ed., ACS Symposium Series 182, 1982, Washington DC, Chapter 6, pp. 59-73.
5. Gunther, F. A.; Iwata, Y.; Carman, G. E.; Smith, C. A. Residue Rev. 1977, 67, 1-139.
6. Nigg, H. N.; Stamper, J. H.; Queen, R. M. Am. Ind. Hyg. Assn. J. 1984, 45, 182-86.

7. Wicker, G. W.; Guthrie, F. E. Bull. Environ. Contam. Toxicol. 1980, 24, 161-67.
8. Wicker, G. W.; Stinner, R. E.; Reagan, P. E.; Guthrie, F. E. Bull. Entomol. Soc. Am. 1980, 26, 156-61.
9. Quinby, G. F.; Walker, K. C.; Durham, W. F. J. Econ. Entomol. 1958, 51, 831-38.
10. Kay, K.; Monkman, L.; Windish, J. P.; Doherty, T.; Pare, J.; Raciot, C. Ind. Hyg. Occup. Med. 1952, 6, 252-62.
11. Roan, C. C.; Morgan, D. P.; Cook, N.; Paschal, E. H. Bull. Environ. Contam. Toxicol. 1969, 4, 362-69.
12. Drevenkar, V.; Stengl, B.; Tralcevic, B.; Vasilic, Z. Int. J. Environ. Anal. Chem. 1983, 14, 215-30.
13. Bradway, D. E.; Shafik, T. M.; Loros, E. M. J. Agric. Food Chem. 1977, 25, 1353-58.
14. Moseman, R. F.; Enos, H. F. J. Environ. Sci. Hlth. 1982, A17, 519-23.
15. Gehring, P. J.; Kramer, C. G.; Schwetz, B. A.; Rose, J. Q.; Rowe, V. K. Toxicol. Appl. Pharmacol. 1973, 26, 352-61.
16. Kohli, J. D.; Khanna, R. N.; Gupta, B. N.; Dhar, M. M.; Tandon, J. S.; Sircar, K. P. Xenobiotica 1974, 4, 97-100.
17. Sauerhoff, M. W.; Braun, W. H.; Blau, G. E.; Gehring, P. J. Toxicology 1977, 8, 3-11.
18. Sauerhoff, M. W.; Chenoweth, M. B.; Karbowski, R. J.; Braun, W. H.; Ramsey, J. C.; Gehring, P. J.; Blau, G. E. J. Toxicol. Environ, Hlth. 1977, 3, 941-52.
19. Lavy, T. L. Human exposure to phenoxy herbicides, 1987, Veterans Administration, Agent Orange Projects Office, Washington, DC 20420, 128 pages.
20. Keil, J. E.; Loadholt, C. B.; Sandifer, S. H.; Weston, W.; Gadsden, R. H.; Hames, C. G. In Pesticides and the Environment: A Continuing Controversy; Diechmann, W. B., Ed.; Intercont. Med. Book Corp., NY, 1973, Vol. 2, p. 203.
21. Klemmer, H. W.; Rashad, M. N.; Mi, M. P. In Pesticides and the Environment: A Continuing Controversy; Deichmann, W. B., Ed.; Intercont. Med. Book Corp., NY, 1973, Vol. 2, p. 53.
22. Lewalter, J.; Korallus, U. Toxicol. Lett. 1986, 33, 153-65.
23. Lentner, C. (ed) Geigy Scientific Tables, Units of Measure, Body Fluids, Composition of the Body, Nutrition. Ciba Geigy: Basle, Switzerland, 1981, Vol. 1, pp. 53-122.
24. Costill, D. L. Ann. N.Y. Acad. Sci. 1977, 301, 160-74.
25. Alessio, L.; Berlin, A.; Dell'Orto, A.; Toffoletto, F.; Ghezzi, I. Inst. Arch. Occup. Environ. Hlth. 1985, 55, 99-106.
26. Araki, S.; Murata, K.; Aono, H.; Yanagihara, S.; Niinuma, Y.; Yamamoto, R.; Ishihara, N. J. Appl. Toxicol. 1986, 6, 245-51.
27. Brown, J. R.; Hughes, H.; Viriyanondha, S. Toxicol. Appl. Pharmacol. 1969, 15, 30-7.
28. Colburn, W. A. J. Pharm. Sci. 1984, 73, 313-17.
29. Swan, A. A. B. British J. Ind. Med. 1969, 26, 322-29.
30. Gollop, B. R.; Glass, W. I. New Zealand Med. J. 1979, 89, 10-11.
31. Wagner, S. L.; Weswig, P. Arch. Environ. Health 1974, 28, 77-9.
32. Lieban, J.; Waldman, R. K.; Krause, L. Ind. Hyg. Occup. Med. 1953, 7, 93-8.

33. Durham, W. F.; Wolfe, H. R.; Elliot, J. W. Arch. Environ. Health 1972, 24, 381-87.
34. Levy, K. A.; Brady, S. S.; Pfaffenberger, C. Bull. Environ. Contam. Toxicol. 1981, 27, 235-38.
35. Kolmodin-Hedman, B.; Hoglund, S.; Akerblom, M. Arch. Toxicol. 1983, 54, 257-65.
36. Kutz, F. W.; Strassman, S. C. Mosq. News 1977, 37, 211-18.
37. Davies, J. E.; Enos, H. F.; Barquet, A.; Morgade, C.; Danauskas, J. X., in Toxicol. Occup. Med., W. B. Deichmann, Ed., Elsevier, New York, 1979, Vol. IV, pp. 369-80.
38. Cohen, B.; Richler, E.; Weisenberg, E.; Schoenberg, J.; Luria, M., Pestic. Monit. J. 1979, 13, 81-6.
39. Hayes, A. L.; Wise, R. A.; Weir, F. W. Am. Ind. Hyg. Assn. J. 1980, 41, 568-75.
40. Wojeck, G. A.; Price, J. F.; Nigg, H. N.; Stamper, J. H. Arch. Environ. Contam. Toxicol. 1983, 12, 65-70.
41. Carman, G. E.; Iwata, Y.; Pappas, J. L.; O'Neal, J. R.; Gunther, F. A. Arch. Environ. Contam. Toxicol. 1982, 11, 651-59.
42. Comer, S. W.; Staiff, D. C.; Armstrong, J. F.; Wolfe, H. R. Bull. Environ. Contam. Toxicol. 1975, 13, 385-91.
43. Franklin, C. A.; Fenske, R. A.; Greenhalgh, R.; Mathieu, L.; Denley, H. V.; Leffingwell, J. T.; Spear, R. C. J. Toxicol. Environ. Health 1981, 7, 715-31.
44. Staiff, D. C.; Comer, S. W.; Armstrong, J. F.; Wolfe, H. R. Bull. Environ. Contam. Toxicol. 1975, 14, 334-40.
45. Wojeck, G. A.; Nigg, H. N.; Braman, R. S.; Stamper, J. H.; Rouseff, R. L. Arch. Environ. Contam. Toxicol. 1982, 11, 661-67.
46. Wojeck, G. A.; Nigg, H. N.; Stamper, J. H.; Bradway, D. E. Arch. Environ. Contam. Toxicol. 1981, 10, 725-35.
47. Lavy, T. L.; Shepard, J. S.; Mattice, J. D. J. Agr. Food Chem. 1980, 28, 626-30.
48. Lavy, T. L.; Walstad, J. D.; Flynn, R. R.; Mattice, J. D. J. Agr. Food Chem. 1982, 30, 375-81.
49. Franklin, C. A.; Muir, N. I.; Moody, R. P. Toxicol. Lett. 1986, 33, 127-36.
50. Grover, R.; Franklin, C. A.; Muir, N. I.; Cessna, A. J.; Riedel, D. Toxicol. Lett. 1986, 33, 73-83.
51. Winterlin, W. L.; Kilgore, W. W.; Mourer, C. R.; Schoen, S. R. J. Agr. Food Chem. 1984, 32, 664-72.
52. Leng, M. L.; Ramsey, J. C.; Brown, W. H.; Lavy, T. L. in Pesticide Residues and Exposure, J. Plimmer, Ed., ACS Symposium Series 182, 1982, Washington, DC, Chapter 11, pp. 133-56.
53. Funckes, A. J.; Hayes, G. R.; Hartwell, W. V. J. Agr. Food Chem. 1963, 11, 455-57.
54. Feldmann, R. J.; Maibach, H. I. Toxicol. Appl. Pharmacol. 1974, 28, 126-72.
55. Wester, R. C.; Maibach, H. I.; Bucks, A. W.; Aufere, M. B. J. Toxicol. Environ. Hlth. 1984, 14, 759-62.
56. Maibach, H. I. Animal Models in Dermatology Churchill Livingstone, Edinburgh.
57. Skinner, C. S.; Kilgore, W. W. J. Toxicol. Environ. Hlth. 1982, 9, 483-90.
58. Stoughton, R. B. Toxicol. Appl. Pharmacol. 1965, 7, 1-6.

59. Riley, R. T.; Kemppainen, B. W.; Norred, W. P. J. Toxicol. Environ. Hlth. 1985, 15, 769-77.
60. Kolmodin-Hedman, B.; Hoglund, S.; Swenson, A.; Akerblom, M. Arch. Toxicol. 1983, 54, 267-73.
61. Akerblom, M.; Kolmodin-Hedman, B.; Hoglund, S., in Hum. Welfare Environ., J. Miyamoto, Ed., Pergamon Press, New York, 1983, pp. 227-32.
62. Nolan, R. J.; Freshour, N. L.; Kastl, P. E.; Saunders, J. H. Toxicol. Appl. Pharmacol. 1984, 76, 264-69.
63. Nolan, R. J.; Rick, D. L.; Freshour, N. L.; Saunders, J. H. Toxicol. Appl. Pharmacol. 1984, 73, 8-15.
64. Morgan, D. P.; Hetzler, H. L.; Slach, E. F.; Lin, L. I. Arch. Environ. Contam. Toxicol. 1977, 6, 159-73.
65. Franklin, C. A.; Greenhalgh, R.; Maibach, H. I., in Hum. Welfare Environ., J. Miyamoto, Ed., Pergamon Press, New York, 1983, pp. 221-26.
66. Wester, R. C.; Noonan, P. K. Int. J. Pharmaceut. 1980, 7, 99-110.
67. Dedek, W. In "Field Worker Exposure during Pesticide Application"; W. F. Tordoir, E. A. H. van Heenstra, Eds.; Elsevier, New York, 1980; pp. 47-50.
68. Spittler, T. D.; Dewey, J. E.; Bourks, J. B. In "Determination and Assessment of Pesticide Exposure"; M. Siewierski, Ed.; Elsevier, New York, 1984; pp. 27-35.
69. Jansen, H. T.; Dellinger, J. A. Neurotoxicol Teratol 1987, in press.
70. Dellinger, J. A.; McKiernan, B. C.; Koritz, G. D.; Richardson, B. C. Neurotoxicol Teratol 1987, 9, 197-201.
71. Dellinger, J. A.; Taylor, H. L.; Porges, S. W. Aviat Space Environ. Med. 1987, 58, 333-38.
72. Birnbaum, S. G.; Richardson, B. C.; Dallinger, J. A. Pharmacol. Biochem. Behavior. 1988, 31, in press.
73. Ferguson, D. B.; Botchway, C. A. Arch. Oral Biol. 1980, 25, 559-68.
74. Stowe, C. M.; Plaa, G. L. Ann. Rev. Pharmacol. 1968, 8, 337-56.
75. Ben Aryeh, H.; Gutman, D. Isr. J. Dent. Med. 1977, 26(2), 5-9.
76. Ben Aryeh, H.; Gutman, D. Isr. J. Dent. Med. 1981, 29(1-2), 7-11.
77. Chang, S. F.; Hanse, C. S.; Fox, J. M.; Ober, R. E. J. Chromatogr. 1981, 226(1), 79-89.
78. Scott, N. R.; Chakraborty, J.; Marks, V. Ann. Clin. Biochem. 1984, 21(Pt2), 120-24.
79. Gross, S. J.; Worthy, T. E.; Nerder, L.; Zimmermann, E. G.; Soares, J. R.; Lomax, P. J. Anal. Toxicol. 1985, 9(1), 1-5.
80. McCurran, M. M.; Walberg, C. B.; Soares, J.; Gross, S. J.; Baselt, R. C. J. Anal. Toxicol. 1984, 8(5), 197-201.
81. Ben Aryeh, H.; Laor, R.; Szargel, R.; Gutman, D.; Naon, H.; Pascal, M.; Hefetz, A. Isr. J. Med. Sci. 1984, 20(3), 197-201.
82. Hambridge, E. M.; Krebs, N. F.; Jacobs, M. A.; Favier, A.; Guyette, L.; Ikie, D. N. Am. J. Clin. Nutr. 1983, 37, 429-42.
83. Ben Aryeh, H.; Gutman, D. In Proceedings of the International

Workshop at Luxembourg; Berlin, A., et al., Eds.; Martin
Nijhoff Publishers, The Hague, 18-22 April 1977.

84. Ben Aryeh, H.; Bergman, S.; Gutman, D.; Barzilai, B.;
Hammerman, H.; Szargel, R. Chest 1977, 72, 131-32.

85. Wotman, S.; Bigger, J. T., Jr.; Mandel, I. D.; Bartelston,
H. J. N. E. J. Med. 1971, 285(16), 871.

86. Gilfrich, H. J. Klin. Wochenschr. 1981, 59(12), 617-21.

87. P'an A. Y. J. Toxicol. Environ. Health 1981, 7(2), 273-80.

88. Gervais, L.; Lacasse, Y.; Brodeur, J.; P'an A. Toxicol. Lett.
1981, B(1-2), 63-6.

89. Nilner, K.; Glantz, P. O. Swed. Dent. J. 1982, 6(2), 71-7.

90. Widerstom, L.; Bratthal, D., Scand. J. Dent. Res. 1984, 92,
33-7.

91. Jemmott, J. B.; Borysenko, M.; Chapman, R.; Borysenko, J. Z.;
McClelland, D. C.; Meye, D. Lancet Apr. 1983, (8339),
1400-02.

92. Elkon, K. B.; Gharave, A. E.; Patel, B. M.; Hughes, G. R. V.;
Frankel, A. Clin. Exp. Immunol. 1983, 52, 75-84.

93. Turkes, A.; Pennington, G. W.; Griffiths, K. Eur. J. Cancer
Oncol. 1984, 20(2), 291-92.

94. Read, G. F.; Wilson, D. W.; Campbell, F. C.; Holliday, H. W.;
Blamey, R. W.; Griffiths, K. Eur. J. Cancer Clin. Oncol.
1983, 19(4), 477-83.

95. Read, G. F.; Bradley, J. A.; Wilson, D. W.; George, W. D.;
Griffiths, K. Eur. J. Cancer Clin. Oncol. 1985, 21(1), 9-17.

96. Walker, R. F.; Wilson, D. W.; Read, G. F.; Riad-Fahmy, D. Int.
J. Andol. 1980, 3(2), 105-20.

97. Walker, R. F.; Hughes, I. A.; Riad-Fahmy, D.; Read, G. F.
Lancet Sept. 1978, 9, 585.

98. Walker, S.; Mustafa, A.; Walker, R. F.; Riad-Fahmy, D. Brit.
J. Obstet. Gynecol. 1981, 88, 1009-15.

99. McGarricle, H. H.; Lachelin, G. C. L. B. J. Med. 1984, 289,
457-59.

100. Robinson, J.; Walker, S.; Read, G. F.; Riad-Fahny, D. Lancet.
May 16 1981, 1111-12.

101. Vining, R. F.; McGinley, R. A.; Symons, R. G., Clin. Chem.
1983, 29(10), 1752-56.

102. Vining, R. F.; McGinley, R. A.; Rice, B. V. J. Clin.
Endocrinol. Metab. 1983a, 56, 454.

103. Zaki, K.; El Hak, R.; Amer, W.; Saleh, F.; El Faras, A.; Ragar,
L.; Nour, H. Biomed. Biochim. Acta 1984, 43(6), 749-54.

104. Cusick, P. E.; Truran, P. L.; Read, G. F.; Alsotn, W. C. Ann.
Clin. Biochem. 1984, 21, 22-5.

105. Lechner, W.; Marth, C.; Daxenbichler, G. Acta Endocrinol.
1985, 109, 266-68.

106. Skalsky, H. L.; Keeling, B. M.; Borzelleca, J. F. Toxicol.
Appli. Pharmacol. 1979, 48(1 Part 2), A140.

107. Skalsky, H. L.; Lane, R. W.; Borzelleca, J. In Toxicol.
Occupat. Med.; Deichmann, W. B., Ed.; Elsvier, New York, 1978,
pp. 349-58.

108. Borzelleca, J.; Skalsky, H. L. J. Environ. Sci. Health [B]
1980, B15(6), 843-66.

109. Lindquist, L.; Augustinsson, K. B. Enzyme 1975, 20, 277.

110. Mahler, J. R.; Chauncey, H. H. J. Dent. Res. 1975, 36, 338.

111. Rosenberg, N. M.; Queen, R. M.; Stamper, J. H.   Bull. Environ. Contam. Toxicol. 1985, 35, 68–72.
112. Sell, C. R.; Maitlen, J. C.; Aller, W. A.   Perspiration as an important physiological pathway for the elimination of 2,4–diclorophenoxyacetic acid from the human body.   Presented at Amer. Chem. Soc. Mtg, Las Vegas, NV, April 1, 1982.
113. Peck, C. C.; Conner, D. P.; Bolden, B. J.; Almirez, R. G.; Rowland, L. M.; Kwiatkowski, T. E.; McKelvin, B. A.; Bradley, C. R.   Pharmacol. Skin   1987, 1, 201–8.
114. Peck, C.; Conner, D.; Bolden, B.; Kingsley, T.; Mell, L.; Kwiatkowski, T.; Hill, V.; Ezra, D.; Dubois, A.; Rahim, M. A.; Murphy, G.   Transdermal chemical collection: A novel research tool.   Presented at Third Annual Symp. Skin Pharmacol. Soc., Karolinska Inst., Stockholm, Sweden, August 1–2, 1986.
115. Peck, C.; Conner, D.; Scheuplein, R.; Dedrick, R.; McDougal, J.   Physiologically based pharmacokinetic modeling of chemical disposition in skin.   Presented at Third Annual Symp. Skin Pharmacol. Soc., Karolinska Inst., Stockholm, Sweden, August 1–2, 1986.
116. Webster, H. L., in CRC Critical Reviews in Clinical Laboratory Sciences, CRC Press, Boca Raton, FL, 1983, 18, 113–338.
117. Costill, D. L. (Moderator)   Ann. N.Y. Acad. Sci.   1977, 301, 183–88.
118. Armstrong, L. E.; Hubbard, R. W.; Szlyk, P. C.; Matthew, B. S.; Sils, I. V.   Aviation, Space and Environ. Med.   1985, August, 765–70.
119. Costill, D. L.; Cote, R.; Fink, W. J.; Van Handel, P.   Int. J. Sports Med.   1981, 2, 130–34.
120. Peck, C. C.; Lee, K.; Becker, C. E.   J. Pharmacokinetics and Biopharmaceutics   1981, 9, 41–58.
121. Nigg, H. N.; Stamper, J. H.   Arch. Environ. Contam. Toxicol.   1983, 12, 477–82.
122. Nigg, H. N.; Stamper, J. H.; Queen, R. M.   Arch. Environ. Contam. Toxicol.   1986, 15, 121–43.
123. Dowdy, S.; Weardon, S., in Stat. for Res., Wiley, New York, 1983, p. 196.

RECEIVED July 5, 1988

Chapter 2

Ways To Reduce Applicator Exposure to Pesticides

J. E. Cowell, S. Dubelman, A. J. Klein, and K. Ohta

Life Sciences Research Center, Environmental Science Department, Technology Division, Monsanto Agricultural Company, Chesterfield, MO 63198

Measurement of applicator exposure to pesticides has allowed scientists the opportunity to evaluate approaches to the reduction of exposure. Both passive dosimetry and biological monitoring applicator exposure studies have been performed by our department on various pesticides. In these studies, four general areas have been identified which have an effect upon reduction of worker exposure. These four areas encompass: worker apparel, product packaging, application equipment and personal hygiene. Worker clothing and rubber gloves have been found effective in reducing personal exposure. Small container size and closed transfer systems have been found to be important in mixer/loader exposure reduction, while tractors with closed cabs have led to reduction in application exposure. Finally, important factors in the reduction of applicator exposure have been found to be the workers' level of instruction for use of the pesticides and the workers' individual personal hygiene practices.

Scientists have been interested in the measurement of worker exposure to pesticides since the 1950s. In 1962, Durham and Wolfe reviewed, in detail, the methods available for measurement of the exposure of workers to pesticides.(1) In 1985, a fairly comprehensive review of the literature from 1951-1984 was conducted by Turnbull (2). Basically there are two approaches used to measure exposure, and these approaches have not changed radically throughout the years. The first approach, pioneered by Durham and Wolfe measures the external deposition or the amount of pesticide with which the worker's body comes into contact. This approach is utilized primarily when little information on the pharmacokinetics (absorption, metabolism and excretion) of the chemical is available. The second approach is the monitoring of the worker's body fluids (usually urine or blood) for levels of the pesticide or metabolites or for changes in enzyme activity.

0097–6156/89/0382–0028$06.00/0
© 1989 American Chemical Society

This has been called biological monitoring. If the pharmacokinetics of a chemical are known, then as the World Health Organization states in their 1982 protocol, "Biological monitoring
provides a quantitative measure of the absorbed pesticide resulting from exposure via all routes" (3).
       Both approaches are valuable in that each provides informa-
tion that the other does not. Since most of the exposure to
pesticide is from the dermal route, the Durham and Wolfe "patch
technique" can estimate the quantity of pesticide that comes into
contact with the skin. It also provides some information on the
exposure at specific sites. This has proven advantageous in
demonstrating avenues for exposure reduction (4). The "biological
monitoring technique" automatically accounts for inhalation,
oral exposure, clothing protection and percutaneous absorption
which all have to be assumed or estimated via additional experiments with the patch technique (5). With sufficient pharmacokinetic data, biological monitoring can provide a quantitative
measure of the total body dose which presents the whole picture
of the applicator's exposure. This capability proves very
advantageous in making risk assessments.
       Although some feel that the two techniques cannot be per-
formed concurrently (6), others including myself feel that the
techniques are compatible (7-9). With proper patch placement and
coordinated hand washes, the techniques can be combined to give
the greatest amount of information from a single study. Consider
the following points:
       1. The patches are attached to the outer clothing. Thus
any normally exposed skin such as face, hands or neck would not
be obstructed from potential dermal deposition or penetration.
       2. In many studies (10-14), normal clothing has approached
100% protection from dermal deposition and therefore in these
cases, patches would have no deleterious impact upon biological
monitoring.
       3. About 10 to 12 patches at 100 square centimeters per
patch are used on the applicator. These patches amount to only
1000 to 1200 square centimeters of body surface area which is
only approximately 6% of the average total body surface area.
       4. Thus the worst case would be that the biological moni-
toring is 6% too low. However inhalation and oral exposure would
be unaffected, thus a 1.06 correction factor may be inappropriate.
       5. Hand washes with alcoholic/aqueous solutions remove the
pesticide deposited on the hands (1) (15-18). Soap and warm
water rinses have also been used. It has been stated that hand
washes may not be accurate since they do not account for the
chemical already absorbed (19). The technique of hand washing is
not incompatible with the conduct of a biological monitoring
study since these hand washes just simulate the normal personal
hygiene practice of the applicator washing his hands after he
finishes working.
       Measurement of applicator exposure to pesticides by both
types of studies has been used to evaluate approaches to the reduction of exposure (20-22). Data developed by our department in
many different studies employing the patch or biological monitoring techniques or at times both, will be used to describe avenues

for exposure reduction. These individual studies will not be described in their entirety as some studies have already been published, others including methodology are described in a companion paper in this symposium (35), and yet others are to be published.

Four general areas have been identified for reduction of worker exposure:

1. Worker Apparel
2. Product Packaging
3. Application Equipment
4. Personal Hygiene

In the worker apparel area, clothing itself reduces exposure (23). Several studies have been performed utilizing patches on the outside and inside of clothing appropriately offset so as to not interfere with penetration of normal clothing. Correction factors obtained by dividing the outside patch residue by the inside patch residue, when found, have typically been in the 215 to 530 fold range (24-25). A Minolta videocamera has been used in our studies since 1983 and one positive effect of this video-taping of mixer/loader and application experiments has been the identification of sources of contamination. For instance, in one study four experiments that consisted of 2 individuals performing 2 replicates of mixing/loading and applying chemical to a 0.5 acre rice paddy each by a different mode, were viewed on tape and it was observed that some of the inside patches may have been contaminated upon removal from the applicator (25). During replicate experiments the next day with the same individuals and conditions, the inside patches were carefully removed with solvent rinsed forceps and the results of these two sets of experimental analyses can be seen in Table I:

Table I. Inside Patch Analyses (micrograms/square centimeter)
          Backpack Spray - Individual Number 1

	DAY 1		DAY 2
Rep 1.	0.0134	Rep 1.	<0.00500
Rep 2.	0.00945	Rep 2.	<0.00500

Mechanical Spreader - Individual Number 2

	DAY 1		DAY 2
Rep 1.	0.196	Rep 1.	<0.00500
Rep 2.	0.0434	Rep 2.	<0.00500

This is not meant to imply that every inside gauze patch that contains a residue is a result of contamination during removal, but only that clothing offers excellent protection and care should be taken to avoid contamination in these types of experiments.

Impermeable gloves are another obvious piece of protective equipment which can be used to reduce exposure. Exposure to the forearms and hands has been found to account for approximately 70-90% or more of the total dermal exposure. Some studies have been performed with cotton gloves worn on the outside and inside of protective rubber gloves (14) (25). Solvent extraction and GC analyses of both outside and inside cotton gloves were performed. Comparison of the analytical results of the outside versus the inside cotton gloves have yielded glove protection factors in our studies of 130 to 233 fold which compares favorably with another literature reported value of 220 fold (21).

Penetration studies with various glove materials have provided data as to which materials are the most impervious to chemical penetration. However, use of impenetrable glove materials in exposure studies has not completely prevented hand dermal exposure. Cotton gloves worn under impenetrable rubber gloves still contained detectable residues (26-27). The results of solvent extraction and GC analysis of individual gauze material worn underneath each rubber glove revealed one hand had significantly higher deposition than the other (24), as shown in Table II:

Table II. Hand Deposition (micrograms/square centimeters)

	Right Hand	Left Hand	
Subject 1.	1.63	0.724	(2.3X)
Subject 2.	11.6	389	(34X)
Subject 3.	18.6	4.14	(4.5X)
Subject 4.	0.976	20.7	(21X)

Although too few replicates were performed to allow statistical interpretation, with help from the videotapes and visual observation it was surmised that the deposition was a result of the glove removal process as one rubber-gloved hand removed one rubber glove and the cotton-gloved hand removed the other rubber glove. In effect, most rubber glove materials are adequate for the duration of worker exposures to most pesticides. Because of this potential route of exposure, EPA is now advising that the outside of rubber gloves be washed before removal.

In the product packaging area, dermal deposition data have been developed which seem to indicate pouring of larger and more difficult to handle containers is a cause of greater chemical exposure. From five studies, generic patch data were compiled from only the mixing/loading of 10-20 gallons of herbicides from two different size containers (12) (14) (26-28). Consider the

two sets of patch data in Table III which have been normalized
for an average body weight and pounds of chemical loaded:

Table III. Container Size Comparison
(Dermal Deposition in μg/kg/lb applied)

Container Size	Replicates	Mean Deposition	S.D.	Range
5.0 gallon	8	0.118	0.150	0.0107-0.279
2.5 gallon	15	0.00830	0.0169	0.000104-0.0544

Use of the 5 gallon containers consistently resulted in
higher dermal deposition values than the smaller 2.5 gallon
containers.
All the examples used to this point have been from patch
data. The remainder of the examples cited will be biological
monitoring of worker's urine. Prerequisite pharmacokinetic
studies have determined the duration of excretion of the pesticide and/or metabolites and the percentage of the administered
dose that is present in the urine. Thus all urine specimens were
collected for the period of excretion plus a baseline interval.
The worker's urinary metabolite levels were normalized for body
weight, amount of chemical handled and corrected for the amount
excreted in the urine to estimate the total body dose (29) (35).
In the next example, Table IV, biological monitoring of
worker's urine was used to measure the differences in total body
doses of workers using a completely closed transfer mini-bulk
package system followed by application to 20 acres of cropland
and an open pour mixer-loading followed by application to the
same amount of crop acreage (29). Closed transfer systems have
been found to reduce mixer/loader exposure in many of our studies
(26-28) and the Shuttle™ system used in this example seems to be
among the most efficient (10).

Table IV. Product Packaging Comparison

Package	Replicates	Mean Total Body Dose (mg/kg/lb Applied)	S.D.	Range (mg/kg/lb Applied)
Mini-bulk (closed system)	16	1.8×10^{-7}	4.7×10^{-7}	$0.0-1.8 \times 10^{-6}$
2.5 gal containers (open pour)	8	7.8×10^{-6}	9.1×10^{-6}	$0.0-2.3 \times 10^{-5}$

As can be seen from the data in Table IV and as others have observed (21) (30), the closed transfer does reduce the body dose of the mixer/loader personnel.

In the area of application equipment, there are many types of selective equipment (recirculating sprayers, shielded sprayers, ropewick applicators, banding applicators, etc.) which deliver the pesticides specifically to the pests with the side benefit of possibly lowering applicator exposure. Data are being developed with shielded sprayers, which show a significant exposure reduction (31). An example of this is a backpack sprayer wand with a small can surrounding the nozzle that ensures that the spray contacts the intended foliage, not adjacent plants or the applicator. Data are currently being completed for this example (32).

Another factor that results in reduction of exposure is the use of the closed cab tractor. A comparison of the absorbed dose in workers using a closed cab tractor with that of workers not using a cab is presented in Table V. All workers used an open pour tank-fill procedure (24) (33).

Again there are too few experiments for much statistical interpretation, but as can be seen from the ranges that there is not very much overlap. The data are suggestive that closed cab tractors offer more protection from exposure during application than open seat tractors.

The last area of reduction of worker exposure is based on the worker himself and his personal habits and hygiene. A biological monitoring study was performed with an open pour mixer-loading and application (12). The major difference from a previous study was that the workers were given safety instructions in the form of a Farmer Education Program (34). As can be seen in the Table VI, this makes a one order of magnitude difference in the means.

Table V. Application Equipment Comparison

Tractor	Subjects	Mean Total Body Dose (mg/kg/lb Applied)	S.D.	Range (mg/kg/lb Applied)
No cab (Cockshutt)	4	5.0×10^{-5}	4.2×10^{-5}	2.0×10^{-5}-1.1×10^{-4}
Closed cab (J. Deere 8450)	8	7.8×10^{-6}	9.1×10^{-6}	0.0-2.3×10^{-5}

Table VI. Worker Instruction Level Comparison

Exposure Study	Subjects	Mean Total Body Dose (mg/kg/lb Applied)	S.D.	Range (mg/kg/lb Applied)
No special directions	8	7.8×10^{-6}	9.1×10^{-6}	$0.0 \text{-} 2.3 \times 10^{-5}$
Farmer education program	20	8.1×10^{-7}	8.6×10^{-7}	$0.0 \text{-} 2.7 \times 10^{-6}$

Cultural hygiene/work practices also play a significant part in exposure reductions. Consider two types of granular applica-tion of a rice herbicide to a paddy. In one case, a mechanical spreader was used with the operator equipped with rubber gloves and rubber paddy shoes. In the other case, the worker applied the granules with his bare hands and waded through the paddies in his bare feet. The obvious speculation is that the bare-handed, bare-footed worker would have a very large exposure when compared to the more protected worker. From biological monitoring exposure studies of these two types of applications (13), the following data listed in Table VII were developed:

Table VII. Worker Hygiene Comparison

Case	Subjects	Mean Total Body Dose (mg/kg/lb Applied)	Range (mg/kg/lb Applied)
Rotary Spreader	3	9.80×10^{-4}	$7.3 \times 10^{-4} \text{-} 1.45 \times 10^{-3}$
Hand Broadcast	3	1.82×10^{-3}	$8.9 \times 10^{-4} \text{-} 2.70 \times 10^{-3}$

Why were the exposures in these two cases not vastly diffe-rent? Well, for two reasons: 1) the active ingredient in the granule did not readily partition to any great extent from the granule material to the skin (i.e., dermal penetration of the active is low) (36), and 2) the cultural practice of the worker was that upon completion of the application, the worker washed his hands and feet in the untreated irrigation ditch alongside the paddy. This practice reduced the worker's chemical contact time (exposure) to a minimum and therefore not too different from a well protected worker.

In conclusion, we have seen in our studies utilizing both techniques for measuring worker exposure, that the following are effective means for exposure reduction:

1. Normal long-sleeved cotton or cotton/polyester blend shirt, long-trouser - typical work clothing and rubber gloves provide good protection.

2. Closed transfer systems which convey chemical via hose or pipe from container to spray tank are the best. When open pouring containers are used, small, easier to handle containers are preferred.

3. Improvement of application equipment such as target delivery applicators and closed cab tractors appear to reduce exposure.

4. The instruction and personal hygiene/work practice of the worker can be very important.

LITERATURE CITED

1. Durham, W. F. and Wolfe, H. R. Bull. Wld. Hlth. Org. 1962, 26, 75-91.
2. Turnbull, G. J. Occupational Hazards of Pesticide Use. Taylor and Francis: London, 1985.
3. Field Surveys of Exposure to Pesticide. World Health Organization. 1982. Standard Protocol: Technical Monograph N 7. Geneva, Switzerland.
4. Reinert, J. C.; Nielsen, A. P.; Lunchick, C.; Hernandez, O. and Mazzetta, D. M. The United States Environmental Protection Agency's Guidelines For Applicator Exposure Monitoring. Toxicology Letters, 1986, 33, 183-191.
5. Cowell, J. E. Applicator Exposure To Pesticides. Proceedings of National Academy of Science-Czechoslovakian Academy of Science Workshop on Agricultural Development and Environmental Research, Ceske Budejovice, Czechoslovakia. 1987, (in press).
6. Ackerman, J. W. August 5, 1986. U.S. Environmental Protection Agency Correspondence.
7. Franklin, C. A. Can. J. Physiol. Pharmacol. 1984, 62, 1037-39.
8. Wojeck, G. A.; Price, J. F.; Nigg, H. N. and Stamper, J. H. Arch. Environ. Contamin. Toxicol. 1983, 12, 65-70.
9. Lavy, T. L.; Shepard, J. S. and Mattice, J. D. J. Agr. Food Chem. 1980, 28, 626-30.
10. Cowell, J. E.; Danhaus, R. D.; Kunstman, J. L.; Hackett, A. G.; Oppenhuizen, M. E. and Steinmetz, J. R. Arch. Environ. Contam. Toxicol. 1987, 16, 327-332.
11. Leavitt, J. R. C.; Gold, R. E.; Holcslaw, T. and Tupy, D. Arch. Environm. Contam. Toxicol. 1982, 11, 57-62.
12. Danhaus, R. G.; Kunstman, J. L.; Oppenhuizen, M. E. and Steinmetz, J. R. Operator Exposure from Open-Pour Transfer and Application of Lasso® EC, Lasso® MT™ and Lasso® WDG Herbicides. Monsanto Report Number MSL-5398, 1986. Submit-

ted to U.S. Environmental Protection Agency, EPA Accession
No. 262907.

13. Ohta, K.; Danhaus, R. G. and Cowell, J. E. Applicator
Exposure to Butachlor from Various Japanese Modes of Machete®
Herbicide Use. Monsanto Report Number MSL-4267, 1985.

14. Cowell, J. E.; Adams, S. A.; Danhaus, R. G. and Graham,
J. A. Aerial Applicator Exposure Studies With Machete®
Herbicide Under Actual Field Conditions. Monsanto Report
Number MSL-3124, 1983.

15. Davis, J. E.; Stevens, E. R.; Staiff, D. C. and Butler, L.
C. Environmental Monitoring and Assessment 1983, 3, 23-28.

16. Davis, J. E. Residue Reviews. 1980, 75, 34-50.

17. Maitlen, J. C.; Sell, C. R.; McDonough, L. M. and Fertig,
S. N. In Pesticide Residues and Exposures, Plimmer, J. R.,
Ed, ACS Symposium Series No. 182, 1982, 8, 83-104.

18. Gold, R. E.; Leavitt, J. R. C.; Holcslw, T. and Tupy, D.
Arch. Environm. Contam. Toxicol. 1982, 11, 63-67.

19. Zweig, G.; Gao, R. Y.; Witt, J. M.; Poppendorf, W. J. and
Bogen, K. T. In Dermal Exposure Related to Pesticide Use:
Discussion of Risk Assessment, Honeycutt, R. C.; Zweig, G.;
and Ragsdale, N. N., Eds. ACS Symposium Series No. 273,
1985, 9, 123-138.

20. Lavy, T. L.; Norris, L. A.; Mattice, J. D. and Marx, D. B.
Environmental Toxicology and Chemistry, 1987, 6, 209-224.

21. Putman, A. R.; Willis, M. D.; Binning, L. K. and Boldt, P.
F. J. Agric. Food Chem. 1983, 31, 645-650.

22. Freeborg, R. P.; Daniel, W. H. and Konopinski, V. J. In
Dermal Exposure Related to Pesticide Use: Discussion of
Risk Assessment, Honeycutt, R. C.; Zweig, G.; and Ragsdale,
N. N., Eds, ACS Symposium Series No. 273, 1985, 20, 287-295.

23. Davies, J. E.; Freed, V. H.; Enos, H. F.; Duncan, R. C.;
Barquet, A.; Morgade, C.; Peters, L. J. and Danauskas, J. X.
Journal of Occupational Medicine, 1982, 24, 6:464-468.

24. Bade, T. R.; Rupel, F. L.; Smith, R. G. and Klein, A. J.
Applicator Exposure Study of Lasso® and Lasso® Micro-Tech™
on a Family Farm in Southern Ontario Using Small Equipment.
Monsanto Report Number MSL-4424, 1985.

25. Cowell, J. E.; Adams, S. A.; Danhaus, R. G. and Graham,
J. A. Worker Exposure Study With Machete® Herbicide Simula-
ting Typical Japanese/Asian Modes of Application. Monsanto
Report Number MSL-3114, 1983.

26. Lauer, R. and Arras, D. D. Aerial and Ground Applicator
Exposure Studies With Lasso® Herbicide Under Field Conditions.
Monsanto Report Number MSL-1889, 1981. Submitted to U.S.
Environmental Protection Agency, EPA Accession No. 70591.

27. Lauer, R. and Arras, D. D. Applicator Exposure Study With
Lasso® ME Under Actual Field Conditions. Monsanto Report
Number MSL-2018, 1981. Submitted to U.S. Environmental
Protection Agency, EPA Accession No. 70840.

28. Arras, D. D. 1983. Applicator Exposure Studies With
MON-097 Herbicide Under Actual Field Use Conditions.
Monsanto Report No. MSL-2887, 1983. Submitted to U.S.
Environmental Protection Agency, EPA Accession No. 71959.

29. Cowell, J. E. and Dubelman, S. In <u>Pesticide Science and Technology</u>; Greenhalgh, R. and Roberts, T. R., Eds; Blackwell Scientific Publications: Oxford, 1987, 573-578.

30. Dubelman, S., Lauer, R., Arras, D. D., and Adams, S. A. J. Agric. Food Chem. 1982, 30, 528-532.

31. Kramer, R. M. Herbicide Applicator Exposure to Glyphosate During Application of Roundup® Herbicide and Field Reentry. Monsanto Report Number MSL-0288, 1978. Submitted to U.S. Environmental Protection Agency, EPA Accession No. 233914.

32. Lavy, T. L.; Mattice, J. D.; Steinmetz, J. R. and Cowell, J. E. 1988-9. (Study in progress).

33. Klein, A. J.; Bade, T. R.; Smith, R. G. and Rupel, F. L. Urinary Excretion of Alachlor Residue Following Normal Application of Lasso® of Lasso® Micro-Tech™ Herbicide Under Commericial Conditions in Indiana. Monsanto Report Number MSL-4207, 1984. Submitted to U.S. Environmental Protection Agency, EPA Accession No. 256623.

34. Monsanto Agricultural Products Company Publication. Guide to the Correct Handling of Lasso® Herbicide. 1985.

35. Dubelman, S. and Cowell, J. E. Biological Monitoring Technology for Measurement of Applicator Exposure. ACS Symposium Series (in press). 1987.

36. Adams, S. A. Butachlor Dermal Penetration Study. Monsanto Report Number MSL-3102, 1983.

RECEIVED March 14, 1988

Chapter 3

Estimating Exposure to Pesticides in Epidemiological Studies of Cancer

Aaron Blair, Shelia Hoar Zahm, Kenneth P. Cantor, and Patricia A. Stewart

Environmental Epidemiology Branch, National Cancer Institute, Landow Building, Bethesda, MD 20892

Epidemiologic studies of cancer and pesticides have proven difficult because of limitations in exposure assessment procedures. Major difficulties include multiple exposures and the length of time between exposure and initial symptoms of cancer. Biochemical monitoring coupled with traditional methods of exposure assessment based on job histories and duties offers the opportunity to evaluate the reliability of, and to improve, exposure assessment procedures.

Pesticides are designed to be toxic to organisms which are considered undesirable. Because of this ability to inflict damage on living organisms, there has been concern regarding their effect on humans. The International Agency for Research on Cancer, an agency which reviews and evaluates the carcinogenicity of chemicals, has concluded that there is sufficient evidence for the carcinogenicity of chlordane, chlordecone, heptachlor, hexachlorobenzene, mirex and toxaphene in laboratory animals (1) and that limited evidence exists for tetrachlorinphos and diallate (2). Epidemiologic studies of cancer and pesticides, however, have proven difficult (3). This paper briefly reviews procedures used to evaluate pesticide exposures in epidemiologic studies of cancer and suggests ways of improving our effort in this area.

Some of the problems are typical of most epidemiologic studies of cancer, i.e. the long period between first exposure and initial evidence of disease and the need for large numbers of study subjects. A particular vexing problem has been the difficulty in documenting exposures. Information on the type of pesticides handled and levels of exposure is crucial for evaluation of exposure-response patterns which is a critical criterion for identifying etiologic factors. Accurate assessment of exposure is important because exposure misclassification reduces estimates of relative risks and dampens dose-response gradients. In addition, misclassification increases the chances of attributing elevated cancer risk among persons exposed to pesticides to the wrong agent.

This chapter not subject to U.S. copyright
Published 1989 American Chemical Society

It is relatively easy to identify persons in occupations where
exposure to pesticides is common and/or heavier than the general
population, but documentation or measurements of exposure to
specific pesticides are seldom available. Furthermore, even if some
monitoring data or other documentation of exposure are available, it
is difficult to evaluate risks associated with specific pesticides
because most applicators have contact with a variety of pesticides
and because variation in work practices can greatly affect delivered
dose. Although the latent period (i.e. the time from first exposure
to diagnosis of disease) associated with pesticides is not generally
known, it is lengthy for most chemical carcinogens which further
complicates exposure evaluation. Precise determination of recent
exposures is not necessarily relevant to the initiation of cancer,
since the most important exposures may be those that occurred 20 or
years before the development of disease.

Despite these difficulties in exposure assessment, epidemiologic
studies of persons having contact with pesticides such as
manufacturers, applicators, and farmers suggest that exposure to
pesticides may increase their risk of cancer. Studies of persons
exposed to pesticides in manufacturing operations and as applicators
have shown relative risks of lung cancer ranging from 1.3 to 1.9 (4-
9). In some studies, risks increase with duration of exposure to
nearly 3-fold among persons exposed for 20 or more years (4,8).
Numerous studies from around the world have also noted excesses for
some cancers among farmers, particularly tumors of the lymphatic and
hematopoietic system (3, 10-15). Despite a considerable number of
studies suggesting that occupations having contact with pesticides
may experience elevated risks for certain cancers, the task of
identifying the specific pesticides involved in these associations
has proven difficult. Recent studies, however, have suggested that
phenoxyacetic acid herbicides may be involved (10-16).

To improve our capabilities of identifying cancer risks associated
with specific pesticides, we need to improve methods for evaluating
relevant historical exposures and to assess their reliability and
validity.

Methods Currently Used to Evaluate Exposures

Case-control and cohort methods have both been used in epidemiologic
studies of cancer and pesticides. Although the procedures for
evaluating exposures need not differ by study design, employment
records have generally been the major source of exposure information in cohort studies, whereas case-control studies have tended
to rely on interviews of subjects to obtain information on pesticide
exposure. Members of cohort studies, however, could be interviewed
and employment or other exposure records could be obtained for
subjects in case-control studies. Information from more than one
source has been sought in some studies, i.e., exposure records for
some subjects were obtained in case-control studies in Sweden (12)
and Kansas (11) and interviews have recently been completed with
selected subjects in a cohort study of Florida applicators (4).

Cohort Studies. Employment records used to identify persons exposed
to pesticides for historical cohort studies (4-9, 16-19) typically
contain personal identifiers (name, social security number, and date
of birth) and employment information, such as dates of employment
and job titles. These records seldom, however, contain sufficient
information to reconstruct a detailed history of pesticide exposure
associated with the job. For example, the cohort of licensed pesticide applicators from Florida (4) was established from licensing
records maintained by the state. The records contained, for each
individual, information on specific years licensed, company where
employed, and job title. However, they lacked information on each
pesticide application, which would be needed to reconstruct a
detailed exposure history. We have recently completed interviews of
next-of-kin of deceased cancer cases and a group of controls from
this cohort. In these interviews we obtained information on job
characteristics that should help in evaluating pesticide exposure,
such as general use of protective equipment, specific pesticides
applied, frequency of skin contact, and the occurrence of symptoms
commonly associated with pesticide poisoning. We did not ask for
information concerning individual applications because accurate
recall of such detail by the next-of-kin seemed unlikely. Although
information obtained from these interviews may improve our understanding of a subject's general exposure, the lack of detail on
dilution rates, volume of mixtures used, frequency of application,
and direct measures of exposure prevents the development of quantitative estimates of exposure to specific pesticides, or to
pesticides in general.

The National Cancer Institute recently initiated a cohort mortality
study of employees of ChemLawn, a major lawn care company. Again,
employment records contain information on job title and years
employed. Because ChemLawn has standardized pesticide formulations
and application procedures for various geographic regions of the
country, it may be possible to develop a semi-quantitative estimate
of exposure to pesticides for employees within these regions using
ambient air and biochemical monitoring data available from the
company. The existence of separate lawn care and tree/shrub
divisions provides another source of exposure information. There
has been little crossover between divisions in recent years, thus
the separation provides the opportunity to identify a group of
employees exposed to insecticides, but not herbicides, since tree
and shrub division employees do not apply herbicides. Despite this
relatively rich source of exposure information, it will not be
possible to reconstruct individual histories of applications.
Instead we must rely upon a general reconstruction of exposure based
on the usual work practices recommended by the company. Neither the
study of Florida applicators, nor of ChemLawn employees, offers the
opportunity to estimate specific daily exposures experienced by
individual cohort members. A record-keeping system that may provide
such detail has recently been brought to our attention. County
Noxious Weed Departments in Kansas are charged with controlling
weeds on private and public lands. These departments appear to
retain a detailed record of each pesticide application. Recorded in
the application records is the name of the applicator, herbicide

used, dilution, gallons applied, acres treated, time and date of treatment, climatic conditions, and type of spray equipment. Although these records represent a considerable improvement over those available in the studies previously described, they are not supported by historical monitoring data. Measurement of levels associated with current operations may provide important quantitative data, if we can establish that current operations are similar to those of the past.

Case-control Studies. Information on pesticide exposures in case-control studies is typically obtained by interview of subjects, or their next-of-kin (10-15, 20, 21). We have conducted studies of cancer in rural areas where the questionnaires have focused on specific pesticides used by farmers (11,13). In these studies we sought lifetime histories of specific pesticides used, earliest and last year of use, number of days per year typically used, type of application equipment, use of protiective equipment, symptoms associated with pesticide poisoning, and the frequency that soiled clothing is changed. Although these interviews obtain information on specific pesticides used, they do not provide information on each application. In addition, no monitoring of exposures has been conducted in conjunction with the interviews. Thus, information from questionnaires in our case-control studies resembles that assembled in most cohort studies in that detailed application histories cannot be reconstructed. Although it is possible to perform some exposure-response evaluations using information obtained from these interviews, it is complicated by the increasing inability of respondents to recall details of exposure with the passage of time, and by the potential for differences in recall between cases and controls. Differential recall is the more serious problem and may occur because cancer cases and their next-of-kin may have spent more time trying to recall past exposure to pesticides than person without cancer. This type of recall bias tends to create associations where none exist. The ability to recall the details regarding pesticide use may also fade with time. Unfortunately because of this problem, the accuracy of the information reported is weakest for earlier uses of pesticides, the very time period that is considered most important for diseases with long latencies such as cancer. On the other hand, a general failure to recall use of pesticides by all subjects (both cases and controls) would tend to have an effect opposite of that of differential recall bias and would generally reduce estimates of risk associated with pesticide exposure.

This type of recall problem would not be an explanation for any excesses observed.

Immediate Needs To Improve Exposure Evaluations

The goal of exposure evaluation is to develop detailed measures of delivered dose over the entire period of exposure. Delivered dose, however, is dependent upon pharmacokinetics and requires more biologic information than is generally available. Air measurements are sometimes available. Air monitoring, however, primarily

provides an indication of dose received by inhalation, which for
pesticides may be insignificant compared to that delivered dermally.
Although the availability of air monitoring and biochemical monitoring data is growing, these data are usually limited or nonexistent
for unregulated chemicals not clearly shown to be carcinogens, or to
present other health problems. In general, however, unless we are
content to wait for years until such monitoring data are assembled,
immediate efforts are needed to improve the quality and reliability
of the evaluation of pesticide exposure in epidemiologic studies
where monitoring data are limited. Assuming that we must continue
to use, at least for the immediate future, information obtained from
interview or personnel records to estimate exposures, we should make
every attempt to evaluate the reliability of these procedures and to
correlate them with measured levels of exposure. Several possibilities to accomplish this come to mind.

Simple Retest Reliability Studies. Although evaluation of test-
retest reliability is a well-establish principle in survey research,
we are unaware of such studies regarding interviews on pesticide
use. Most interview studies routinely include a small number of re-
interviews, primarily as a check on the interviewers. These could
easily be expanded to include crucial questions regarding pesticide
use to develop information on the reliability of subject recall.
Epidemiologists have conducted many such reliability studies for
other interview items such as tobacco use and diet, but we have not
adequately considered reported use of pesticides.

Comparison of Information from Different Sources. Confidence in
exposure estimates is improved when there is agreement between
evaluations from different experts or between evaluations based on
different information sources. Several possibilities for such
comparisons exist.

1. In a case-control study of lymphoma and soft-tissue sarcoma in
    Kansas (11), we attempted to corroborate farmers' reported
    pesticide use by contacting their pesticide suppliers. When
    available, supplier's records were reviewed to document pesti-
    cide purchases, otherwise we relied upon the memory of the
    supplier for corroboration. Overall, agreement between farmer
    and supplier regarding pesticide purchases was not high, i.e.
    about 50%. This is not surprising given the number of pesti-
    cides purchased, the long period of time over which farmers had
    made such purchases, the lack of historical purchase records
    retained by many suppliers, the large number of suppliers
    generally available to farmers, and the closing of establish-
    ments that had previously supplied farmers with pesticides.
    There was little difference in agreement rates, however, between
    cases and controls. For 2,4-D, agreement was 83% among cases of
    non-Hodgkin's lymphoma and 74% among controls. This is
    comforting in that at least risks associated with herbicide use
    seen in this study could not be attributed to recall bias. As
    expected, agreement was better for more recent, rather than for
    earlier years. Level of agreement also varied by type of
    pesticide and was better for herbicides than for insecticides.

In these comparisons it is not always clear whether the report by the subject or supplier is correct, since either the memory or the records of the supplier could also be incomplete.

Such duplicate assessments of exposure provide the opportunity to evaluate the influence of different reports of exposure on the estimate of relative risk. In this study adjusting the data for herbicide use as reported by suppliers had little effect on estimates of relative risk for non-Hodgkin's lymphoma. Further evaluation of these data and additional comparisons are needed to assess the magnitude and type of reporting errors from subjects and the influence of these errors on risk estimates.

2. The availability of detailed records on individual herbicide applications from County Noxious Weed Departments in Kansas offers the opportunity to compare information on herbicide use obtained from current interviews of applicators with information from records prepared at the time of the application. This would be especially useful in evaluating memory loss over time and the specific aspects of herbicide application that are most susceptible to inaccurate recall, including names of pesticides, application rates, formulations, frequencies of application, and use of protective equipment. Other opportunities of this type may exist elsewhere.

3. Comparison data from application records or interviewing with biochemical monitoring results offers the greatest potential to evaluate the reliability of, and to improve, our exposure assessment techniques. Biochemical monitoring for pesticide exposure has been conducted on small populations for a number of years and many new methods for biochemical monitoring are appearing. Monitoring studies generally indicate that the type of application equipment used and procedures followed at the time of application correlate with the exposure level measured. For epidemiologic studies of cancer it would be helpful to know how well individuals can recall pertinent details regarding application episodes that took place several years in the past. Re-interview of participants in early biochemical monitoring studies could assess how well individuals can recall important events surrounding these applications episodes. If accurate, data from recent interviews could be used to develop models to predict exposure levels measured at the time of the application. We are interested in exploring opportunities for developing such collaborative projects with researchers who may have biochemical monitoring data obtained several years ago.

4. Another approach to evaluate individual reports of pesticide use obtained by questionnaires would be to assemble a panel of experts to assess the plausibility of the types of pesticides used and the methods of application reported by study subjects. This would be a population, rather than an individual, comparison. Obviously, it would generally not be possible to determine whether or not a particular individual used a particular pesticide in a particular year. It might be possible, however, to

evaluate whether or not it was likely that a certain percentage
of subjects would have used a particular pesticide in a specific
year for a particular purpose. This is probably the weakest
approach for corroborating individual reports, because as
implausible as a reported practice may seem, it may in fact be
exactly what happened. This evaluation of the plausibility of
reports is often performed by the study of investigators, but it
would work better if entomologists, agricultural scientists,
toxicologists, and industrial hygienists knowledgeable in use of
pesticides perform the activity.

Ultimate Needs for Evaluation Of Pesticide Exposures

The ultimate goal of exposure evaluation in epidemiologic studies of
cancer is to identify the delivered dose of the active chemical to
the target tissue at the time relevant for tumor initiation or
promotion. The difficulties in achieving this goal for epidemiologic studies of cancer are many and may never be achieved.
Coupling biochemical measures with traditional exposure evaluation
procedures used in epidemiologic studies of cancer offers the best
opportunity for improving our assessment of historic pesticide
exposures. Although the utility of biochemical measures has been
clearly demonstrated for associating acute symptoms with pesticide
exposure, studies of cancer impose additional requirements.

As discussed above, the major limitation of biochemical measures is
that they are seldom available for the time period of greatest
interest. For early stage carcinogens, the time between first
exposure and diagnosis of disease is typically 20 or more years.
Unfortunately, many measures of pesticides or their metabolites in
body fluids or tissues reflect relatively recent exposures and must
be evaluated carefully to assess whether or not they are similar to,
or reflect, those from earlier times. Changes in the preferred
pesticide for a particular pest, in concentration and application
procedures, and in work practices make evaluation of exposure to
specific pesticides difficult. Biochemical measurements can,
however, help in relating intermittent exposures experience by
workers to exposures in bioassays.

Biochemical measures could, of course, be utilized in prospective
studies. Prospective cancer studies, however, require very large
populations which would need to be followed many years. Single
biochemical measures in prospective studies, although useful, would
not by themselves provide sufficient information to evaluate
cumulative dose, because they would provide an estimate of exposure
for a short period of time. Given the cost and complexity of sample
collection and analysis, repeat measurements on large numbers of
study subjects may not be practical.

Inclusion of biochemical monitoring in case-control studies offers
the advantage of much smaller numbers of subjects than are necessary
in prospective studies. A major drawback to case-control studies is
that the disease process itself, or its treatment, may affect the
concentration of the chemical being measured.

Another limitation in most epidemiologic studies of pesticides and cancer is the difficulty in assessing the independent effects of specific pesticides. Biochemical monitoring is no more useful in tackling this problem than the more traditional exposure evaluation methods, since the fundamental problem is multiple exposures and identification of which agent is responsible for the disease, not the precision with which measurements are made.

We have not addressed many pertinent technical issues including reliability of the laboratory analyses, difficulty in preserving and transporting the samples, effects of interferences from other environmental exposures, and half-life and metabolism of the substances. Obviously some pesticides are rapidly eliminated from the body, while others may be measured years after exposure. These are very important issues for epidemiologic studies, but measurement of pesticides with long half-lives could provide a general indication of cumulative exposure.

Conclusions

Biochemical measures can supplement traditional methods of exposure evaluation used in epidemiologic studies of cancer and exposure to pesticides. Such measures can provide more solid estimates of delivered dose than estimates based on patches, on ambient air measures, on those strictly from job descriptions, or on subject reports of pesticide use. The limited number of biochemical measures likely to be available (on only a sample of the study population, for only a few pesticides, for only a few points in time) implies that other procedures for evaluating pesticide exposure will still be required. Biochemical measures can be very useful in developing more reliable procedures to estimate exposures based on work practices by relating differences in exposure associated with tank size, type of spray system, use of protective equipment and other information that may be obtained from work history records or interview. Efforts to evaluate the reliability and validity of procedures combining data from various sources are needed.

Literature Cited

1. International Agency for Research on Cancer. IARC Monographs on the Evaluation of the Carcinogenic Risk of Chemicals to Humans. Vol. 20. Lyon, France. 1979.
2. International Agency for Research on Cancer. IARC Monographs on the Evaluation of the Carcinogenic Risk of Chemicals to Humans. Vol. 30. Lyon, France. 1983.
3. Blair, A.; Malker, H.; Cantor, K.P.; Burmeister, L.; Wiklund, K. Scand. J. Work Environ. Health. 1985, 11, 397.
4. Blair, A.; Grauman, D.J.; Lubin, J.H.; Fraumeni, J.F., Jr. J. Nat. Cancer Inst. 1983, 71, 31.
5. Kauppinen, T.P.; Partenen, T.J.; Nurminen, N.M.; Nickels, J.I.; Hernberg, S.G.; Hakulinen, J.R.; Pukkala, E.I.; Savonen, E.T. Br. J. Industr. Med. 1986, 43, 84.

6. Wang, H.H.,; MacMahon, B.   J. Occupat. Med. 1979, 21, 741.
7. Ditraglia, D.; Brown, D.P.; Namekata, T.; Iverson, N.   Scand. J. Work Environ. Health 1981, 7 (Suppl. 4), 140.
8. Barthel, E.   J. Toxic. Environ. Health. 1981, 8, 1027.
9. Wang, H.H.; MacMahon, B.   J. Occupat. Med. 1979, 21, 745.
10. Hardell, L.; Eriksson, M.; Lenner, P.; Lundgren, E.   Br. J. Cancer. 1981, 43, 169.
11. Hoar, S.K.; Blair, A.; Holmes, F.; Boysen, C.; Robel, R.J.; Hoover, R.; Fraumeni, J.F., Jr.   J. Amer. Med. Assoc. 1986, 256, 1141.
12. Hardell, L.; Sandstrom, A.   Br. J. Cancer. 1979, 39, 711.
13. Blair, A.; Cantor, K.P.; Zahm, S.H.; Burmeister, L.; Van Lier, S.; Gibson, R.; Schuman, L.   Proceedings of Pesticides and Groundwater. St. Paul, MN. October, 1986.
14. Woods, J.S.; Polissar, L.; Severson, R.K.; Heauser, L.S.; Kulander, B.G.   J. Nat. Cancer Inst. 1987, 78, 899.
15. Vineis, P.; Terracini, B.T.; Ciccone, G.; Cignetti, A.; Colombo, E.; Donna, A.; Maffi, L.; Pisa, R.; Ricci, P.; Zanini, E.; Comba, P.   Scand. J. Work Environ. Health. 1987, 13, 9.
16. Lynge, E.   Br. J. Cancer. 1985, 52, 259.
17. Riihimaki, V.; Asp, S.; Hernberg, S.   Scand. J. Work Environ. Health. 1982, 8, 37.
18. Ott, M.G.; Holder, B.B.; Olson, R.D.   J. Occupat. Med. 1980, 22, 47.
19. Axelson, O.; Sundell, L.; Andersson, K.; Edling, C.; Hogstedt, C.; Kling, H.   Scand. J. Work Environ. Health. 1980, 7, 73.
20. Smith, A.H.; Pearce, N.E.; Fisher, D.O.; Giles, H.J.; Teague, C.A.; Howard, J.K.   J. Nat. Cancer Inst. 1984, 73, 1111.
21. Pearce, N.E.; Smith, A.J.; Howard, J.K.; Sheppard, R.A.; Giles, H.J.; Teague, C.A.   Br. J. Industr. Med. 1986, 43, 75.

RECEIVED July 5, 1988

Chapter 4

Evaluation of Field Worker Exposure to Chlordimeform by Using Urine Monitoring

K. Balu

Agricultural Division, Ciba–Geigy Corporation, Greensboro, NC 27419

Chlordimeform, the active ingredient of Galecron 4E, is
an effective insecticide-ovicide used in cotton.
Chlordimeform is readily absorbed and is rapidly excreted
in urine following dermal, oral and inhalation exposure.
     CIBA-GEIGY Corporation has conducted extensive urine
monitoring of field workers for several years under field
use conditions which employ aerial applications on cotton.
Over 38,000 urine samples have been analyzed for chlordimeform and metabolites during 1978-1984 for approximately 4,600 field workers. These data provide a significant statistical validity for assessing the field worker
exposure during actual use.

Chlordimeform, N'-(4-chloro-o-tolyl)N,N-dimethyl formamidine, the
active ingredient of Galecron 4E, is an effective insecticide-
ovicide used in cotton. CIBA-GEIGY Corporation conducted extensive
urine monitoring of field workers during the years 1978-1984 growing
seasons under field use conditions using aerial applications of
chlordimeform on cotton. Over 38,600 urine samples were analyzed
during this period for approximately 4,600 field workers. The
purpose of the urine monitoring of field workers was to provide a
measure of the daily worker exposure and adherence to safe work
practices. This report summarizes the results of these studies
along with additional supportive data on the urine monitoring of
chlordimeform.

STUDY DESIGN AND LIMITATIONS

Because the worker exposure of chlordimeform was conducted under
actual field use conditions for a large number of field workers, the
urine monitoring program had a few necessary limitations which were
a) urine residues were determined on a grab sample rather than on a

0097–6156/89/0382–0047$06.00/0
○ 1989 American Chemical Society

24-hour total collection for the field worker, b) total daily urine output of individual workers was not measured, and c) exposure of field workers during the work period was variable. This is significantly different from a controlled field experiment where individual work activity would be extensively monitored for an exposure of short duration.

The exposure estimate obtained from a single grab sample is only approximate for a field worker. However, when a large number of samples are analyzed in the monitoring program (e.g., 13,779 urine samples analyzed from 866 field workers in 1978 alone), the exposure estimates become meaningful. However, it is recognized that collection of urine samples were not randomized in a true statistical sense and hence an unknown bias may exist in the statistical interpretation of the data. Daily exposure values for field workers are expected to show a range of values distributed around mean and median values. Some of the higher exposure values may be caused by uncontrolled variables such as accidental spills, clean-up operations, exposure to contaminated surfaces, etc. The mean or median value for exposure is more relevant for risk estimation of chlordimeform than individual excursions from the mean.

The concentration of chlordimeform and its metabolites in a urine specimen will fluctuate according to normal physiological variables. Urine volume is influenced by fluid intake and non-urinary fluid losses which are influenced by climatic conditions, individual health status, physical activity, etc. Hence, the concentration of chlordimeform and its metabolites in urine collected arbitrarily during the day provide only a qualitative indication of the exposure on a particular day. Attempts were made initially to obtain the first urine void of the morning; however, because of the large number of people involved in the monitoring program, the time of sampling could not be strictly controlled.

The urinary elimination of dermally absorbed chlordimeform as a single dose is expected to follow the plasma level and approximate a log normal distribution as a function of time as shown by the excretion curve in Figure 1 (1). In contrast, the urinary excretion curve for a continuous exposure is expected to show a large plateau. The exposure to field workers handling chlordimeform under field conditions is expected to be intermittent with varying amounts of dose depending on the work activity. The excretion curve under this circumstance will result in broader peak but also troughs, i.e., something in between the sharp peak and the plateau. Hence, urine sample taken at any time during the day is expected to be unpredictable as to whether it represents a peak or a trough in the excretion pattern.

Dermal absorption studies on human volunteers in which chlordimeform was applied up to nine hours dermally, showed that the majority of the absorbed dose is excreted in the urine rapidly within 24 hours with a peak maximum of 8-12 hours. Details of these studies are presented in unpublished reports (1,2). Also, urine monitoring studies conducted by Maddy et. al. (3) on California farm workers in 1982 have shown close agreement between chlordimeform concentrations measured in urine specimens collected the following morning. Under certain circumstances when significant exposures are encountered through accidental spills, there could be differences in

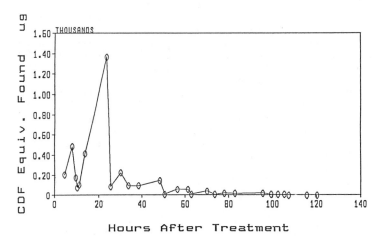

Figure 1. Excretion curve for chlordimeform. Single-dose dermal application to human.

the urinary residues in the evening of the day of exposure and the next morning. However, it should be recognized that collection of urine samples at a specified interval is impractical when dealing with a large number of field workers for a long period.

METHODS

Field Monitoring

The label directions for Galecron 4E specified for mixing and loading, using closed system equpment, personal protective clothing requirements and precautions were followed during the study. Bulk handling systems were employed for closed-system storage and transfer of Galecron 4E through 1981. Bulk system was largely replaced with an automated Captain Crunch® device using 5-gallon containers at later periods to meet the closed system requirements.

Protective clothing requirements were specified on the Galecron 4E label to reduce worker exposure during handling, mixing and aerial applications. These protective clothing requirements included heavy-duty, long-sleeve, one-piece work suit; cloth caps; rubber or neoprene-type gloves; and heavy-duty work boots. Special protective clothing and equipment specified for cleaning or spill situations included complete waterproof rubberized or plastic rain suits with head coverings and approved pesticide respirators. It should be noted that these protective clothing and equipment requirements may not have been strictly followed under actual use conditions. However, because of closed-system requirements, the mixing and loading operation provides very little opportunity for exposure. Exposures to mixer/loaders and applicators at the site where thought to be primarily caused by the cleanup operation of the aircraft, inadequate use of gloves during adjustments of the spray nozzle and other indirect causes.

CIBA-GEIGY Corporation also conducted extensive worker exposure studies in 1982 under an Experimental Use Permit for aerial applications of chlordimeform in oil using ultra-low-volume (ULV) sprays. Because the study was conducted under actual use conditions, use of oil as the only carrier during the growing season was not practical and most participating aerial application sites applied Galecron 4E in both oil and water. Field worker exposure during this period is thought to have occurred during clean-up of aircraft and equipment during switching of the carriers.

Laboratory Studies

Laboratory studies have shown that chlordimeform is readily absorbed and excreted in urine following dermal, oral and inhalation exposure. Oral dosing of ring ^{14}C-labelled chlordimeform to rats or mice showed that approximately 85% and 74%, respectively, of the applied radioactivity was excreted in the urine during the initial 24 hours (4). These results are in good agreement with the data obtained by Knowles and Sengupta (5) in which 88% of the applied dose in the rat was recovered in urine.

An absorption/excretion study was conducted in 1978 in which a
human volunteer received a single dermal dose of Galecron 4E in
water for a duration of nine hours (1). This study showed that
chlordimeform and its metabolites are rapidly excreted in the urine.
Majority of the metabolites of chlordimeform appeared as conjugates
which were released as 4-chloro-o-toluidine by base hydrolysis.
Analyses of 48-hour urine sample by the 4-chloro-o-toluidine common
moiety method accounted for approximately 40% of the dermally
absorbed dose. This formed the basis for the method to determine
the exposure of chlordimeform to field workers.

CIBA-GEIGY Corporation conducted an additional dermal study in
1983 using eight human volunteers who received a single dose of
Galecron 4E in water for a period of four hours (2). This study
also confirmed that an average of 38.3% of the absorbed dose was
accounted for by urine analyses for chlordimeform and its metabolites containing the 4-chloro-o-toluidine common moiety. The half-
life for excretion varied between subjects from 5.9 hours to 12.1
hours with an average of 8.8 hours.

The excretion pattern found in the human study is consistent
with that found in the rat and the mouse study using oral dosing
(4). Based on the results of ^{14}C-metabolism studies on animals, the
majority of the undetected portion represents metabolites in the
urine which the analytical method does not recover. A buildup of
chlordimeform residues in any tissue is unlikely, since animal
studies have shown exclusively the entire radioactive dose in the
excreta.

Analytical Procedure

The urine samples collected in the field worker exposure studies
were analyzed for total chlordimeform residues containing the
4-chloro-o-toluidine common moiety (6). In this method, the urine
sample was hydrolyzed to 4-chloro-o-toluidine by heating with sodium
hydroxide.

The hydrolyzed urine was cooled and partitioned with hexane and
an aliquot of the organic phase was analyzed by gas chromatography
or high pressure liquid chromatography (HPLC). The limit of detection for the method was 0.05 ppm, expressed in chlordimeform equivalents. The method for the analyses of chlordimeform and metabolites
in urine and other unpublished reports cited in the references will
be available on request.

Estimation of Worker Exposure

Worker exposure values were calculated from the urine residues using
some reasonable assumptions. Assuming an average excretion volume
of 1,500 ml/day, 90% elimination in urine (10% eliminated other than
urine, primarily feces based on animal data) and 40% detection of
chlordimeform residues in urine by the total method (based on the
accountability in the human volunteer studies), the urinary
residues, in ppm, was correlated with the dermal dose using the
following relationship:

$$\text{Body Burden} = (\text{Urine Residue, ppm}) \times 1{,}500 \text{ ml} \times \frac{100}{90} \times \frac{100}{40}$$

$$= (\text{Urine Residue, ppm}) \times 4.16 \text{ mg/day}$$

Where the body burden is the amount of the dermal dose absorbed through the skin.

Assuming an average weight of 70 kg for a field worker, the average exposure estimate for the field worker using chlordimeform is calculated from the urine monitoring data as

$$\text{Body Burden} = (\text{Urine Residue, ppm}) \times .0595 \text{ mg/kg/day}$$

RESULTS AND DISCUSSION

The number of samples, workers monitored and the distribution profiles for mixer/loaders and other workers (including pilots) during the years 1978-1984 are summarized in Tables I and II. These results show a remarkable similarity in the distribution profiles during different years.

TABLE I: SUMMARY OF PERCENT DAILY VALUE DISTRIBUTION FOR MIXER/LOADERS EXPOSED TO CHLORDIMEFORM DURING 1978-1984

Year	1978[1]	1979[1]	1980[1]	1981[1]	1982[2]	1984[2]	Total
No. of Samples	8,223	4,408	2,886	1,986	505	96	18,104
No. of Workers	352	597	650	381	34	7	2,021

PPM Range				%			
<0.05-0.10	78[3]	46	51	55	52	53	
0.1 -0.3		23	22	18	10	28	
0.3 -0.5	16[3]	10	8.1	6.8	7.4	6.3	
0.5 -1.0		11	8.5	7.7	12	10	
1.0 -5.0	5.6	9.2	9.1	10	18	2.1	
>5.0	0.5	1.9	1.0	1.6	1.4	0	

[1]Used water as a carrier.
[2]Used both water and oil carrier in ULV (with 1984 predominately using oil-ULV).
[3]Combined values for <0.3 ppm and 0.3-1.0 ppm, respectively.

The results of the 1982 worker exposure study showed a two-fold increase in exposure values exceeding 0.5 ppm to mixer/loaders (Table I) compared to the previous years, when water only was used as a carrier. However, during the 1982 study period, most of the application sites switched between water and oil carriers and excursions in exposure might have been caused by the additional equipment handling when switching between water and oil as a carrier. In exposure studies conducted in 1984 (where predominantly oil-ULV was used), the distribution profile was quite similar to the years in which only water was used as a carrier. Also, the 1984 values showed daily urine residues generally close to the detection limit and very few exceeding 1 ppm. Hence, it appears from the 1984 study and earlier data that chlordimeform exposure to field workers using closed systems and protective clothing was probably caused by uncontrollable factors, such as site contaminations, work habits, or cleanup operations.

The median for the daily value distribution for field workers is less than 0.1 ppm; 52-70% of the daily urine values were below 0.1 ppm (Table II).

TABLE II: SUMMARY OF PERCENT DAILY VALUE DISTRIBUTION (PPM) FOR PILOTS AND OTHER WORKERS EXPOSED TO CHLORDIMEFORM DURING 1978-1984

Year	1978[1]	1979[1]	1980[1]	1981[1]	1982[2]	1984[2]	Total
No. of Samples	5,556	8,380	3,806	2,021	730	81	20,574
No. of Workers	514	1,826	787	402	47	5	2,581
PPM Range				%			
<0.05-0.10	90[4]	66	63	68	74	74	
0.1 -0.3		19	21	17	11	20	
0.3 -0.5	6.9[4]	5.3	5.4	4.7	7.7	3.7	
0.5 -1.0		4.8	5.7	5.8	2.9	1.2	
1.0 -5.0	3.0	4.1	4.5	4.4	4.2	1.2	
>5.0	0.3	0.4	0.7	0.4	0.3	0	

[1]Used water as a carrier.
[2]Used both water and oil carrier in ULV (with 1984 predominately using oil-ULV).
[3]Combined values for <0.3 ppm and 0.3-1.0 ppm, respectively.

These results also show that approximately 75% of the daily urine values for all field workers were below 0.3 ppm. Only 6-7% of all the samples for the field workers (10.1% or 3.8% of the mixer/ loaders or pilots and other workers, respectively) showed daily urine values exceeding 1 ppm. It is important to note that although urine values exceeded 1 ppm for some field workers on some days, these values for the individual workers decreased on subsequent days. Hence, considering only the maximum daily exposure for a field worker will over-estimate exposure on a seasonal basis. The median value for the daily value distribution found in the CIBA-GEIGY urine monitoring studies of Galecron is in close agreement with the daily average value of 0.13 ppm obtained by Maddy et al. (3) for worker exposure to chlordimeform in the Imperial Valley in California during the 1982 cotton growing season.

A seasonal cumulative value distribution for all the field workers during the years 1978 and 1979 is summarized in Table III. The cumulative seasonal exposure value for a field worker is the projected sum of all the average daily urine values during the entire growing season.

TABLE III: CUMULATIVE VALUE DISTRIBUTION (PPM) FOR ALL FIELD
             WORKERS AS MEASURED FROM URINE SAMPLES

Cumulative Range (ppm)	No. of Workers	1978 % Distribution	No. of Workers	1979 % Distribution
<5	530	61.2	1,015	73.3
5-10	175	20.2	259	15.6
10-20	100	11.5	185	11.2
20-30	34	3.9	78	4.7
30-60	21	2.4	48	2.9
>60	6	0.7	38	2.3
Total No. of Personnel	866	100.0	1,623	100.0

These data show that 61.2-73.3% of the 2,489 monitored workers
during these years showed a total cumulative seasonal value of <5
ppm. For the purpose of calculation of the cumulative values, all
the urine samles containing residues below the 0.05 ppm screening
level were assigned a value of 0.05 ppm and hence the total cumulative value is expected to be conservatively higher than they would
be using the actual values for samples <0.05 ppm. A small percent
(3.1-5.2%) of the field workers showed seasonal cumulative values
exceeding 30 ppm.
       California Department of Food and Agriculture (CDFA) conducted
extensive urine monitoring of chlordimeform in California during the
1982-1985 growing seasons. These data were presented by
Maddy et al. (7) at the 6th International Conference on Pesticide
Chemistry (IUPAC) at Ottawa, Canada. In the four years of monitoring, approximately 8,800 field applications of chlordimeform were
made at 0.25 lbs. ai/acre on an average size of 80 acres, and
approximately 200 field workers were monitored. These studies
showed that the chlordimeform urine residues for the field workers
averaged 0.09 ppm, and did not increase during the work season. The
level of chlordimeform residues in urine at the end of the work
shift was similar to that found 8 to 10 hours later. The urine
monitoring data in the CDFA studies are in good agreement with the
extensive data obtained by CIBA-GEIGY on urine monitoring of the
field workers exposed to chlordimeform.

CONCLUSIONS

Based on laboratory animal metabolism and studies with human
volunteers, the amount of total chlordimeform residues containing
the 4-chloro-o-toluidine common moiety recovered in the urine
following dermal application of chlordimeform is approximately 40%
of the dermally absorbed dose. These studies have also shown that
chlordimeform and its metabolites are rapidly excreted in the urine.
This approach has been used by CIBA-GEIGY Corporation to monitor
exposure of a large number of field workers and applicators.

The extensive urine monitoring conducted by CIBA-GEIGY provides a large data base for evaluating worker exposure to chlordimeform under actual use conditions. The reproducibility of the urinary distribution profiles of chlordimeform in these data allow for evaluation of the field worker exposure to chlordimeform under actual use conditions.

REFERENCES

1. Camp, H. B., ABR-78005, "Chlordimeform Residues in Human Urine Following Dermal Applications," CIBA-GEIGY Corporation, Greensboro, NC, January 1978.
2. Nixon, W. B., B. E. Neal, "Chlordimeform Residues in Human Urine Following Dermal Applications," July 11, 1983.
3. Maddy, K. T., P. H. Kurtz, Dennis Gibbons, Linda O'Connell, "Preliminary Report on Health Monitoring of Pest Control Workers Exposed to Chlordimeform in Imperial Valley During the 1982 Cotton Growing Season," Report No. HS-1064, Division of Pest Management, California Department of Food and Agriculture, Sacramento, CA, April 1, 1983.
4. Ifflaander, U., Project Report 39/77, "Comparison of the Urinary Metabolite Pattern of Mice and Rats After Oral Application of ^{14}C-Chlordimeform," CIBA-GEIGY Limited, Basle, Switzerland, August 18, 1987.
5. Knowles, C. O., Sen Gupta, A. K., J. Econ. Entomol., 1970, 63, 856-9.
6. Cheung, M., "Chlordimeform Methods for Biological Monitoring," CIBA-GEIGY Corporation, Greensboro, NC. Presented at ACS Symposium on Biological Monitoring, September 1987, New Orleans (Not Published), available on request.
7. Maddy, K. L., J. B. Knaak, D. B. Gibbons, "Monitoring of the Urine of Pesticide Applicators in California for Residues of Chlordimeform and Its Metabolites," 1982-1985, Sixth International Conference of Pesticide Chemistry (IUPAC), Ottawa, Canada, 1986.

RECEIVED June 24, 1988

Chapter 5

Convenient Field Sampling Method for Monitoring Volatile Compounds in Exhaled Breath

Michael S. Morgan, Gary S. Phillips, and Eileen M. Kirkpatrick

Department of Environmental Health, University of Washington, Seattle, WA 98195

A modified half-face air purifying respirator was developed as a technique for large-scale monitoring that will be acceptable to workers, simple to apply, and relatively sensitive. Exhaled air was directed through the respirator exhaust port and then through a two-part cartridge. The first part contained four layers of activated charcoal cloth which adsorbed organic solvent vapors; the cloth was subsequently desorbed for gas chromatographic analysis. The second part contained 70 g of 8-12 mesh molecular sieve whose weight gain (water) was proportional to the volume of air exhaled. The proportionality was determined by independent measurement of volume in subjects while at rest and while exercising. Controlled atmospheres containing toluene at relative humidities near saturation were passed through the cartridge at steady flows equal to resting human ventilatory rates. Toluene recovery was 70% for simulated breath concentrations of 0.75 mg/m^3 to 60 mg/m^3 (0.20 ppm to 16 ppm). Normal adults volunteered to breathe toluene in air at 150 mg/m^3 (40 ppm) or 340 mg/m^3 (90 ppm) for four hours (TLV = 375 mg/m^3 or 100 ppm, 8 hr TWA). About eighteen hours later their breath was sampled, to simulate a worksite measurement at the start of the next shift. Samples of at least 140 liters were taken from each subject, and the mean exhaled concentrations were 344 µg/m^3 and 600 µg/m^3 (0.23% and 0.18% of exposure TWA), respectively, in good agreement with literature reports using more complicated methods not appropriate for field application. The device can be used to collect samples of up to 300 liters in 30 minutes, and its sensitivity and selectivity are then limited only by the desorption and analysis of the charcoal adsorbent. The lower limit of quantitation for toluene, with conventional GC analysis, was about 65 µg/m^3 (18 ppb). The technique can be applied to most solvents capable of adsorption on charcoal, and will permit sampling large numbers of workers with minimal job disruption. In a limited field application, automobile body painters showed levels of toluene in their exhaled breath that could not be

0097–6156/89/0382–0056$06.00/0
© 1989 American Chemical Society

explained by inhalation exposure alone; observations
of frequent skin contact with the solvent suggested
that important skin absorption also occurred, and the
breath levels reflected the workers' total solvent
exposure.

Among methods available for biological monitoring, exhaled breath
analysis offers potential advantages as it is less intrusive than
drawing blood and often gives a better reflection of blood
composition than does urinalysis. The appearance of volatile
compounds in exhaled breath after industrial exposure has been
demonstrated in several instances (1-7). Table I shows some
examples, together with solubility data which suggest means of
identifying other compounds as candidates for this form of
biological monitoring. However, breath analysis has not become
widespread in the workplace because of practical problems in
sampling large numbers of workers and in interpreting the results.
Because concentrations of contaminants in exhaled air are low and
the air is moist, previous research has relied either on elaborate
and expensive equipment or on sampling methods subject to
moisture-related loss of contaminant. Further, evaluating the
results of breath sampling requires consideration of the complex
excretion kinetics of most volatile compounds and of the effects
of respiratory dead space on the composition of exhaled breath.
The last point has led to efforts to sample alveolar air by
procedures requiring much cooperation from the worker. This work
addresses some of these problems. A portable, simplified breath
sampling system has been developed which is suitable for mass
screening, is capable of collecting a relatively large sample, and
gives good performance in sampling moist air.

Table I.   Materials Shown to be Present in Exhaled Breath after
Industrial Exposure

| Compounds | --Partition Coefficients-- | | | Found in | |
	Blood/Air	Fat/Air	Oil/Air	Breath at[A]	Ref.
Benzene	6 - 8	425	492	20 hours	15,24
Toluene	10-16	962	1470	20 hours	12
Xylene	26-38	-	3700	20 hours	25
Methyl Ethyl Ketone	200	140	260	2 hours	26
Ethylene Oxide	90	-	-	0 hours	27
Trichloroethylene	8-10	560-660	700-940	20 hours	5
Chloroform	8-10	280	400-560	0 hours	28
Methylchloroform	3	250		20 hours	29
Carbon Tetrachloride	2-6	360		6 hours	30

[A] Time measured from the end of the exposure period

The primary value in breath sampling lies in the fact that
alveolar gas is very nearly in equilibrium with arterial blood
(Figure 1). Mixed expired air, however, is not equal in
composition to alveolar air, because of the addition of air from
the respiratory dead space. Nevertheless, for samples taken over
periods of ten minutes or more, such that all the expired air is

collected and its volume measured, there is usually a predictable
relationship between alveolar and mixed expired air, so that the
latter can still be used to make estimates of the blood levels of
trace compounds.(1-3)   A more serious problem in sampling either
alveolar or mixed expired air is the effect of the passage of time
after exposure has ended. Models and experimental measurements of
excretion kinetics of volatile compounds have shown that within
two to four hours after the end of exposure, the breath levels
decrease rapidly, and are strongly correlated with the
concentration in the inhaled air at the end of exposure.(4-6)   At
longer times post-exposure, the breath levels are less time
dependent, and are more closely proportional to the time weighted
average exposure, or body burden, of the compound.(5)
      The use of breath analysis in monitoring pesticide exposure
has not yet been reported, but this general approach has potential
value for certain kinds of pesticide formulations. Table II
presents some examples of pesticide components which have
physicochemical properties which favor their excretion, at least
in part, in breath. Suitable compounds must be volatile, and must
have solubility properties in blood and body fat that are close to
the ranges given in Table I. Many of the fumigants used in
agriculture meet these requirements, and a few have actually been
found in the breath of workers exposed in experimental or
industrial settings. In addition, many of the vehicles used in
pesticide formulations are good candidates for breath monitoring,
and examples are included in Table II.

Table II. Pesticide Components with Physicochemical Properties
Favoring the Use of Exhaled Breath for Biological Monitoring

Compound	Volatile	Lipid Soluble	Breath Data Available	Refs
Chloropicrin	x			
Methylisocyanate	x			
Ethylene Dichloride	x	x	x	28
HCN	x			
Sulfuryl Fluoride	x			
Vapam	x			
Dichloropropylene	x	x		
Dichloropropane	x	x		
Methyl Chloroform	x	x	x	29
Ethylene Oxide	x	x	x	27
Naphthalene	x	x		
p-Dichlorobenzene	x	x		
Methyl Bromide	x	x		
Methyl Isothiocyanate	x			
Diesel fuel	x	x		
Kerosene	x	x		
Methanol	x	x	x	31
Petroleum distillates	x	x		
Xylene	x	x	x	25
Toluene	x	x	x	12

      The goal of the work described here was to design and
demonstrate a field-portable technique for sampling mixed expired

air for volatile compounds, at times long after exposure when the breath level is indicative of body burden. The use of mixed expired air represents a concession to the need for simplicity in sampling, but the method should still give a result useful in biological monitoring. The sampling method was demonstrated in human volunteers long after a relatively low inhalation exposure (as low as 20% of the occupational Threshold Limit Value, TLV), as a severe test of performance. Results will also be presented for field studies with workers exposed to solvents in the automobile repair industry.

Materials and Methods

Sampler Design and Performance

The sampler is based on a half-face, dual cartridge respirator whose inhalation ports are fitted with standard air purifying elements.(7) On the exhalation port is mounted a special cartridge for sampling exhaled air. The operating principle of this cartridge is based on: a.) quantitative adsorption of organic vapors and subsequent analysis by standard methods, and b.) determination of the air volume sampled by taking advantage of the nearly invariant concentration of water vapor in expired air among individuals over a wide range of activity levels.(8,9)

The sampling cartridge is shown in cutaway view in Figure 2. The upper section contains four layers of activated charcoal cloth mounted in pairs separated by teflon gaskets. This adsorbent is a woven material (Charcoal Cloth Limited, Maidenhead, United Kingdom) having properties similar to granular charcoal, except that its collection performance, based on studies with volatile anesthetics, is reported to be much better at high water vapor content.(10) The lower section contains 70 g of 8 - 12 mesh molecular sieve of 3 Å pore size which collects the water vapor (maximum capacity 14 g water vapor per 100 g adsorbent). The organic vapors collected on the charcoal cloth were recovered by desorption of paired layers in 10 ml carbon disulfide for one hour. The eluent was analyzed by gas chromatograph using a flame ionization detector following recommended procedures.(11) Generally, the cloth layer pairs were analyzed separately to permit detection of breakthrough past the first pair of layers. The collected water vapor was determined gravimetrically. The cartridge was fabricated from poly vinyl chloride pipe with stainless steel screens to retain the adsorbents. The loaded cartridge weighed about 180 ± 10 g, and thus added about 60% to the weight of the respirator. Resistance to airflow through the cartridge was less than 2 cm $H_2O/L/s$ at flow rates up to 1 L/s.

The sampling cartridge was tested for recovery efficiency with controlled atmospheres designed to simulate human breath containing low levels of organic vapor. Toluene was selected for this study as it is used in large quantities in industry and studies of its toxicokinetics have been reported by several authors.(2,12-15) The atmospheres were generated in a 90 liter glass mixing chamber equipped with a cooled-mirror dew point hygrometer and a photoionization detector. The detector was calibrated before and after the study using a capillary diffusion tube (16). Compressed breathing quality air was passed through a high efficiency filter and a bed of granular charcoal before entering the chamber at 40 L/min. Water was atomized into the chamber, and liquid toluene was metered via motor-driven syringe through a heated metal tube.

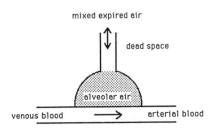

Figure 1 -- Schematic diagram of the relationship among venous
blood, arterial blood, alveolar air and mixed expired air, with
respect to concentration of a volatile material. "p" refers to
the partial pressure of the volatile component of interest.

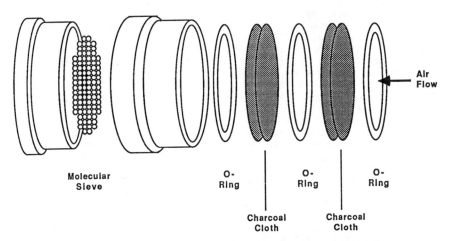

Figure 2 -- Cutaway view of the breath sampling cartridge
showing the section for organic solvent vapor collection and
the section for moisture collection; the two sections nest
tightly together when in use. The solvent section is threaded
to fit a standard respirator cartridge holder which is mounted
in the exhaust port of the mask.

Both relative humidity (RH) and solvent concentration were
monitored continuously. The generator was capable of producing
stable atmospheres at between 5% and 95% RH and containing between
0.38 mg/m^3 (0.1 ppm) and 1500 mg/m^3 (400 ppm) of toluene.
Recovery data were obtained over a range of RH and air
temperatures, whose selection was based on preliminary
measurements of the air stream leaving respirators while being
worn. Cartridges were challenged with 10 L/min air containing
toluene at levels between 0.75 mg/m^3 (0.20 ppm) and 150 mg/m^3 (40
ppm) for 30 minutes based on the results of toxicokinetic studies.

To determine the relationship between water vapor collected
and the volume of expired air sampled, a group of six volunteers
wore the respirator while at rest or while walking on a treadmill
at various work levels. The resulting pulmonary ventilation rates
ranged from 4 L/min to 28 L/min. Expired air was passed through
the sampling cartridge in series with a calibrated
pneumotachometer. The flow signal from the pneumotachometer was
integrated electronically to give an accurate measurement of air
volume. The weight gain of the molecular sieve in the cartridge
was then compared to the independent measurement of volume. The
sampling periods were between fourteen and twenty minutes.

Performance in Controlled Human Exposures

As a demonstration of the device under realistic conditions of
use, healthy adult male volunteers were recruited for a laboratory
study. After giving informed consent, each subject was sampled
for the baseline level of toluene in expired breath. Then air at
50% RH containing toluene at 150 mg/m^3 (40 ppm) or 340 mg/m^3 (90
ppm) was passed through a mask covering the subject's nose and
mouth at 35 L/min, for four hours. Between 17 and 20 hours later,
corresponding to the start of the next work shift, a breath sample
was taken and analyzed. The sampling procedure consisted of first
wearing the respirator without the special sampling cartridge for
seven to ten minutes to allow air temperature and RH inside the
mask to stabilize. Then the sampling cartridge was attached and
the subject continued to breathe at rest for 15 to 20 min. The
cartridge was then disassembled and the adsorbents were analyzed
within one hour. Routine sampling of laboratory ambient air
indicated that toluene levels were always less than 10 µg/m^3.

The observed breath concentrations were corrected for the
dilution effect of the respirator cavity dead space. In a
separate experiment, the correction factor for each subject was
estimated by measuring the concentration of carbon dioxide in
mixed expired air collected: a.) at the respirator outlet port and
b.) at the mouth. It was assumed that the dilution of expired
carbon dioxide by the respirator dead space approximates closely
the dilution of expired trace organics.

Performance in Industrial Settings

Eleven painters employed in five automobile body repair and
repainting shops were then studied, with the intent of determining
whether or not breath concentrations of toluene used as a solvent
compared to traditional measurements of the solvent in breathing
zone ambient air. Breath samples were collected for fifteen
minutes before the beginning of each shift for five consecutive
days in each painter. During the sampling period no painting was
done, and standard organic vapor cartridges were attached to the

inlet ports of the sampling respirator, to ensure that no exposure occurred. During each shift toluene concentrations in each worker's breathing zone were measured, as the 8 hour time-weighted average, using a passive dosimeter incorporating activated charcoal.(17) Samples were collected using the Model 530-11 dosimeter of SKC Inc., Fullerton, CA. The charcoal elements were desorbed in 2.0 ml carbon disulfide and the eluent analyzed by the procedure cited earlier. Recovery efficiency for dosimeters was taken from manufacturer's literature. All painters were observed during at least part of each shift, to determine the use of gloves and respiratory protection, and to estimate the extent of skin contact with liquid paint solvent.

Results

Overall recovery of toluene from the charcoal cloth was calculated as the mass determined after collection and desorption, divided by the mass presented to the charcoal determined from air volume and toluene concentration. Results of recovery are presented in Table III. The recovery dropped at concentrations above 60 mg/m^3 (16 ppm), presumably due in part to breakthrough. At 60 mg/m^3 or less, the recovery coefficient of variation was less than 15%.

Table III.
Overall Recovery of Toluene from Charcoal Cloth

Toluene Concentration (mg/m^3)	Temp (°C)	RH (%)	No. of Layers	%Recovered[A]
0.75	22	80	4	69.1 ± 6.2 (n = 7)
1.30	30	90	4	63.6 ± 7.5 (n = 6)
2.00	30	90	4	70.5 ± 7.5 (n = 6)
7.4	22	80	4	68.8 ± 5.2 (n = 5)
60.0	22	80	6	67.0,70.0 (n = 2)
150.	22	80	6	38.0,25.0 [B] (n = 2)

[A] Mean ± standard deviation (no. of replicate runs)
[B] Breakthrough detected on second pair of layers in each replicate run

The results for the comparison of exhaled air volume and water vapor collected are given in Figure 3. There was a good correlation between the two, despite the fact that among the subjects there was considerable variation in tidal volume, breathing pattern and rate of ventilation. The data suggest that there is a simple, reliable relationship between weight gain of the desiccant and exhaled volume which can be applied as the calibration for the sampler when used under the conditions described. From linear regression, this calibration is: Moisture gain (g) = 0.0268 x Expired volume (L) + 0.73 g. The correlation coefficient (r) was 0.9789.

When the subjects' breath was sampled 17 to 20 hours after
controlled exposure, toluene was readily quantitated in each
person, while no toluene was detected in background breath samples
and blanks. In the post-exposure samples, the amount of toluene
found on the second pair of charcoal cloth layers was less than 5%
of the total recovered. Table IV summarizes the results for all
subjects given controlled exposure, and indicates the range of
sample volumes and resulting toluene concentrations, corrected for
recovery efficiency and for respirator dead space. The toluene
levels after exposure to 150 mg/m^3, showed an overall mean exhaled
concentration that was 0.23% of the exposure concentration inhaled
the previous day. The results for the exposures to 335 mg/m^3 gave
a mean exhaled concentration of 0.18% of that breathed on the
previous day.

Table IV. Results for 4 Hour Controlled Exposure of
Human Volunteers to Toluene

Subject	Exposure Concentrations (mg/m3)	Hours After	Sample Volume (L)	Breath Toluene[A] (mg/m^3)
1	145	18	174	0.246
2	152	20	311	0.356
3	160	18	231	0.389
4	148	17	184	0.309
5	147	18	214	0.453
6	155	19	200	0.246
7	140	19	237	0.211
8	147	19	137	0.606
9	156	18	200	0.282
			mean	0.344
			std.dev.	0.125
10	338	19	168	0.465
11	331	20	125	0.438
12	338	20	118	0.436
13	342	19	164	0.638
14	335	19	83	0.434
15	338	21	155	1.14
16	338	19	149	0.664
17	327	20	207	0.600
			mean	0.602
			std dev.	0.238

[A] Corrected for recovery efficiency and for mask dead space.

The results of the field study in automobile painters are
shown in figure 4, where the concentration of toluene found in
breath is plotted against the ambient air concentration measured
on that worker's lapel during the previous day's shift. Also
shown are the estimated levels of toluene in breath that would be
observed if the previous shift ambient air concentrations had been
equal to the TLV, and to one-half this level. These breath levels
were estimated from the results of the controlled laboratory
exposures.

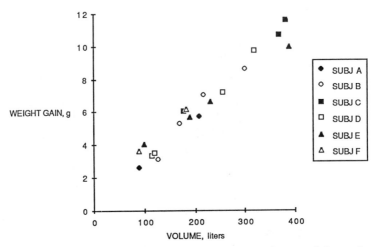

Figure 3 -- Relationship between molecular sieve weight gain
and exhaled volume measured by an independent method (see text)
in volunteer subjects, measured at 20C and 40% RH ambient
conditions.

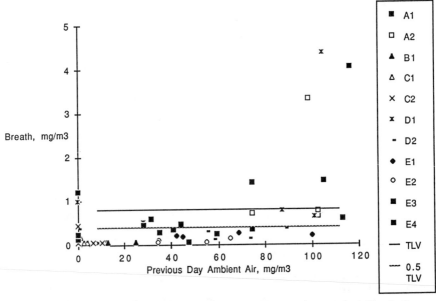

Figure 4 -- Breath concentrations of toluene in automobile body
painters at the start of each shift, plotted against the time-
weighted average air concentration during the previous shift.
Legend identifies individual painters. The horizontal lines
indicate estimated breath levels corresponding to exposure at
the TLV and one-half the TLV for toluene in air.

Discussion

In designing the breath sampling cartridge the primary goal was to measure toluene in breath at the start of the next shift. This was based on the predictions from toxicokinetic models, and limited experimental data, showing that one must wait at least two to four hours after the end of exposure before the breath level of solvent reflects the integrated dose over the previous shift (or shifts), rather than the most recent concentration inhaled. (4-6) Since it appears impractical to ask workers to remain at work until two to four hours after the shift ends, the first chance to obtain the desired sample is 16 to 20 hours after the shift ends. Then the breath levels of solvent are expected to be less than 1% of the previous time-weighted-average exposure concentration. (4) The sampling and analytical procedure must therefore have a quantitation range that extends much lower than that required of methods for sampling workroom air for contaminants at concentrations near the Permissible Exposure Limits (PEL) or the Threshold Limit Values.

The performance of the sampling cartridge was satisfactory, considering the conditions employed: very moist expired air containing toluene at concentrations between 0.75 mg/m^3 and 60 mg/m^3, as compared to the PEL of 750 mg/m^3 and the TLV of 375 mg/m^3 which are usually measured at RH levels less than 75%. Granular forms of activated charcoal have been reported to show serious degradation in capacity and breakthrough time at RH levels above 80%. (18) In addition, collection efficiency of solvents on granular charcoal is known to be adversely affected by low sampling flow rates. (19) Recovery is also lower for vapor loading as compared to liquid loading. (20,21) It should be noted that recovery efficiency was determined for a range of air concentrations which was above the levels found in breath. The accuracy of breath levels reported is thus uncertain to the degree that the recovery efficiency is uncertain.

The relationship between moisture collected and the volume of breath exhaled was approximately 27 mg/L. This is in good agreement with the work of others who have reported values between 25 and 31 mg/L using more sophisticated methods. (9,22) Those authors also reported that the moisture content of exhaled breath is moderately dependent on ambient temperature and RH. Variation in breath moisture is very small for temperature or RH above room conditions, but it becomes important below 10C or below 20% RH. Under such conditions the volume measuring portion of the breath sampler described here would have to be recalibrated.

When the sampler is used as reported in this work, the lower limit of quantitation for toluene in breath is 65 $\mu g/m^3$ (0.018 ppm). This is based on a sample volume of 240 liters, correction for dead space, desorption of the cloth in 10 ml of carbon disulfide with a recovery efficiency of 70%, injection of 1.0 μl eluate and a rather modest gas chromatograph quantitation limit of 0.87 ng. With the exception of dead space, each of these factors is subject to improvement so that a much better detection limit could be achieved readily. However, a breath level of 65 $\mu g/m^3$ would correspond to a previous day's exposure to toluene at an eight hour time-weighted average of about 15 mg/m^3, or 4% of the present TLV. Thus even with moderate analytical sensitivity, relatively low exposures may be monitored with this technique.

The findings from the controlled human exposure may be compared to other published reports of breath sampling for toluene in which plastic bags, glass tubes, or more elaborate methods (not suitable for workplace screening) were used. Figure 5 shows the data from this study, corrected for dilution by the respiratory dead space (assuming a physiological dead space of 30% of tidal volume) and mask dead space. The figure also shows results from other studies.(2,12-15) All concentrations have been normalized to the inhaled dose calculated as the product of exposure concentration and duration. Note that only one previous study included data at 18 hours post-exposure, and that value is close to the result from this work. At earlier sampling times, the data from other studies show considerable variation. That variation might be attributed to differences in sampling technique or to variable excretion kinetics at short post-exposure times.

Field measurements of toluene in the breath of painters indicated that the breath level correlated with inhalation exposure only when the ambient air concentration exceeded about 70 mg/m^3, and then the correlation was not strong. Ambient concentrations were derived from passive dosimeters, whose performance under field conditions has not been fully validated. (17) The extent to which uncertainty in ambient concentration contributed to the lack of correlation with breath data is not known. Observation of the work practices employed in the workplaces revealed that there was significant skin exposure in many employees, and that respirator usage was highly variable among them. These factors would confound any relationship expected between inhalation exposure, as estimated by air concentration, and breath levels. On the other hand, the levels of toluene found in the breath of all workers corresponded to equivalent airborne exposures at a significant proportion of the health guideline, and suggest that the workers were receiving important exposure by a route other than inhalation. The most likely explanation appears to be skin contact, which was frequently observed. If this finding is confirmed in wider studies of workers who are exposed by both routes, the value of biological monitoring will be reinforced.

The sampling method used in this work offers several advantages over other techniques. The sampling respirator would not be intimidating to the majority of workers exposed to solvents, as many are undoubtedly familiar with air purifying respirators already. The sampling and analytical techniques are relatively simple and inexpensive, and thus many workers can be monitored simultaneously. The ability to sample a large volume of expired air gives the method very good sensitivity. Finally, leakage of expired air around the face seal produces no error as this lost air does not reach the adsorbent or desiccant in the cartridge. Therefore the device measures only the volume of air from which organic vapor is also collected.

There are some features which could limit the value of this approach under certain circumstances. The sampler as described is rather heavy, and sampling for longer than fifteen to twenty minutes may prove uncomfortable. Use of lighter weight materials in constructing the cartridge should reduce this problem. The need to correct for the effect of mask dead space is a disadvantage relative to use of bags or other methods permitting sampling directly at the mouth. The range of correction factors in adult males at rest was relatively narrow, however, so that using a group mean correction for dead space would have produced a

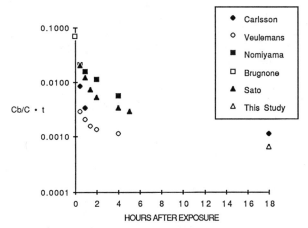

Figure 5 -- Breath toluene after controlled laboratory exposure (Cb), normalized to dose expressed as exposure concentration (C) multiplied by exposure duration (t) in hours. Note that the ordinate is a logarithmic scale. Results are shown for this study and for five others, identified by first author of report.

deadspace error of less than 15% for any individual in our group of subjects. The technique also does not permit the estimation of true alveolar concentration, but there is some doubt that any of the published methods could accomplish this in the field. When the features of this device are weighed, it may be an attractive means of monitoring the body burdens of volatile organic compounds in a wide variety of industries and processes.

This preliminary study has shown that the respirator-based technique for sampling mixed expired breath appears to be a potentially useful method for pre-shift monitoring. Its use in practice will require measuring the efficiency of recovery of compounds of interest from the sampling cartridge. Some data are available now for toluene and additional data are being developed for the xylene isomers, methyl ethyl ketone and methyl isobutyl ketone. Other sampling conditions, such as temperature, relative humidity and presence of possible interfering compounds, may affect sampler performance in applications such as pesticide biomonitoring. More extensive field studies must be done, in which present biological monitoring methods, such as urinalysis for parent compounds or metabolites, are compared with breath analysis in the same exposed workers.

Acknowledgments

Supported by Grant No. 5 R01 OH01490-02 from the National Institute for Occupational Safety and Health

Literature Cited

1.   Wilson. H.K. Scand. J. Work Environ. Health. 1986, 12:174-192.
2.   Veulemans, H.; Masschelein, R.   Int. Arch. Occup. Environ. Health. 1978, 42:91-103.
3.   Berlin, M.; Gage, J.C.; Gullberg, B.; Holm, S.; Knutsson, P.; Tunek, A. Scand. J. Work Environ. Health. 1980, 6:104-111.
4.   Fiserova-Bergerova, V.; Vlach, J.; Singhal, K. Br. J. Ind. Med. 1974, 31:45-52.
5.   Fernandez, J.G.; Droz, P.O.; Humbert, B.E.; Caperos, J.R.; Br. J. Ind. Med. 1977, 34:43-55.
6.   Stewart, R.D. In Essays in Toxicology. W.L. Hayes, Ed. Academic Press, New York 1974, pp 121-148.
7.   Sherwood, R.J.; Carter, F.W.G.   Ann. Occup. Hyg. 1970, 13:125-146.
8.   Mitchell, J.W.; Nadel E.R.; Stolwijk J.A.J. J. Appl. Physiol. 1972, 32:474-476.
9.   Caldwell, P.B.; Gomez, D.M.; Fritts, H.W. J. Appl. Physiol. 1969, 26:82-88.
10.   Maggs, F.A.P.; Smith, M.E. Anaesthesia. 1976, 31: 30-40.
11.   Eller, P.M. Ed. NIOSH Manual of Analytical Methods; 3rd Ed. U.S. Dept. of Health and Human Services Publication 1984, No. 84-100. Cincinnati, pp 1500.1-1500.4.
12.   Carlsson, A. Scand. J. Work Environ. Health. 1982, 8:43-59.
13.   Brugnone, F.; DeRosa, E.; Perbellini, L.; Bartolucci, G.B.; Pasini, F.; Faccini, G. Appl. Ind. Hyg. 1986, 1:21-24.

14. Sato. A.; Nakajima, T.; Fujiwara, Y.; Hirosawa, K. Int. Arch. Arbeitsmed. 1974, 33: 169-182.
15. Nomiyama, K.; Nomiyama, H. Int. Arch. Arbeitsmed. 1974, 32: 85-91.
16. Altshuller, A.P; Cohen, I.R. Anal. Chem. 1960, 32, 802-810.
17. Rose, V.E.; Perkins, J.L. Am. Ind. Hyg. Assoc. J. 1982, 43, 605-621.
18. Nelson, G.O.; Correia A.N.; Harder, C.A. Am. Ind. Hyg. Assoc. J. 1976, 37:280.
19. Levine, M.S.; Schneider, M. Am. Ind. Hyg. Assoc. J. 43:423.
20. Krajewski, J.; Gromiec, J.; Dobecki, M. Am. Ind. Hyg. Assoc. J. 1980, 41:531.
21. Dommer, R.A.; Melcher, R.G. Am. Ind. Hyg. Assoc. J. 1978, 39:240.
22. Burch, G.E. Arch. Int. Med 1945, 76:315.
23. Sato, A.; Nakajima, T. Scand. J. Work Environ. Health. 1987, 13, 81-93.
24. Sato, A.; Nakajima, T. Br. J. Ind. Med. 1979, 36, 231-234.
25. Riihimaki, V. Scand. J. Work Environ. Health. 1979, 5, 143-150.
26. Perbellini, L.; Brugnone, F.; Mozzo, P.; Cocheo, V.; Caretta, D. Int. Arch. Occup. Environ. Health. 1984, 54, 73-81.
27. Brugnone, F.; Perbellini, L,; Faccini, G.; Pasini, F. Am J. Ind. Med. 1985, 8, 67-72.
28. Morgan, A.; Black, A.; Belcher, D.R. Ann. Occup. Hyg. 1970, 13. 219-233.
29. Monster, A.C. Int. Arch. Occup. Environ. Health. 1979, 42, 311-317.
30. Stewart, R.D.; Gay, H.H.; Erley, D.S.; Hake, C.L.; Peterson, J.E. J. Occup. Med. 1961, 43, 586-590.
31. Dutkewicz, B. In Industrial and Environmental Xenobiotics; Fouts, J.R.; Gut, J.; Eds.; Excerpta Medica: Amsterdam, 1978, pp 106-109.

RECEIVED May 4, 1988

Chapter 6

Validation of Environmental Monitoring by Biological Monitoring

Fluorescent Tracer Technique and Patch Technique

Richard A. Fenske

New Jersey Agricultural Experiment Station, Department of Environmental Science, Rutgers University, New Brunswick, NJ 08903

Environmental monitoring of pesticide exposure allows identification of exposure
pathways and appropriate exposure reduction
strategies. Biological monitoring studies
which collect total urinary metabolites
from a single exposure episode provide a
relative index of exposure for evaluating
the validity of environmental monitoring
methods. Essential validation study design
factors include selection of an appropriate
pesticide for biological monitoring, and
elimination of extraneous and interfering
exposures. Most studies which have reported poor correlations between patch
estimates of dermal exposure and metabolite
excretion exhibit deficiencies in one or
more of these design factors. A recent
study of malathion exposure during airblast
applications demonstrated a high correlation between fluorescent tracer measurements of dermal deposition and malathion
metabolite excretion (r=.84). Patch deposition values were also correlated with
excretion (r=.71).

Environmental and biological monitoring are complementary
approaches to characterizing human exposure to chemicals
in occupational and general populations. The combination
of these two techniques provides a comprehensive evaluation of exposure magnitude and the pathways by which
exposure occurs. Biological monitoring has been an important part of pesticide exposure assessment for nearly
forty years due to the importance of the dermal route of
exposure (1). Cholinesterase and urinary metabolite
monitoring have often been conducted in conjunction with
estimates of dermal deposition to determine the relative

0097–6156/89/0382–0070$06.00/0
© 1989 American Chemical Society

contribution of dermal exposure to total exposure, and to determine the accuracy of dermal exposure measurements.

This paper examines the general principles involved in field validation of environmental monitoring methods, and reviews studies which have employed biological monitoring as a relative index of pesticide exposure to evaluate dermal exposure estimates. Studies employing the patch technique are compared to a recent study which measured pesticide deposition on the skin with fluorescent tracers and video imaging. The strengths and limitations of these techniques are discussed together with suggestions regarding future areas for research in pesticide exposure assessment.

Human Exposure Assessment Methods

Environmental monitoring provides a measure of exposure; i.e., amount of material reaching a body barrier and available for absorption. Air sampling, patch monitoring and handwashing are examples of environmental monitoring methods employed routinely in pesticide exposure assessment. Such techniques allow study of the relative importance of routes of exposure and provide the foundation for the development of appropriate control strategies. Since environmental monitoring techniques need not be compound-specific, they have often been employed to measure entire classes of compounds (e.g., air sampling of volatile organics), or to provide a generic examination of production processes (e.g., auto body painting or pesticide applications). Finally, environmental monitoring is the only means of assessing exposure for the many chemicals which do not have a reliable biological endpoint to measure.

Biological monitoring provides a measure of absorption in body tissue or fluids, or involves measuring change in a physiological parameter. Such monitoring integrates exposure from all routes and allows estimation of an absorbed dose. Since a dose estimate is the ultimate goal of any exposure assessment, a well-conducted biological monitoring procedure can provide important information unattainable with environmental monitoring. Clearly both of these approaches are essential to reducing exposures and setting appropriate occupational and environmental health standards. Under many circumstances they can be conducted simultaneously to provide a comprehensive exposure assessment. The American Conference of Governmental Industrial Hygienists considers biological monitoring to be an important supplement to environmental monitoring, and has recently established Biological Exposure Indices to provide guidance in this area (2). Similar biological exposure guidelines have been developed in Europe, where biological monitoring is an established exposure assessment procedure (3).

Exposure Assessment Method Validation

The relative accuracy of an exposure assessment technique can be established by demonstrating its ability to monitor changes in exposure consistently. Measurements produced by the technique are compared to a reliable measure of exposure or exposure potential. The absolute accuracy of a method is normally demonstrated by calibrating the measurement system against a known standard. If such a standard is not available, accuracy is determined by calculation of error or uncertainty. Validation of dermal exposure assessment methods has proven problematic. Laboratory facilities which create well-defined exposures are commonly employed to evaluate respiratory measurement techniques (e.g., controlled test atmospheres and inhalation chambers). No such procedures are available for the study of dermal exposure. Instead, investigations must be conducted in the field where numerous variables cannot be controlled. As a result, the dermal exposure assessment methods in current use have never been validated in terms of absolute accuracy. Dermal exposure validation studies have instead focused on relative accuracy by comparing environmental monitoring data to a relative index of exposure.

Two field study parameters are often employed as relative indicators of exposure: work rate and active ingredient applied. Implicit in the use of such variables is an assumption that a strong association exists between the variable and exposure; i.e., exposure is proportional to time worked or amount of material handled. Work rate is commonly employed in industrial settings where exposure potential is predictable (e.g., ambient air levels in a factory), and where work activity is routine. In a recent study of timber mill workers exposed to tetrachlorophenol, for example, it was demonstrated that skin deposition of tetrachlorophenol was directly related to the amount of time worked (4). This association was expected since workers pulled and sorted timber at a rate controlled by the speed of a conveyor belt. Such work conditions contrast sharply with pesticide mixing and application in agriculture, where both exposure potential and work rate are highly variable.

A 1979 study of sixteen mixer/applicators demonstrated that when workers employ their own equipment and work at their own speed, work rate is highly variable (5). Regression analysis resulted in no significant correlation between time worked and 48 hr excretion of azinphosmethyl metabolites (r=.43). However, a strong correlation (r=.77) was found when the amount of active ingredient handled by each worker and 48 hr excretion were compared. Several other investigators have confirmed these results (6). Most recently a study of 2,4-D applicators in Canada found strong correlations between the urinary excretion of eight workers and amount sprayed (r=.90), as well as with spraying time (r=.93) (8). The association of amount of active ingredient applied and exposure suggests that this parameter is useful as a relative indicator of exposure potential. Work rate may be an appropriate indicator in some cases, but can be highly variable for pesticide applications.

Study Design for Biological Monitoring Validation

Most pesticide studies aimed at validating dermal expo- sure measurements have employed biological monitoring as a relative index of exposure. An ideal validation study design would attempt to demonstrate a strong correspon- dence between dermal exposure and internal dose. In lieu of a measure of internal dose for humans, the use of urinary metabolite excretion as an indicator of relative dose has gained widespread use in industrial hygiene and applied toxicology (9). This approach assumes a linear relationship between exposure and absorbed dose, and may not be appropriate for all compounds.

Most successful validation studies are based on a "single exposure" design. Subjects work for a defined exposure period, and total urine samples are then col- lected until metabolite excretion is negligible. The duration of urine collection is a function of the ki- netics of the absorption and excretion of the pesticide applied. If virtually all metabolites are collected, the amount of pesticide metabolites excreted is a direct reflection of the single period exposure, though not necessarily a measure of absorbed dose. Three criteria can be employed to evaluate the soundness of a validation study design: (1) control of extraneous exposure before and after the study period, (2) control of interfering exposure during the study period, and (3) selection of an appropriate pesticide for biological monitoring.

Extraneous Exposure. Subjects are asked to avoid expo- sure prior to the study for a time sufficient to allow urinary metabolite levels of the study compound or inter- fering compounds to reach background levels. Following the application period no additional exposure is allowed until urine collection is completed. This protocol is difficult to implement if workers must maintain a regular work schedule. Furthermore, even if workers do not mix or apply pesticides before and after the study, they may come into contact with contaminated equipment or reuse exposed clothing.

Interfering Exposure. Biological monitoring integrates exposure from all sources. If the environmental monitor- ing technique under study measures only a portion of the potential exposure, then other exposures should be mini- mized. When dermal exposure is of interest, for example,

oral and respiratory exposure should be controlled for
the study period. Similarly, a study of hand exposure
would require protection of all other dermal surfaces.

Pesticide Selection. The central decision in designing a
validation study is the choice of the pesticide to monitor. Compound selection requires knowledge of the excretion kinetics following dosing, ideally by the dermal
route in humans. The compound should be rapidly excreted
in the urine either unchanged or as a major metabolite.
Table I presents absorption and excretion data in humans
reported by Feldmann and Maibach for four of the compounds which have been employed in validation studies to
date (10). The study involved an intravenous dose followed by a single topical application left on the skin
for 24 hours. Total urine was collected for 5 days in
each case. The intravenous dose half-lives of the compounds exhibited nearly a five-fold range, from 3 hours
for malathion to 14 hours for ethion. The percentage of
the dermal dose excreted ranged from 3.3% for ethion to
9.7% for parathion, or nearly three-fold. Column 3 of
Table I was calculated from the 5 day excretion data
presented in the study. The values are the percentages
of the total metabolites which were excreted on the final
day of collection. Less than 2% of the malathion was
excreted on day 5, whereas more than 11% of 2,4-D was
excreted on the final day of sampling. Data of this kind
allow basic comparisons among pesticides in the selection
of suitable candidates for biological monitoring.

Table I. Dermal Absorption and Excretion Characteristics
of Four Pesticides in Humans*

Compound	Half-life** (hours)	Percent Dermal Dose Excreted	Day 5 Excretion as Percent of Total
Ethion	14	3.3	8.0
2,4-D	13	5.8	11.1
Parathion	8	9.7	7.2
Malathion	3	8.2	1.5

* Data adapted from (10); mean of 6 subjects
** Half-life following intravenous administration

Patch Technique Validation

The patch technique has been the most widely employed
method for estimating dermal exposure since its formal
publication by investigators from the U.S. Public Health
Service (11). It is now an approved protocol for both
the World Health Organization and the U.S. Environmental
Protection Agency (12-13). However, the method has never
been validated, and there are many investigators who

consider patch technique data inadequate (14-16). This
judgment is based on the questionable accuracy of the
method, but also stems from the repeated observation that
patch data do not correlate with urinary metabolite excretion data. A review of published studies which have
attempted to demonstrate a correlation between dermal
exposure and metabolite excretion indicates shortcomings
in study design or execution. The study design criteria
discussed above are employed here to examine five studies
which have collected patch and metabolite data simultaneously. These studies are summarized in Table II.

Table II. Patch Technique Validation Studies

Study	Pesticide	N	r	Extraneous Exposure	Interfering Exposure	Urine Sample
18	parathion	11	.69	possible	hand	unknown
19	2,4,5-T	21	.45	yes	hand/resp	5 days
20	ethion	17	.36	possible	hand	spot
21	phenoxy	17	.67	possible	hand/resp	spot
22	2,4-D	8	-	no	resp	7 days

Durham and Wolfe first attempted to validate the
patch technique by monitoring a single exposure and determining total parathion metabolite excretion (17).
Extraneous exposure apparently was not controlled: no
pre-exposure urine samples were reported and the length
of urine sampling was expressed simply as until "levels
were no longer of significance". Interfering exposures
were not controlled: respiratory exposure and hand exposure both contributed to metabolite levels. Parathion
appears to have been a good choice as a study compound
due to its relatively rapid absorption and excretion.

The study reported a "good correlation" between
patch exposure and excretion, but no statistical analysis
was conducted. A correlation coefficient of r=.69 for
the 11 subjects can be calculated, but this value is
heavily influenced by very high results for one subject.
When this subject is removed from the data set, there is
no significant correlation (r=.19). The influence of a
single high value is an inherent weakness of the Pearson
correlation coefficient, and correlations based on one
extreme value are generally not considered adequate evidence of a positive association. thus, these data do not
demonstrate a correlation between the two measures.

A study by Lavy and co-workers of 2,4,5-T exposure
was based on a single exposure design and was conducted
twice (18). The importance of reducing extraneous exposure was clearly recognized, as indicated by the recruit-
ment of participants who had not used 2,4,5-T for two
weeks, and the collection of 24 hour pre-exposure urine

samples. Unfortunately, background levels of 2,4,5-T
were very high for a number of the workers, particular in
the second study, calling into question the utility of
the excretion data for comparative purposes. In regard
to interfering exposures, respiratory exposure was measured and was determined to be only a small fraction of
the dermal exposure. However, hand exposure was not
measured or controlled. Thus, hand exposure represents
an important confounding factor, particularly since applications with backpack systems and mist blowers commonly result in significant hand exposure.

This study was also hampered by the choice of compounds. The herbicide 2,4,5-T is excreted almost totally
in urine, but excretion following dermal exposure extends
beyond 5 days. Several workers exhibited their highest
excretion levels on the fifth and last day of collection.
On average the excretion on the last day represented 14%
of the total 5 day excretion, suggesting that a significant fraction of the compound continued to be excreted
beyond this period. The study reports a low correlation
coefficient (r=.45) for the 21 workers studied. In light
of problems with extraneous exposure, interfering exposure, and incomplete metabolite collection, however, this
result is not unexpected. Thus, the study does not
provide clear evidence that patche exposure estimates and
excretion are not correlated.

Wojeck and co-workers examined the relationship
between ethion exposure and dialkylphosphate excretion in
17 Florida citrus mixers and applicators (19). Extraneous exposure was monitored by a single urine sample one
week before the study. Metabolite levels on the day
prior to the study were not measured. Spot sampling of
urine was conducted rather than total 24 hour collections. These sampling procedures clearly limit the utility of the urine values as relative indicators of exposure. Respiratory exposure was limited by use of respirators. Cotton gloves were worn by all workers to measure hand exposure, but workers did not wear gloves as
protective devices. The use of cotton gloves represents
a particularly complex confounding factor, wherein the
dermal sampling procedure itself is likely to alter the
biological monitoring data in unpredictable ways.

Regression analysis produced a low correlation coefficient (r=.36) for the group mean total dermal exposure
(dermal patches + hands) and the group mean metabolite
concentration when these values were compared on a daily
basis. Considering the limitations in urine sampling and
the potential confounding effect of the cotton gloves,
this study does not provide an adequate test of patch
technique validity.

Manninen and co-workers conducted a study of 17 workers exposed to phenoxy acid herbicides (20). No evaluation of prior exposure among workers is mentioned, and no pre-exposure urine samples were collected. Two spot samples were taken: one after the working day in the evening and one on the following morning. Respiratory exposure and hand exposure were left uncontrolled. Some workers wore respirators or gloves but others did not, introducing an unknown amount of variability into the total exposure reflected by the metabolites. This study analyzed urine for four different phenoxy herbicides: MCPA, dichlorprop, mecoprop, and dicamba. Workers used formulations with different combinations of these compounds. Clearly the variable dermal penetration and pharmacokinetics of these compounds make the spot urinary excretion values difficult to interpret.

The authors conducted a regression analysis of urine excretion and dermal patch estimates for the 17 workers, resulting in a positive correlation coefficient (r=.67). However, variability in the higher exposure values were pronounced. Highly exposed workers with similar levels of skin exposure (approximately 2 mg) varied by more than an order of magnitude in the excretion of metabolites (2-28 umol/L). The lack of control over extraneous and interfering exposures, together with spot sampling of a variety of compounds raises questions regarding the correlation of exposure and excretion.

The final study to be reviewed was conducted by Canadian researchers on 8 farmers exposed to 2,4-D amine (21). Pre-exposure urine samples were collected to determine background levels. Total 24 hour urine samples were collected during the study and for 4-7 days thereafter. Some of the participants sprayed 2,4-D again within a few days after the initial study period, precluding use of a strict single exposure design. However, all urine was collected from the first exposure through the last and for 4-7 days after the last, providing adequate data for developing a relative index of exposure. Each exposure was measured by the patch and hand wash techniques. Workers did not use respirators or protective gloves. This study was well conducted, avoiding problems regarding extraneous exposure seen in the other studies, and collecting urine for a period appropriate to the excretion of 2,4-D.

Cumulative urinary excretion was associated only with hand exposure (r=.67). Patch exposure estimates and total dermal exposure (patch estimates + hand exposure) did not correlate with urinary excretion. The authors concluded that the lack of correlation between total dermal exposure and urinary excretion was attributable to the variable nature of dermal deposition and the inability of the patch technique to estimate such deposition.

In summary, the studies reviewed here do not provide definitive evidence regarding the relative accuracy of the patch technique. Confounding factors of extraneous exposure, interfering exposure and inadequate urine collection introduce an unknown degree of variability which cannot be separated from variability due to the measurement technique.

Fluorescent Tracer Technique Validation Study

The fluorescent tracer technique was first employed in field studies in 1979 (5). Subsequently, a quantitative video imaging system was developed to measure dermal fluorescence. The relationship between the tracer and pesticides during application was examined, and the technique was field tested (22-24). A detailed account of the validation study discussed here has been reported recently (Fenske, R.A. Am. Ind. Hyg. Assoc. J., in press).

The study included seven mixers and 14 applicators. Each applicator sprayed four tanks on a high-volume air-blast spray schedule typical for citrus in the region. The fluorescent whitening agent, 4-methyl-7-diethylaminocoumarin, was employed as a tracer. Deposition of the tracer compound and malathion on gauze patches attached to the spray rig was highly correlated (r=.94). The instrument employed to quantify dermal fluorescence was a computer-based image processing system interfaced with a television camera. The traditional patch technique was also employed (25). Hand washes were not conducted due to use of the tracer compound.

The primary concern in designing this study was the selection of a pesticide which would be rapidly excreted in the urine proportional to absorbed dose. Several laboratory studies provide support for the use of organophosphorus pesticide metabolite levels excreted in the urine as relative indicators of exposure. A controlled study in humans with methyl and ethyl parathion demonstrated a strong association between two oral dose levels and excretion levels (26). More recently a study of azinphosmethyl applied dermally to rats demonstrated that dimethylthiophosphate excretion was proportional to dose over a four-fold dose range. Studies with human volunteers also suggested a proportional dose-excretion pattern (27).

One of the most rapidly excreted organophosphorus compounds is malathion, due to its hydrolysis in mammals to form carboxylic acid metabolites (28). Feldman and Maibach demonstrated that excretion of malathion metabolites following dermal application in acetone peaked within 12 hours following exposure, and that over 90% of the intravenous administration was recovered as metabolites in urine (10). Bradway and Shafik demonstrated a similar pharmacokinetic pattern for malathion in mice (29). Thus, malathion appeared to be an excellent candidate for this validation study.

The second study design issue involved minimizing extraneous exposures. Subjects were asked to avoid all exposure to malathion or any other dimethyl organophosphorus compounds for at least 3 days prior to the study. Pre-exposure samples were collected at the beginning of the study period to determine prior exposure. In one case metabolite levels were found to be above background levels, necessitating exclusion of this subject's data from analysis. All urine was collected for 72 hours from the commencement of the study, and subjects were removed from any further exposure during this collection period. The relatively short 3 day period of collection favored subject cooperation, and the time period was adequate to recover approximately 95% of the metabolites which would be excreted in 5 days (10). Thus, the total amount of malathion metabolites recovered in the 3 day urine sample appeared to accurately reflect the relative exposure which workers received. Interfering exposure was minimized by providing all workers with respirators and chemical resistant gloves. Dermal exposure was monitored by the fluorescent tracer technique (body + hands) and by the patch technique (body only) during a single study period for each worker.

Table III. Correlation of Exposure Measurements with 24-Hr Malathion Metabolite Excretion

Exposure Measurements	Corr. Coeff.*	R-Squared	Rank Corr.**
Fluorescent Tracer	.84+	.71	.62+
Patch: Mean Value	.71+	.51	.39++
Patch: Head Exposure	.63+	.40	.33

* Pearson correlation coefficient
** Spearman rank correlation coefficient
+ Statistically significant; $p < .001$
++ Statistically significant; $p < .05$

A plot of fluorescent tracer exposure and metabolite excretion for the 20 workers is presented Figure 1, and results of regression analysis are listed in Table III. All workers had their peak excretion within the first 24 hours, and the fluorescent tracer measurements were highly correlated with excretion (r=.84). The correlation coefficient and R-squared value for the association of fluorescent tracer measurements and 24-hr metabolite excretion were compared to the same statistics for two measurements derived from patch data. The two patch data values are 1) the mean of the eight outer patches above

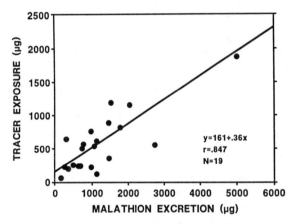

Figure 1. Regression analysis of fluorescent tracer
exposure and 24 hr malathion metabolite excretion.

the waist on each worker, and 2) the estimated exposure
to the head and neck based on extrapolation from four
patches (chest, back and two shoulder). The head and
neck were the only exposed regions. Since the study did
not include a full set of patches beneath the clothing,
no attempt was made to extrapolate patch data to determine dermal exposure to the whole body. Both the mean
patch value (r=.71) and the head exposure estimate
(r=.63) were significantly correlated with excretion.

The R-squared value indicates the proportion of the
metabolite excretion variable that can be explained by
the exposure variable, and is the most useful statistic
for comparison of the different exposure measurements.
The tracer data explained approximately 70% of the total
variance, whereas the patch data explained at best about
50%. All of the correlations were significant, however,
demonstrating that the patches do provide a general indication of relative exposure potential.

The Spearman Rank Correlation statistic ($r[s]$) was
also applied to these data, since the Pearson Correlation
Coefficient requires an assumption of normal distribution
and is highly influenced by large values. Here the
contrast in the association of excretion and tracer data
as compared to patch data was even more pronounced. The
tracer rank correlation was highly significant ($r[s]=.62$;
$p<.001$), whereas the mean patch data were only marginally
correlated ($r[s]=.39$; $p<.05$), and patch-estimated head
exposure has no significant correlation ($r[s]=.33$).

Current Status of Dermal Exposure Assessment Methods

The patch technique can provide a relative indication of
exposure, but may not be able to rank exposures with a
high degree of accuracy. With large data sets the variability reflected in patch data may be overcome. The
establishment of a generic data base of all patch technique data is a promising development in this regard
(30). The patch technique is inherently limited due to
its reliance on the assumption that exposure is uniform
over various body parts. Studies with the fluorescent
tracer and with the whole body technique in the United
Kingdom have illustrated the inappropriateness of this
assumption for applicator exposures (31-32). The patch
method may also suffer from a systematic error; i.e., for
some mixing and application procedures the patch estimates are consistently high, while for other procedures
the estimates are consistently low (31).

The validation study discussed here provides evidence that measurement of fluorescent tracer deposition
on the skin is a valid method in regard to relative
accuracy. As discussed earlier, the technique also
showed a high correlation between exposure and time

worked among timber mill workers, where time worked is a
valid parameter of exposure potential. Additionally,
this approach has successfully demonstrated quantitative
differences in exposure as a function of the type of
protective clothing worn (33). The fluorescent tracer
technique provides new information regarding dermal exposure, as both the investigator and worker can see patterns of deposition and immediately analyze possible
causes. The method requires relatively few pesticide
residue analyses, since most of the exposure data are
collected and analyzed automatically with the imaging
system.

The major disadvantage of this technique when compared to the patch technique is its relative complexity
in the field. The stability of UV-A illumination and the
instrument's performance must be monitored. The ratio of
pesticide and tracer deposited on the skin surface must
be determined empirically in each study through field
sampling. In some cases clothing penetration may be
different for the two compounds, requiring a correction
factor.

The quantitative accuracy of fluorescent tracer
measurements has not been demonstrated and is currently
under investigation. Laboratory experiments are aimed at
determining the behavior of the fluorescent tracer once
it reaches the skin. Recent studies suggest that the
tracer produces a stable fluorescent emission on the skin
for at least six hours. Further studies will examine the
effects of sunlight and perspiration on tracer stability.
Finally, the problem of quenching is inherent to any
method measuring dermal fluorescence. When excess fluorescent material is deposited on the skin the fluorescence
produced is no longer proportional to deposition. Thus,
areas of very high exposure may be underestimated with
this technique. Proper choice of tracer concentration at
the outset of a study can do much to mitigate this
problem.

Conclusion

The validation of exposure methods is an essential step
in developing a scientific basis for the evaluation of
human health risks. Biological monitoring has enormous
potential for providing estimates of internal dose and
for identifying early indicators of clinical effects of
exposure. Environmental monitoring plays a vital role in
reducing health risks by determining the magnitude of
exposure and documenting exposure pathways. The fluorescent tracer technique and patch technique serve as independent and complementary approaches for evaluating and
reducing dermal exposure in agriculture.

Acknowledgments

The cooperation of the administration and staff of the University of California Lindcove Field Station is acknowledged and greatly appreciated. Field work was supported by the National Institute for Occupational Safety and Health (1 R01 01234-01 Al). Data analysis was supported by state funds through the New Jersey Agricultural Experiment Station (Publication No. F-07123-1-87).

Literature Cited

1. Kay, K.; Monkman, L.; Windish, J.P.; Doherty, T.; Pare, J.; Racicot, C. Ama Arch. Ind. Hyg. & Occ. Med. 1952, 6, 252-252.
2. TLV - Threshold Limit Values for Chemical Substances in the Work Environment, 1986-87, American Conference of Governmental Industrial Hygienists, Cincinnati, Ohio, 1986.
3. Lowry, L.K. J. Occup. Med. 1986 28, 578-582.
4. Fenske, R.A.; Horstman, S.W.; Bentley, R.K. Appl. Ind. Hyg. 1987, 2, 143-147
5. Franklin, C.A.; Fenske, R.A.; Greenhalgh, R.; Mathieu, L.; Denley, B.V.; Leffingwell, J.T.; Spear, R.C. J. Toxicol. Environ. Health 1981, 7, 715-731
6. Hackathorn, D.R.; Eberhart, D.C. In Dermal Exposure Related to Pesticide Use Honeycutt, R.C.; Zweig, G.; Ragsdale, N.N., Eds.; ACS Symposium Series No. 273; American Chemical Society: Washington, D.C., 1985; pp. 341-356.
7. Reinert, J.C.; Severn, D.J. In Dermal Exposure Related to Pesticide Use Honeycutt, R.C.; Zweig, G.; Ragsdale, N.N., Eds.; ACS Symposium Series No. 273; American Chemical Society: Washington, D.C., 1985; pp. 357-368.
8. Grover, R.; Cessna, A.J.; Muir, N.I.; Riedel, D.; Franklin, C.A.; Yoshida, K. Arch. Environ. Contam. Toxicol. 1986, 15, 677-686.
9. Bernard, A.; Lauwerys, R. J. Occup. Med. 1986, 28 558-562.
10. Feldman, R.J.; Maibach, H.I. Toxicol. Appl. Pharmacol. 1974, 28 126-132.
11. Durham, W.F.; Wolfe, H.R. Bull. World Health Organization 1962, 26, 75-91.
12. World Health Organization Toxicol. Letters 1986, 33, 223-235.
13. Pesticide Assessment Guidelines, Subdivision U: Applicator Exposure, U.S. Environmental Protection Agency, NTIS, Virginia, 1986.
14. Bonsall, J.L. In Occupational Hazards of Pesticide Use; Turnbull, G.J.; Ed.; Taylor & Francis: London, 1985; pp. 13-34.
15. Lavy, T.L.; Mattice, J.D. Toxicol. Letters 1986, 33, 61-71.

16. Lunchick, C.; Burin, G.; Reinert, J.C.; In Chemical Basis of Biological Monitoring ACS Symposium Series (this volume).

17. Durham, W.F. Bull. World Health Organization 1963, 29, 279-281.

18. Lavy, T.L.; Shepard, J.S.; Mattice, J.D. J. Agric. Food Chem., 1980, 28 626-630.

19. Wojeck, G.A.; Nigg, H.N.; Stamper, J.H.; Bradway, D.E. Arch. Environ. Contam. Toxicol. 1981, 10, 725-735

20. Manninen, A.; Kangas, J.; Klen, T.; Savolainen, H. Arch. Environ. contam. Toxicol. 1986, 15, 107-111.

21. Grover, R.; Franklin, C.A.; Muir, N.I.; Cessna, A.J.; Riedel, D. Toxicol. Letters 1986, 33 73-83.

22. Fenske, R.A.; Leffingwell, J.T.; Spear, R.C. In Dermal Exposure Related to Pesticide Use Honeycutt, R.C.; Zweig, G.; Ragsdale, N.N., Eds.; ACS Symposium Series No. 273; American Chemical Society: Washington, D.C., 1985; pp. 377-393.

23. Fenske, R.A.; Leffingwell, J.T.; Spear, R.C. Am. Ind. Hyg. Assoc. J. 1986, 47 764-770

24. Fenske, R.A.; Wong, S.M.; Leffingwell, J.T.; Spear, R.C. Am. Ind. Hyg. Assoc. J. 1986, 47, 771-775.

25. Davis, J.E. Residue Reviews 1980, 75 33-50.

26. Morgan, D.P.; Hetzler, H.L.; Slach, E.F.; Lin, L.I. Arch. Environ. contam. Toxicol. 1977, 6, 159-173.

27. Franklin, C.A.; Muir, N.I.; Moody, R.P. Toxicol. Letters 1986, 33, 127-136

28. Chen, R.R.; Tucker, W.P.; Dauterman, W.C. J. Agric. Food Chem. 1969, 17, 86.

29. Bradway, D.E.; Shafik, T.M. J. Agric. Food Chem. 1977, 25, 1342-1344.

30. Honeycutt, R.C. In Dermal Exposure Related to Pesticide Use Honeycutt, R.C.; Zweig, G.; Ragsdale, N.N., Eds.; ACS Symposium Series No. 273; American Chemical Society: Washington, D.C. 1985; pp. 369-375.

31. Fenske, R.A. In Pesticide Science and Biotechnology; Greenhalgh, R.; Roberts, R.R.; Eds.; Blackwell Scientific Publications: London, 1987; pp. 579-582.

32. Chester, G.; Ward, R.J. Human Toxicology 1983, 2, 555-556.

33. Fenske, R.A. In Performance of Protective Clothing; American Society for the Testing of Materials: Philadelphia, 1988.

RECEIVED May 4, 1988

Chapter 7

Biological Markers To Study Exposure in Animals and Bioavailability of Environmental Contaminants

L. R. Shugart, S. M. Adams, B. D. Jiminez, S. S. Talmage, and J. F. McCarthy

Environmental Sciences Division, Oak Ridge National Laboratory, Oak Ridge, TN 37831

Epidemiologic studies of agents present in the environment seek to identify the extent to which they contribute to the causation of a specific toxic, clinical, or pathological endpoint. The multifactorial nature of disease etiology, long latency periods and the complexity of exposure, all contribute to the difficulty of establishing associations and causal relationships between a specific exposure and an adverse outcome. These barriers to studies of exposure and subsequent risk assessment cannot generally be changed. However, the appropriate use of biological markers in animal species living in a contaminated habitat can provide a measure of potential damage from that exposure and, in some instances, act as a surrogate for human environmental exposures. Quantitative predictivity of the effect of exposure to environmental pollutants is being approached by employing an appropriate array of biological end points.

Human exposure to environmental pollutants is often exceedingly complex. Sources of exposure are multiple, and the importance of a particular source may depend on individual practices. Humans are highly mobile, and direct study, particularly when physiological testing is required, is generally expensive and logistically difficult. For these reasons, a simpler animal model which provides a parallel biological marker in humans would be useful.

Small mammals have frequently been used to monitor the presence of metals and other contaminants in the environment. Such biomonitoring can be essential for determining bioavailability and resultant biological effects under natural conditions. Small mammals can be particularly effective biomonitors of soil contaminants if the species used are abundant, easily caught, do not migrate long distances, and have well documented food habits

This chapter not subject to U.S. copyright
Published 1989 American Chemical Society

(1). Good biomonitors are in equilibrium with the environment and should show a graded response to a range of pollutants.

Data are sparse on the amounts of hazardous substances released to the environment. Measuring concentrations of these substances in soil, plants, and animals would require an exhaustive monitoring program which would be costly, especially since many chemicals will not be present as the parent compound in living organisms due to their rapid metabolism. The important question is not whether these substances are present, but rather whether these substances enter the biota in chemical forms and concentrations that will result in an adverse biological effect. Thus, monitoring the biological availability of these substances in biota becomes a critical parameter for determining whether they have potential for being hazardous and whether they could result in significant exposures to humans (2).

The estimation of the risk resulting from exposure to environmental pollutants requires knowledge of the dose and pharmacokinetics of the chemicals in the animal. A systemic dose in an individual can be obtained by quantitation of the chemical or its metabolites in body fluids such as blood, urine, feces, sputum, or milk, however, a major drawback to this approach is that the analysis must be performed shortly after exposure, that is, prior to the clearance of the metabolites from the body. Alternative procedures for monitoring exposure to hazardous substances are needed. In particular, new methods are needed for measuring reaction products of chemicals, such as metabolites and adducts, in animals and humans that correlate with patterns of associated biological change and pathological conditions (3,4).

Our approach to detecting exposure to hazardous chemicals in the environment, and to estimating the potential for subsequent adverse effects, is to monitor biological endpoints in wild animals. Biological endpoints include indicators that: (a) quantify exposure by measuring chemical interaction with critical molecular targets (adducts in nucleic acids and proteins); (b) measure alterations in specific, sensitive, and critical physiological and biochemical processes (detoxifying enzyme activities and metal-binding proteins); and, (c) monitor early expression of cellular dysfunction (neoplasia or loss of immune competence). Using this approach the organism is seen to function as an integrator of exposure, accounting for abiotic and physiological factors that modulate the dose of toxicant taken up from the environment. The biological marker is used to detect the response of the organism to the environmental insult. Because of the often long latent period between exposure and subsequent irreversible deleterious impact on health, it would be desirable to have sensitive biological indicators that could detect exposure early enough so that preventive or remedial measures could be taken. Three elements are critical to our approach: (a) marker selection based on toxicological mechanisms; (b) field studies to establish correlations between environmental contamination and markers; and, (c) laboratory confirmation of causal relationships between exposure, biological markers, and adverse effects.

Biological monitoring can be used as a cost-effective survey of contaminated sites, for routine monitoring of uncontaminated sites,

to provide evidence for contaminant impact on biota, and to
establish priorities for site cleanup.

A suite of biomarkers that we currently use to monitor for
exposure to selected environmental pollutants, is shown in Table I.
Information obtained upon monitoring the response of these
biomarkers is compared to long-term adverse effects in the organism
(reduced fecundity, decreased disease resistance, and tumor
formation).

Table I. Biological Markers of Exposure and Bioavailability
of Environmental Contaminants

Environmental Pollutant	Biological Marker	Reliability Index*
A. Toxic Metals:		
Cu, Hg, Ag,	DNA integrity/m^5dCyd	s
Zn, Cd, Pb,	metal-binding proteins	s,d
	porphyrin biosynthesis	s,d,p
	immune response	s
	xenobiotic metabolism	s
B. Organic Cmpds:		
1. PAH's	DNA/hemoglobin adducts	s,d,p
	xenobiotic metabolism	s,d
	immune response	s
	DNA integrity/m^5dCyd	s
2. PCB's &	xenobiotic metabolism	s
TCDD	porphyrin profile	s
	immune response	s
	DNA integrity/m^5dCyd	s
	DNA/hemoglobin adducts	s,d

* s: signal of potential problem
  d: definitive indicator of type or class of pollutant
  p: predictive indicator of long-term adverse effect

Studies with Cellular Biomarkers

DNA Modification. As a result of exposure to hazardous substances
in the environment, it is not unreasonable to expect that damage to
DNA may occur that goes uncorrected, with subsequent adverse
effects to the organism.

The rationale underlying the strategy of chemical dosimetry by
determining levels of compounds which become covalently bound to
cellular macromolecules is based on our understanding of the mode
of action of genotoxic compounds (5-7). The metabolism of
chemicals is a relatively complex phenomenon and detoxification by
cellular mechanisms is not always complete, sometimes resulting in
highly reactive electrophilic metabolites. These metabolites can

undergo attack by nucleophilic centers in macromolecules such as
lipids, proteins, DNA and RNA which often results in cellular
toxicity. Binding with DNA, however, can cause formation of
altered bases that can be repaired, be innocuous, or result in
alterations which become fixed and are transmitted to daughter
cells. Current research suggests that reaction of chemicals with
DNA and the ensuing changes which result can cause cancer.

Given that genotoxic agents exert their activity through
irreversible reactions with nucleophilic atoms (adducts), the
amount of such reaction products will be proportional not only to
the in vivo concentration of the electrophile, but also to the time
this concentration is maintained. Therefore, the amount of
metabolite bound to cellular DNA (in vivo dose), provides a
reliable dosimetric basis upon which to assess the risk connected
with exposure to a genotoxic compound (3,7,8).

It should be noted that the detection and quantitation of DNA
adducts is not a simple task because there are few analytical
techniques currently available. The reasons for this are: (a) the
assay often has to accommodate the unique chemical and/or physical
properties of the individual compound or its adduct; (b) the
percentage of total chemical that becomes attached to the DNA in
the target tissue is quite small because most of it is usually
detoxified and excreted; (c) not all adducts that form between the
genotoxic agent and DNA are stable or are involved in the
development of subsequent deleterious events in the organism; and,
(d) the amount of DNA available for analysis from the target tissue
or organ is often quite limited.

Recently our laboratory demonstrated an alternative method to
radiometric, immuno, or postderivatization detection of the
polycyclic aromatic hydrocarbon, benzo[a]pyrene (BaP) binding to
DNA (9). Essentially, the technique consists of the acid-induced
removal of the diolepoxide adduct of BaP from the macromolecule as
the strongly fluorescent free tetrols which are then separated and
quantitated by fluorescence/HPLC analysis. The resulting
chromatographic profile can be used to establish the stereochemical
origin of the diolepoxide involved in adduct formation (10).

Benzo[a]pyrene-DNA Adduct Detection. Our initial research with the
fluorescence/HPLC technique has demonstrated that we can detect,
identify, and quantitate, subsequent to several routes of exposure,
the binding of BaP with cellular DNA of mice (10-12) and
fish (13). The detection and quantitation of adduct formation in
fish exposed to BaP demonstrate that aquatic species are similar to
other organisms in that they possess cellular enzymes capable of
metabolizing BaP to the ultimate carcinogenic form of the chemical,
the diolepoxide. A comparison of BaP-adducts formed with the DNAs
of mice and fish demonstrate similarities (Table II), and suggest
the feasibility of extrapolation of exposure data, based on the
detection and quantitation of DNA adduct levels, between species.

Field Studies with Beluga Whale. Large quantities of PAHs,
including the strongly carcinogenic BaP, have been reported in the
main habitat of the St. Lawrence beluga whale population. These
compounds are the probable cause of the increased frequency of

Table II. Comparison of DNA Adduct Formation in the Mouse
and Bluegill Sunfish after an Acute Exposure to
Benzo[a]pyrene

Species	Macromolecule	DNA Adduct Formation*		
		I-1	II-2	%I-1
Mice	Skin DNA**	588	220	73
Fish	Liver DNA***	928	127	88

* DNA adduct formation determined 72 hours subsequent to
BaP exposure and expressed as nanograms of tetrol I-1 or
II-2 per gram of DNA. Data taken from (10-13).
** Topical application of BaP at 3 micrograms per gram
body weight.
*** Intraperitoneal injection of BaP at 5 micrograms per
gram body weight. Fish maintained at 20°C.

bladder tumors seen among aluminum workers from the same area (14),
and since the compounds contaminate the beluga whale food chain,
they are considered to be the etiological factor for the high
frequency of tumors seen in this population (15).

Detectable levels of BaP-DNA adducts were found in the brains
of beluga whales from the St. Lawrence estuary, while the
occurrence of BaP-DNA adducts of the brain and liver of belugas
taken from the Mackenzie estuary was not observed (Table III).

Table III. Detection of Benzo[a]pyrene Adducts in DNA of
Beluga Whales (*Delphinapterus leucas*)

Sample	Tissue	BaP Adduct Formation	
		binding*	level**
St. Lawrence Estuary			
#1	Brain	206	2.15
#2	Brain	94	0.98
#3	Brain	69	0.73
Mackenzie Estuary			
#1 - #4	Brain	none detected	
#1 - #4	Liver	none detected	

* BaP adducts to DNA expressed as nanograms of tetrol I-1
per gram of DNA. Data taken from (15).
** Level of adduct formation expressed as BaP adducts per
10^7 DNA nucleotides.

The data obtained are important for several reasons. First,
they provide evidence that the whales from the St. Lawrence estuary
had been exposed to BaP, and had metabolized it to the diolepoxide,
which subsequently became covalently bound to the DNA of the brain
tissue. Over the past several years a strong and convincing
argument has developed for a causal relationship between the
carcinogenic potency of BaP and the amount bound to an organism's
DNA as a result of cellular metabolism (6,16). This is reinforced
by the premise that the integrity of DNA is essential for survival.
Alterations, if left uncorrected, could trigger a sequence of
events that culminates in the appearance of an overt malignancy.
Second, the level of adducts detected approaches that found in
animals, both terrestrial and aquatic, exposed under controlled
laboratory conditions to a carcinogenic dose of BaP (12,13,17,18).
Third, cells in brain tissue are known to have slow turnover rates
and lack or have very low capacity for excision repair of DNA
damage. Therefore, significant accumulation of DNA adducts could
occur in this tissue from long-term chronic exposure to
environmental levels of BaP too low to induce neoplasia (19). It
should be noted that the health of an animal may influence the
formation of adducts. The whales from the Mackenzie estuary were
hunted animals and not known to be diseased at the time of their
capture, while those from the St. Lawrence were beached animals.

Non-adductive DNA Damage. Certain genotoxic compounds or agents
such as metals, radionuclides, some chemicals, etc., do not
covalently bind to DNA, but nevertheless induce damage. If this
damage is expressed as strand breakage (or the potential for strand
breakage), it can be detected by measuring the rate of alkaline-
induced strand separation (20).
    Analysis by a modified alkaline unwinding assay (21)
demonstrated that chemically induced DNA strand breakage could be
detected in bluegill sunfish and fathead minnows exposed to
chronic, low levels of BaP. This technique has been used to
determine the relative DNA damage, as measured by strand breakage,
in bluegill sunfish taken from several sites in White Oak Creek,
which is a small stream that flows through the Department of Energy
reservation at the Oak Ridge National Laboratory and terminates in
White Oak Lake. Biomonitoring activities are being conducted in
this system (27).
    The data in Table IV show that the integrity of the DNA of the
fish in the White Oak Creek System, except for those at the 3.0-3.4
km site, is similar to that of fish taken from a control site
(Brushy Fork Creek, which is located some distance from the ORNL
reservation) for both the Spring and Fall collection times.
Additonal studies with fish collected at the 3.0-3.4 km site are in
progress. These data, although preliminary, indicate the potential
for measuring DNA damage as a general biological marker of exposure
of indigenous animals to contaminants that occur in their
environment.

Hemoglobin Modification. Because it meets a number of essential
requirements, hemoglobin has been proposed as an alternative
cellular macromolecule to DNA for estimating the in vivo dose of

Table IV. Relative DNA Strand Breaks in Bluegill
from the White Oak Creek Watershed

Site	n*	
	Spring 1987	Fall 1987
W.O.C.(3.0-3.4 km)	4.77	2.01
W.O.C.(2.6 km)	0.68	0.03
White Oak Lake	0.75	1.13
Brushy Fork Creek	0.91	1.15

* $n = (\ln F_s/\ln F_c) - 1$ = number of breaks per
alkaline unwinding unit of DNA (see refs 20,21).
F_s represents fraction of DNA in double stranded
form from fish at sample sites listed. F_c represents fraction of DNA in double stranded form from
fish at Melton Branch, a small stream that enters
the White Oak Creek (W.O.C.) at 2.5 km. A minimum
of five fish were analyzed at each site.

chemicals subsequent to exposure (22-25). First, it has reactive
nucleophilic sites and the reaction products with electrophilic
agents are stable. Over fifty compounds to date have been shown to
yield covalent reaction products with hemoglobin in animal
experiments. These compounds include representatives from most of
the important classes of genotoxic chemicals currently known. No
tested mutagenic or cancer-initiating compound has failed to
produce covalent reaction products with hemoglobin. Secondly,
hemoglobin has a well established life-span, is readily available
in humans and animals, and its concentration in an individual is
not subject to large variation. Thirdly, modification of
hemoglobin has been shown to give an indirect measure of the dose
of reaction product that binds to the DNA in the target cells.

Biomonitoring of hemoglobin-bound metabolites represents a
novel approach to the estimation of exposure to potentially harmful
chemicals (26). Although these adducts have no putative
mechanistic role in carcinogenesis, they do relate quantitatively
to exposure and to activation since they may approximate the
systemic dose (in vivo dose) of a chemical. They can be a measure
of the chemical's genotoxic potency as well. Furthermore, since
the adducts which form with hemoglobin are stable and have life-
spans equal to that of the circulating erythrocyte (23),
quantitation of these adducts can be used to integrate the dose
obtained from chronic low-level types of exposure which most likely
occur in chemically-polluted environments.

Field Studies with Terrestrial Animals. A floodplain on East Fork
Poplar Creek (EFPC) was selected as a study site. EFPC originates
at New Hope Pond, a point source of industrial pollution, and the
study site is about 4 kilometers downstream. The floodplain is low
and the creek periodically overflows, depositing sediment. There

is abundant vegetation. Measured BaP concentrations in the soil
was 70 nanograms/gram, although 10 times this amount have been
reported. Concentrations in plants was less than 1/10th of that in
the soil. Small animals were trapped at this site to determine the
practicality of using hemoglobin as a suitable biological marker of
BaP pollution.

Preliminary data (Table V) indicate detectable concentrations
of BaP adducts with hemoglobin were present in some individuals of
species which have intimate contact with the sediment or soil. The
shorttail shrew burrows into the ground and eats earthworms and
insects, while muskrats feed on invertebrates found in the creek
bed and browse on muddy vegetation along the creek bank. BaP
adducts were not detectable in herbivores such as the white-footed
mouse.

Table V.   Concentration of Benzo[a]pyrene Adducts in the
            Hemoglobin of Animals on the EFPC Floodplain

Species	Number Analyzed	BaP-hemoglobin Adducts*
White-footed mouse (Peromyscus leucopus)	15	0.00
House mouse (Mus musculus)	1	0.00
Shorttail shrew (Blarina brevicauda)	2	0.35
Black rat snake (Elaphe obsoleta obsoleta)	1	0.00
Snapping turtle (Chelydra serpentina)	1	0.16
Norway rat (Rattus norvegicus)	1	0.15
Muskrat (Ondatra zibethica)	6	0.23

*   BaP adducts to hemoglobin expressed as nanograms of
tetrol I-1 per gram of hemoglobin. Data taken from (27).

BaP-hemoglobin Adducts in Humans. Human daily exposure to BaP
increases dramatically in smokers, as one cigarette contains
between 10 and 50 nanograms of BaP. Since the life-span of a human
red blood cell is several months, continual exposure to BaP at one
or more packs of cigarettes per day should result in a measurable
steady state concentration of BaP-hemoglobin adducts. A
preliminary study was conducted in a limited population of humans
to determine whether BaP-hemoglobin adducts could be detected. The
data in Table VI (methodology according to (25,26)) show that
adducts were present in five out of six individuals who smoked
while similar analyses of non-smokers gave lower levels relative to
smokers. These data demonstrate the feasibility of the technique,

however, intrinsic factors such as age, sex, health, and nutritional status, as well as extrinsic factors such as the presence of other chemicals, may influence the pharmacokinetics of BaP metabolism, and the incidence of adducts with hemoglobin.

Table VI.   Benzo[a]pyrene Adducts in Hemoglobin of Smokers and Non-smokers

No.	Sex	Age	Race	Smoking Habit*	BaP-hemoglobin Adducts**
1	m	23	C	none	64
2	m	44	B	none	24
3	f	54	C	20	nd
4	f	56	C	none	69
5	m	36	O	none for 8 yrs	73
6	m	40	C	none for 15 yrs	nd
7	f	28	C	none	nd
8	m	42	C	20	24
9	m	49	O	40	159
10	m	27	B	none	129
11	f	56	C	none for 1 yr	1402***
12	m	49	C	20	468
13	f	50	C	40	272
14	m	57	C	40+	229

*   Cigarettes per day.
**   BaP adducts to hemoglobin expressed as picograms of tetrol I-1 per gram of hemoglobin; nd: none detected.
*** Numerous fluorescent peaks present in chromatogram in addition to tetrol I-1 peak.

Xenobiotic Metabolism. Xenobiotics in the environment, if taken up by an organisms, may induce microsomal enzymes (mixed function oxidases, MFO's) that can detoxify many of these compounds (28). The MFO's catalyze a variety of reactions, including aromatic and aliphatic N-hydroxylation, N-dealkylation, and O-dealkylation. Paradoxically, the MFO's may activate certain chemicals to their carcinogenic metabolite(s) (29). The biochemical systems in fish responsible for these types of reactions are similar to those found in mammalian species (30,31). The use of enzyme assays in biological monitoring programs was reviewed by Payne (32) for different phyla of aquatic animals and was found to be useful in detecting known point sources of pollution.

Field Studies in Aquatic Organisms. Activities of several MFO parameters have been measured in fish collected from stations along East Fork Poplar Creek (33). A multivariate discriminant analysis was used to examine the pattern of several measures of the MFO system (ethoxyresorufin deethylase, NAD reductase, NADP reductase,

cytochrome P-450, and cytochrome b_5 levels) in fish from the
different stations. The statistical analysis (Figure 1) confirm
that female bluegill sunfish at station no.1 (EFPC at New Hope
Pond), a source of industrial pollution, exhibited a significantly
different pattern of MFO responses than fish collected 20
kilometers down stream (station no. 5) or from a pristine stream
(control). In addition, histopathological analysis of various
organs from fish along EFPC showed higher levels of lesions in the
fish closest to station no.1.

      These results (Figure 1) suggest that the MFO enzyme system can
be useful as a biological marker in a monitoring program if the
response of the system to environmental and physiological
influences such as temperature, season, food, hormonal (sex), etc.,
are taken into consideration.

Summary and Conclusions

Effective environmental management requires knowledge of the
transport and fate of contaminants in natural systems (34). Small
mammals can serve as indicators of the presence and bioavailability
of contaminants and selected monitoring species can be used to
measure the accumulation of contaminants. Furthermore, knowledge
of food habits and habitat may indicate pathways of contaminants to
organisms

      Monitoring biological endpoints in wild animals can be used as
an alternative to extensive sampling and chemical analyses,
particularly where a large area is involved and the origin or
extent of contamination is unknown or poorly defined. Evidence of
exposure of biota as determined by biological monitoring could help
to establish the need for cleanup.

      Our laboratory has been interested in devising methods for
detecting the exposure of living organisms to hazardous chemicals
and physical agents in the environment. Initial studies with
chemical dosimetry analysis began with the development of a
fluorescence/HPLC assay for the detection and quantitation of BaP-
DNA adducts with a sensitivity sufficient for detecting
environmental exposures. Subsequent research demonstrated the
applicability of this technique to animal models, both aquatic and
terrestrial, under various experimental conditions. Furthermore,
hemoglobin modification by chemicals was shown to be equivalent to
DNA binding as a dosimeter.

      Studies in aquatic organisms, both in the laboratory and in the
field, have demonstrated the feasibility of measuring MFO enzyme
activities associated with the metabolism of xenobiotics, such as
BaP, in conjunction with non-adductive DNA damage as potentially
useful biomarkers for exposure and bioavailability of environmental
pollutants.

      Other biological markers are currently being investigated for
their capacity to detect and quantitate exposure to contaminants.
These include: (a) parameters of the immune response (interferon
induction, antibody-forming cells, and lymphocyte response to
mitogens); (b) induction of metal-binding proteins; and, (c) minor
nucleoside content of DNA.

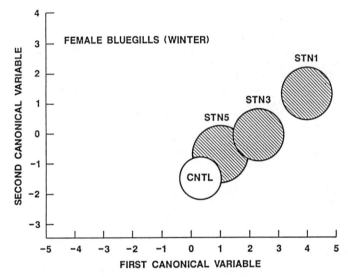

Figure 1. Segregation of integrated variable groups by discriminant analysis using several measures of the MFO system. Circles represent 95% confidence radii of control and respective test stations. Station no. 1 (New Hope Pond) is the headwaters of East Fork Poplar Creek; increasing station numbers are further down stream. Data taken from (33).

Acknowledgments

Portions of this work were sponsored by the Department of
Environmental Management in the Health, Safety, Environment and
Accountability Division of the Oak Ridge Y-12 Plant; and the ORNL
Director's R&D Program. The Oak Ridge Y-12 Plant and the Oak Ridge
National Laboratory are operated by Martin Marietta Energy Systems,
Inc., under contract DE-AC05-84OR21400. Environmental Sciences
Division, Oak Ridge National Laboratory Publication No. 3088.

Literatute Cited

1. Beardsley, A., Vogg, J., Beckett, P.H.T., and Sanso, B.F.
   Environ. Pollut. 1978, 16, 65-71.
2. Maugh, T.H. Science 1984, 219, 1032-1033.
3. Perera, F.P., Poirer, M.C., Yuspa, S.H., Nakayama, J.,
   Jaretski, A., Curnern, M.M., Knowles, D.M., and Weinstein,
   I.B. Carcinogenesis 1982, 3, 1405-1410.
4. Montesano, R., Rajewksy, M.F., Pegg, A.F., and Miller, E.
   Cancer Res. 1982, 42, 5236-5239.
5. Gelboin, H., and T'so, P.O.P. Polycyclic Hydrocarbons and
   Cancer: Molecular Biology and Environment; Academic: New York,
   1979.
6. Harvey, R.G. Am. Scientist 1982, 70, 386-393.
7. Wogan, G.N., and Gorelick, N.J. Environ. Health Perspec.
   1985, 62, 5-18.
8. Shamsuddin, A.K.M., Sinopoli, N.J., Hemminki, K., Boesch,
   R.R., and Harris, C.C. Cancer Res. 1985, 45, 66-68.
9. Rahn, R., Chang, S., Holland, J.M., and Shugart, L.R.
   Biochem. Biophys. Res. Commun. 1982, 109, 262-269.
10. Shugart, L.R., Holland, J.M., and Rahn, R. Carcinogenesis
    1983, 4, 195-199.
11. Shugart, L.R., J. Toxicol. Environ. Health 1985, 15, 255-263.
12. Shugart, L.R., and Kao, J. Environ. Health Perspec. 1985, 62,
    223-226.
13. Shugart, L.R., McCarthy, J.F., Jimenez, B.D., and Daniel, J.
    Aquatic Toxicol. 1987, 9, 319-325.
14. Theriault, G., and Tremblay, C. The Lancet 1984, 1, 947-950.
15. Martineau, D., Legace, A., Beland, P., Higgins, R., Armstrong,
    D., and Shugart, L.R. Proc. 7th Biennial Conf. on Biology of
    Marine Mammals 1987, p 45.
16. Phillip, D.H. Nature 1983, 303, 468-472.
17. Varanasi, U., Stein, J.E., and Hom, T. Biochem. Biophys. Res.
    Commun. 1981, 103, 780-787.
18. Stowers, S.J., and Anderson, M.W. Chem.-Biol. Interact. 1984,
    51, 151-166.
19. Stowers, S.J., and Anderson, M.W. Environ. Health Perspec.
    1985, 62, 31-39.
20. Rydberg, B. Rad. Res. 1975, 61, 274-287.
21. Shugart, L.R. Mar. Environ. 1988, 24, 321-325.
22. Osterman-Golkar, S., Ehrenberg, L., Segebrack, D., and
    Halstrom, I. Mut. Res. 1976, 34, 1-20.
23. Calleman, C.J. Ph.D. Thesis Department of Radiobiology,
    University of Stockholm, Sweden, 1984.

24. Shugart, L.R. <u>Toxicol</u>. 1985, <u>34</u>, 211-220.
25. Shugart, L.R. <u>Anal</u>. <u>Biochem</u>. 1986, <u>152</u>, 365-369.
26. Pereira, M.A., and Chang, L. In: <u>Banbury</u> <u>Report</u> #13; Bridges, B.A., Butterworth, B.E., and Weinstein, I.B., Eds.: Cold Spring Harbor Laboratory, New York, 1982; pp 177-187.
27. Walton, B.T., Talmage, S.s., and Meyers, L.J. In: <u>First</u> <u>Annual</u> <u>Report</u> <u>on</u> <u>the</u> <u>ORNL</u> <u>Biological</u> <u>Monitoring</u> <u>and</u> <u>Abatement</u> <u>Program</u>: Loar, J.M., Ed.; ORNL-TM-10399, 1987, Oak Ridge National Laboratory, Oak Ridge, TN; pp 234-244.
28. Parke, V.D. <u>J</u>. <u>Aquatic</u> <u>Toxicol</u>. 1981, <u>1</u>, 367-376.
29. Cummings, S.W., and Prough, R.A. In: <u>Biological</u> <u>Basis</u> <u>of</u> <u>Detoxification</u>: Caldwell, J., and Jakoby, W.B., Eds.: Academic; New York, 1983; pp 1-30.
30. Bend, J.R., and James, M.O. <u>Biochem</u>. <u>Biophys</u>. <u>Perspec</u>. <u>Mar</u>. <u>Biol</u>. 1979, <u>4</u>, 125-188.
31. Chambers, J.E., and Yarbrough, J.D. <u>Comp</u>. <u>Biochem</u>. <u>Physiol</u>. 1976, <u>55c</u>, 77-84.
32. Payne, J.F., In: <u>Ecological</u> <u>Testing</u> <u>for</u> <u>the</u> <u>Marine</u> <u>Environment</u>: Personne, E., Jasper, E., and Clares, C., Eds.; State University of Ghant, Belgium, 1984; pp 625-655.
33. Loar, J.M., (Ed.) 1988. <u>First</u> <u>Annual</u> <u>Report</u> <u>on</u> <u>the</u> <u>Y-12</u> <u>Plant</u> <u>Biological</u> <u>Monitoring</u> <u>and</u> <u>Abatement</u> <u>Program</u>. Draft ORNL/TM. Oak Ridge National Laboratory, Oak Ridge, TN.
34. Wren, C.D. <u>Environ</u>. <u>Monit</u>. <u>Assess</u>. 1986, <u>6</u>, 127-144.

RECEIVED June 1, 1988

Chapter 8

Use of Urine for Monitoring Human Exposure to Genotoxic Agents

Richard H. C. San[1], Miriam P. Rosin[1,2], Raymond H. See[1], Bruce P. Dunn[1], and Hans F. Stich[1]

[1]Environmental Carcinogenesis Unit, British Columbia Cancer Research Centre, 601 West 10th Avenue, Vancouver, BC V5Z 1L3, Canada
[2]School of Kinesiology, Simon Fraser University, Burnaby, BC V5A 1S6, Canada

We have recently assessed the feasibility of using two approaches for biological monitoring of pesticide-exposed individuals: (a) the detection of chromosome-damaging components in urine specimens, and (b) the analysis of urothelial cells for the presence of chromosomal damage, as measured by the frequency of micronuclei. Urine specimens were collected from non-smoking orchardists in the Okanagan Valley, B.C. during the pre-spraying and pesticide spraying periods of the fruit growing season. The urine was concentrated by preparative reversed-phase high-pressure liquid chromatography, and assayed for chromosome-damaging activity using Chinese hamster ovary cell cultures. A significant elevation in chromosome-damaging activity was observed only in the urine collected during the spraying period. Samples from the same individuals obtained during the pre-spraying period did not differ from non-smoking controls. Urothelial cells collected by centrifugation of urine from a single void proved to be insufficient in number for analysis of micronuclei. This approach may be applicable if multiple urine samples are obtained. A brief description of our experience with micronuclei analysis in urothelial cells from individuals in other populations is also presented.

Short-term *in vitro* assays of pure chemicals have aided in the discovery of the genotoxic action of many chemicals. However, such tests do not permit the assessment of human exposure to environmental agents. The tests also do not simulate the number of complex ways in which chemical agents may interact in biological systems. At present, two methods are widely applicable for monitoring the effects of genotoxic chemicals on exposed populations. One method involves the analysis of *in vitro* target indicators such as microbial or mammalian cells for genotoxic damage after exposure to body fluids (e.g., urine) from exposed individuals. The other approach involves the analysis of cells and tissues of the exposed individual for evidence of cytogenetic damage such as micronuclei or chromosomal aberrations.

0097–6156/89/0382–0098$06.00/0
© 1989 American Chemical Society

The rationale behind the analysis of urine is based on the knowledge that ingestion or metabolic transformation of endogenous and exogenous substances may result in the excretion of metabolites into the urine (1). The detection of the metabolites in urine would indicate that absorption of the precursor compound has occurred, and that cells in various organs are at risk of exposure during systemic distribution of the parent compound. Unfortunately, the concentration of genotoxic metabolites in the urine may be relatively low, requiring extraction and concentration procedures for adequate detection. This difficulty was alleviated by Yamasaki and Ames (2), who used non-polar Amberlite XAD-2 resin to concentrate compounds from the urine of cigarette smokers. Since then, this approach has been used to examine many types of exposure through lifestyle (3), diet (4-6), occupation (7-11), and medical treatment (12,13). Recently, preparative reversed-phase high-pressure liquid chromatography was shown to be superior to XAD-2 resins in terms of performance and recovery in the extraction of non-polar urinary genotoxic constituents (14).

The micronucleus test has been successfully applied to exfoliated urinary bladder cells of smokers and coffee drinkers (15), as well as of bilharzial patients (16). Micronuclei are acentric chromosome fragments derived from aberrant chromosomes (17). Their presence in the cytoplasm of exfoliated cells as DNA-containing bodies indicates the capacity of genotoxins to inflict genetic damage on the dividing basal cells of the epithelium (15). An increase in the micronucleus frequency of the bladder cells, together with a demonstration of genotoxic activity in the urine, would provide strong evidence of exposure to environmental contaminants.

In this paper we report on our study of urine genotoxicity and micronucleus frequency in exfoliated urinary bladder cells of individuals occupationally exposed to pesticides.

Methodology

Study Groups. In this study, urine samples were collected from 21 orchardists (all non-smokers) in the Okanagan Valley, B.C., when they were engaged in the application of pesticides during the fruit growing season. As controls, urine was collected from these same individuals during the pre-spraying as well as the post-spraying seasons. In addition, 16 individuals from an agricultural research station in the Okanagan region were recruited to provide urine samples during the same time period as the orchardists. As controls outside the fruit growing region, non-smoking individuals from Vancouver and Grand Forks, B.C. were recruited to provide one urine specimen.

Collection of Urine Samples. It was decided that a longitudinal study would be most ideal for this project since variables such as metabolic and lifestyle differences would be essentially eliminated.

At least one single urine sample was collected from each of the orchardists during the peak pesticide spraying season. Initially, the specimen consisted of all voids collected between 16 and 24 hours after pesticide application. Based on the observations made on these samples, it was suspected that the collection of urine at 16 to 24 hours post-spraying may have passed the time at which pesticides

are metabolized and excreted. Consequently, all urine specimens were
collected from the orchardists within the entire first 8 hours after
pesticide application. A late afternoon sample was also collected
from the same individuals during the pre-spraying season to serve as
a control. Urine samples from all control groups were collected late
in the afternoon (4 to 8 p.m.).

All urine specimens were collected in sterile 500-ml polyethylene bottles (Nalgene, Rochester, NY) without any preservatives.
Bottles were refrigerated by the participants during the collection
period until full. Before freezing, each sample was centrifuged to
obtain exfoliated urinary bladder cells. The supernatant was stored
at -20°C until analysis. The volume, pH, and creatinine content of
each urine sample were measured. The creatinine determination,
obtained using a modification of the procedure described by
Iosefsohn (18), served to adjust for varying urine concentrations
and differences in body weights between individuals.

Preparation of Concentrates from Urine Samples. Urine specimens were
concentrated by reversed-phase high-pressure liquid chromatography
using a Waters Prep LC/System 500A preparative liquid chromatograph
(Waters Scientific, Milford, MA) and a Waters Prep Pak 500/C18
reversed-phase column. All the organic material on the column was
eluted with 50% acetone/50% 2.5 mM phosphoric acid (v/v) (4). The
eluate was rotary evaporated at 40°C to remove the acetone, neutral-
ized with 1 M sodium hydroxide, and freeze-dried. After drying, the
powdered urine extract was stored at -20°C and redissolved in double-
distilled water immediately before use.

Assay for Clastogenic (Chromosome-Damaging) Activity in Urine. Urine
extracts were assayed for their capacity to induce chromosome and
chromatid damage in cultured Chinese hamster ovary (CHO) fibroblasts.
Dilutions of the urine extracts were prepared to obtain various
concentrations of creatinine equivalence (14). Following addition
of the urine extract for 3 hours, the CHO cells were incubated for a
further 16 hours, then arrested at metaphase with colchicine for 3
hours, harvested, stained, and analyzed for the presence of chromosome as well as chromatid breaks and exchanges (19). Using this
experimental protocol, the cytogenetic damage observed was predominantly (≥96%) of the chromatid type.

Analysis of Micronuclei in Exfoliated Urothelial Cells. Exfoliated
urothelial cells were obtained from freshly collected urine samples
by centrifugation, fixed in ethanol/glacial acetic acid (3:1, v/v),
dropped onto precleaned slides, air-dried overnight, and stained
according to the procedures described by Stich et al. (20). A
minimum of 300 intact urothelial cells were analyzed to determine
the frequency of micronucleated cells (20-22).

Statistical Analysis. All statistical comparisons were performed
using non-parametric methods. The clastogenic activity of urine
samples from the agricultural research station workers before and
during pesticide exposure was evaluated for significance using the
Wilcoxon paired-sample test. Tukey's multiple comparisons test was
used to evaluate differences in the clastogenic activity of urine
from orchardists during different pesticide exposure periods. This
test was also used to examine differences in the mean clastogenic

activity among the three study groups (orchardists, agricultural
research station workers, and reference controls). The Mann-Whitney
U test was used to evaluate urinary creatinine values and urinary pH.

Results

Clastogenic Activity in Urine from Reference Control Group. The
urine of the reference control group exhibited low but significant
levels of clastogenic activity compared to those found for control
distilled water concentrates (P<0.001; Mann-Whitney U test) (Table
I). Dose-related increases in clastogenic activity were observed
for many urine extracts (data not shown). Clastogenic responses
were generally found at concentrations between 2.0 and 5.0 mg/ml
creatinine equivalence. Beyond this concentration range, CHO cells
showed evidence of mitotic inhibition in addition to toxicity, the
latter indicated by a decrease in cell number and the presence of
pycnotic nuclei.

Table I. Effect of Pesticide Exposure on Urine Clastogenicity

Group	Percent Metaphases with Chromatid Aberrations (Mean±S.D.)[a]
Reference controls (n=22)	5.2±2.3[b]
Research station personnel (n=11):	
Before spraying	5.4±2.0
During spraying	6.3±3.1 (P>0.05)[c]
Orchardists (n=22):	
Before spraying	4.9±3.5
During spraying:	
Afternoon void	19.9±10.2 (P<0.001)[c,d]
Next morning void	7.1±3.9 (P>0.05)[c]
Distilled water concentrate controls	1.0±1.0

[a]Average of the maximum value obtained for each individual over the
dose range tested (1.0 to 8.0 mg/ml creatinine equivalence).
[b]Significant increase (P<0.001; Mann-Whitney U test) compared to
value for distilled water concentrates.
[c]Statistical significance of difference between pre-spraying and
spraying urine samples, as determined by the Wilcoxon paired-sample
test.
[d]Highly significant (P<0.001) relative to value obtained for the
reference control group, as determined by the Mann-Whitney U test.

    Figure 1-F describes the distribution of urine clastogenicity
among the reference control individuals at a creatinine equivalence
of 4.0 mg/ml. At this concentration, the urine extracts of 76% of
the subjects did not induce more than 5% metaphases with chromatid
aberrations. The urine extracts of 19% of the individuals demonstrated clastogenic activity between 6 and 10% metaphases with chromatid
aberrations, while only 5% of the control group subjects showed 11
to 15% metaphases with chromatid aberrations.
    The maximum clastogenic activity found over the dose range
tested (1.0 to 8.0 mg/ml creatinine equivalence) is shown for each
individual in Figure 2-C. For the group, a mean percentage of
5.2±2.3 metaphases contained at least one chromatid aberration.
These figures strongly suggest (P<0.001; Mann-Whitney U test) that

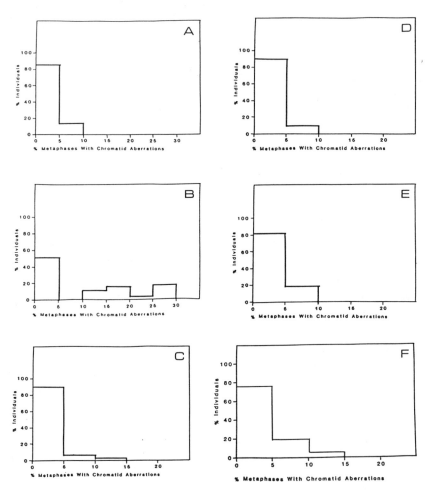

Figure 1.   Frequency distribution of the clastogenic activity of urine extracts from orchardists (A-C) and controls (D-F), measured as the capacity to induce chromatid aberrations in Chinese hamster ovary (CHO) cell cultures.   Urine samples were obtained from orchardists prior to spraying (A) and on two occasions during the spraying season: 6-8 hours post-spraying (B), and 16-24 hours post-spraying (C).   Values shown in D are from research station personnel sampled during the pre-spraying period, with E displaying these same individuals during the spraying period.   Values shown in F are from urine samples taken from individuals in a non-agricultural area.   All samples were measured at 4.0 mg/ml creatinine equivalence.

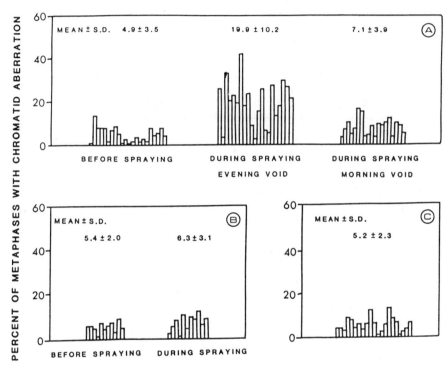

Figure 2.   Individual variations in the clastogenic activity of
urine extracts from the orchardists (A) and control groups (B and C).
Each bar represents the maximum percentage of metaphases with
chromatid aberrations in CHO cell cultures obtained over the dose
range tested (1.0 to 8.0 mg/ml creatinine equivalence).   Values
shown in B were obtained from urine samples of individuals at the
agricultural research station, while C gives control values from
urine of individuals from a non-agricultural area.

relative to the baseline levels of clastogenic activity observed
with distilled water concentrates, urine contains materials capable
of inducing genetic damage (Table I).

Clastogenic Activity in Urine from Agricultural Research Station
Personnel. Unlike the reference control group, where pesticide
exposure was known to be small or non-existent, individuals from the
agricultural research station may have experienced some exposure to
pesticides during the spraying period due to the possible drift of
pesticides from the site of application. Urine samples obtained from
11 non-smoking agricultural research station personnel during the
pre-spraying and spraying periods were concentrated as described
previously, and assayed for the presence of clastogenic materials.
For the majority of urine extracts, dose-related responses were
observed (two examples are shown in Figures 3-C and 3-D). Clastogenic activity was generally detectable at 3.0 mg/ml creatinine
equivalence, with signs of toxic effects appearing at about 6.0
mg/ml concentration.

The frequency distribution of urinary clastogenic activity for
the pre-spraying and spraying periods at 4.0 mg/ml creatinine
equivalence is shown in Figures 1-D and 1-E. Little difference was
apparent in the frequencies during the pre-spraying and spraying
periods. During both these periods, over 80% of the individuals
exhibited urine clastogenicity within the range of 0 to 5% metaphases
with chromatid aberrations. Over both periods, no individuals showed
urine clastogenicity of more than 10% metaphases with chromatid
aberrations.

Illustrated in Figure 2-B is the observed maximum clastogenic
activity over the dose range tested (1.0 to 8.0 mg/ml creatinine
equivalence). For the pre-spraying period, an average of 5.4±2.0
aberrant metaphases were found for the urine specimens tested.
During the spraying period, the urines demonstrated an average of
6.3±3.1% metaphases with chromatid aberrations. Comparison of these
mean values by the Wilcoxon paired-sample test (23) showed no
significant difference (P>0.50).

It therefore appears that indirect exposure to pesticides may
be insufficient to induce any further chromosome-damaging activity
in the urine above that of normal/baseline levels.

Clastogenic Activity in Urine from Orchardists (Urine Collected
Within 16 to 24 Hours of Pesticide Application). Pesticide exposure
did not make the urine more toxic towards the CHO cells, since the
reference control urine samples demonstrated the same extent of
toxicity.

The frequency distribution of urinary clastogenic activity at
4.0 mg/ml creatinine equivalence during both the pre-spraying
(Figure 1-A) and spraying (Figure 1-C) periods appears to be similar.
During these two time periods, the urines of about 90% of the
subjects were unable to induce more than 5% aberrant metaphases.
Therefore pesticide spraying did not appear to affect the urinary
clastogenic activity of the orchardists. The maximum clastogenic
activity obtained over the dose range of 1.0 to 8.0 mg/ml creatinine
equivalence is presented in Figure 2-A (before spraying, and at 16
to 24 hours post-spraying). Despite intra- and inter-individual
variations, the group mean values of clastogenic activity for these
two sets of samples were not significantly different (Table I).

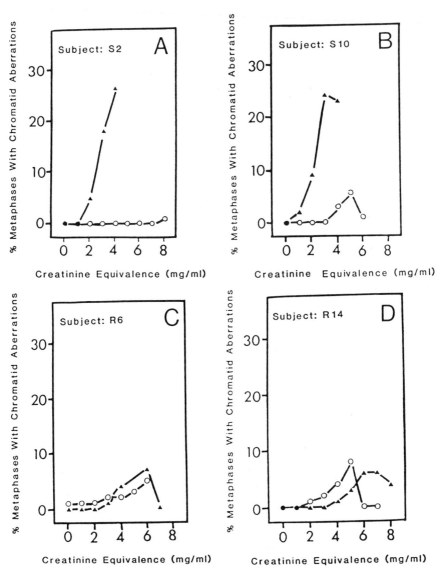

Figure 3. Dose-response curves for the clastogenic activity of extracts prepared from urine collected during the pre-spraying and spraying periods from two orchardists (A and B), and two controls from the agricultural research station (C and D). The percentage of metaphases with chromatid aberrations in CHO cell cultures induced by urine extracts from the pre-spraying (o) and spraying (▲) periods are shown for each subject. All subjects are non-smokers.

Table II lists the different types of pesticides used by the orchardists during the days of urine collection. In many instances, more than one pesticide was applied by an individual sprayer during the course of the day. Many of these pesticides possess genotoxic properties. With the exception of one or two individuals, all of the orchardists applied at least one genotoxic pesticide. However, even though genotoxic pesticides were used by many orchardists, no overall increase in urinary clastogenic activity beyond normal limits was observed.

Table II. Pesticides Used by the Orchardists

Pesticides	Use[a]	Genotoxicity[b]	Reference
Azinphos-methyl	I	+	24
Benomyl	F	+	25
Captan	F	+	26
Carbaryl	I	+	27
Cyhexatin	M	−	28
Diazinon	I	+	29
Dimethoate	I	+	30
Dinitrocresol	I	ND	
Dodine	F	−	31
Endosulfan	I	−	32
Ethephon	PG	−	28
Ethion	I	−	28
Nabam	F	ND	
Paraquat	H	+	33
Phosalone	I	ND	
Simazine	H	+	34
Ziram	F	−	28

[a]I, insecticide; F, fungicide; M, miticide; PG, plant growth regulator; H, herbicide.
[b]+, positive result; −, negative result; ND, no information available for the chemical.

Clastogenic Activity in Urine from Orchardists (Urine Collected Within 6 to 8 Hours of Pesticide Application). Owing to the lack of an increase in genotoxic activity in urine collected within 16 to 24 hours of pesticide spraying, the timing of urine collection was changed to within 8 hours of pesticide application. This decision was influenced by a recently published report that changes in urine genotoxicity may be time-dependent (35).

Dose-response curves of urine samples from two representative pesticide sprayers are shown in Figures 3-A and 3-B. Compared to urine from the pre-spraying period, urine specimens collected during the spraying period exhibited potent clastogenic activity, as indicated by the sharply increased frequency of chromatid aberrations. The clastogenic activity was dose-dependent but not linear, and occurred over a narrow concentration range. The predominant type of damage was chromatid exchange, and their prevalence did not appear to change with dose. The percentage of metaphases with chromatid aberrations generally increased with urine dose to a maximum, then decreased with a further increase in dose. In many cases, the highest activities were found at near toxic urine concentrations. Toxicity was usually noted between 5.0 and 8.0 mg/ml creatinine equivalence.

At these concentrations, a decrease in clastogenic activity was typically observed since severely aberrant cells lyse rapidly and are not detected. Toxicity was prominent at high creatinine doses in urines collected during both the pre-spraying and spraying periods.

Figures 1-A and 1-B contrast the distribution of urinary clastogenic activity for the two periods at 4.0 mg/ml creatinine equivalence. In the pre-spraying period, no individuals demonstrated any activity beyond 10% cells with chromatid aberrations. Eighty percent of the subjects showed 0 to 5% metaphases with chromatid aberrations. However, a change in distribution was observed after exposure to pesticides. At 4.0 mg/ml creatinine concentration, the urines of a larger proportion of individuals showed the ability to induce high frequencies of chromatid aberrations. For example, the urines of 38% of the sprayers, after pesticide usage, demonstrated more than twice the typical baseline levels of aberrations (i.e., 0 to 5% metaphases with chromatid aberrations).

The maximum clastogenic activity over the dose range tested (1.0 to 8.0 mg/ml creatinine equivalence) for each orchardist is depicted in Figure 2-A. During the pre-spraying period, an average of $4.9\pm3.5\%$ of the metaphases exhibited chromatid aberrations. With exposure to pesticides, the aberration frequency was significantly elevated to $19.9\pm10.2\%$ cells with chromatid aberrations ($P<0.001$; Wilcoxon paired-sample test). Multiple exchanges and fragmentation of the chromosomal complement were frequently observed.

The most commonly used pesticides on the day of urine collection were the insecticides azinphos-methyl and phosalone. On average, each subject sprayed a total of 4.2 hours per day. The Spearman rank correlation test indicated no correlation between the total number of hours of spraying and the observed maximum clastogenic activity ($r_s=0.317$; $P>0.20$). Since many orchardists used a combination of pesticides during the course of one day, a correlation of a specific pesticide with the urinary clastogenic activity was not feasible. However, it is worth pointing out that four orchardists, who used only a single pesticide on that day, demonstrated high urinary clastogenic activity when spraying either phosalone, simazine, or paraquat.

Of the 17 pesticides sprayed on the day of urine sampling, 8 (47%) had been reported to exhibit genotoxic activity *in vitro*. The use of such genotoxic pesticides may explain the increase in urinary clastogenic activity associated with pesticide exposure.

It should be noted that all of the above effects were obtained without metabolic activation *in vitro*, suggesting that the clastogenic agents in the urine were direct-acting. The effect of including an S9 microsomal activation system in the assay on the clastogenic activity has not been examined. In a large proportion of the urine samples tested, low but significant (relative to solvent controls) levels of clastogenic activity were observed in the urine of unexposed non-smokers, indicating the role of other factors in the appearance of urine clastogenicity. Urinary pH and creatinine did not differ among the study groups.

Analysis of Micronuclei in Exfoliated Bladder Cells. An attempt was made to analyze the exfoliated urothelial cells of pesticide sprayers for the presence of micronuclei, an *in vivo* indication of genotoxic damage. Unfortunately, exfoliated urothelial cells in the urine of

male subjects are not abundant, and large volumes of urine are
generally required to obtain an adequate number of cells. Because
of the scarcity of cells in the slide preparations, only a limited
number of specimens provided sufficient cells for analysis. As
shown in Table III, 3.36% of the exfoliated urothelial cells collected from the orchardists within 6 to 8 hours of pesticide application
were micronucleated. This represents a 5.6-fold increase in micronucleated cells compared to specimens collected during the pre-
spraying period. It should be noted that these samples were obtained
from individuals 10 to 12 days into the spraying season. Genotoxic
damage by environmental agents occurs in dividing epithelial cells.
It requires one to two weeks for the daughter cells to migrate up
through the epithelium and exfoliate.

Table III. Frequency of Micronucleated Cells from Population
Groups at Elevated Risk for Cancer

| | Percent Cells with Micronuclei | | |
	Controls	Exposed Group	Relative Increase
Egypt: *Schistosoma*	0.57[a]	7.56	
haematobium infection	(0.2-0.9)	(4.7-12.5)	13.3
	(n=11)	(n=19)	
Vancouver: cigarette	0.56	3.34[b]	
smokers	(0.0-0.8)	(1.6-6.5)	5.96
	(n=20)	(n=20)	
Okanagan Valley:	0.60	3.36	
pesticide sprayers	(0.2-0.8)	(1.1-5.3)	5.6
	(n=10)	(n=5)	

[a]Figures represent average percentage of micronucleated exfoliated
cells, with the range given in parentheses.
[b]40-65 cigarettes per day.

Discussion

Urine Clastogenicity Associated with Pesticide Exposure. The current
investigation indicates that individuals exposed to high concentrations of pesticides show substantial genotoxic activity in their
urine. In contrast, pre-spraying urine samples collected from the
same subjects demonstrated only low "baseline" levels of clastogenic
activity. The mean percentage of CHO cells with chromatid aberrations increased fivefold for the group during the peak spraying
season, strongly implying the association of pesticide exposure with
the high urinary clastogenic activity.
     Genotoxicity of urine from pesticide sprayers has not been
previously reported. However, evidence of the ability of pesticides
to induce cytogenetic damage in humans is known. Yoder et al. (36)
noted a marked increase in the chromatid lesions of lymphocyte
cultures prepared from individuals exposed during heavy spraying
periods. The aberrations were particularly striking among workers
exposed primarily to herbicides. Crossen et al. (37) and Dulout et
al. (38) both found a significantly elevated incidence of sister-
chromatid exchanges (another endpoint for genotoxic damage) in
peripheral lymphocyte chromosomes of subjects occupationally exposed
to pesticides. However, some of these findings have not been

substantiated by other investigators (39-42). Differences in the degree of exposure or the use of different pesticides may have contributed to the negative findings.

The high urine clastogenicity associated with pesticide exposure was only observed in urine specimens collected within 6 to 8 hours of pesticide spraying. Urine collected within 16 to 24 hours of spraying demonstrated no significant increase in clastogenic activity over control baseline values. It can be speculated that the maximum excretion rate of pesticides generally occurs within hours of exposure. This indicates the importance of collecting urine at a period when the metabolite excretion rate is high or optimal.

Interindividual variations were found in the levels of clastogenic activity in urine collected during the spraying period. Some individuals had extremely high activity, whereas a few showed moderate to low levels of activity. These variations may reflect differences in absorption, distribution, metabolism and excretion of pesticides between individuals. Alternatively, they may also be an indication of the variations in personal working habits and hygiene. The inclusion of a conventional patch test to determine pesticide exposure may help to explain some of the variability observed in clastogenic activity (43). High urinary clastogenic activity may be interpreted in one of two ways. The rapid clearance of clastogens from the body may be taken as evidence of diminished risk. On the other hand, such facile excretion may mean that organs such as the bladder will be exposed to high concentrations of genotoxic material (44).

It should be emphasized that the tested doses of organic material in the urine extracts are not very different from those present in urine in the bladder. Creatinine concentrations in the urine typically ranged from 0.5 to 2.5 mg/ml. Many of the urine extracts obtained from the orchardists during the spraying period were active *in vitro* at 4.0 mg creatinine equivalence per ml of tissue culture medium or less. Thus the concentrations of genotoxic materials used in the assay are reasonably comparable to the concentrations to which bladder mucosal cells may be exposed.

Monitoring Urine Genotoxicity as a Means of Detecting Exposure to Environmental Carcinogens and Mutagens: Limitations and Applications. The present study demonstrates the value of using urine analysis as a means of assessing human exposure to environmental contaminants. It is necessary to emphasize here that the study is only an attempt to make a qualitative association between exposure to a potential carcinogen or mutagen and abnormalities observed in the proposed genetic endpoints. Several advantages of the bioassay of urine are illustrated in this investigation. Unlike epidemiological studies, urine analysis for genotoxicity takes into account the variations in exposure regimes, and thus the screening procedure can pinpoint individual risk (45). With the implementation of such screening techniques, exposure to high risk environments may be minimized long before the occurrence of any irreversible pathological changes.

The assay of urine for genotoxicity does not measure the activity of just one chemical component, but the activity of a combination of the pesticides *per se* and the metabolites present in the urine as a result of complex exposures. Within the urine are thousands of chemicals, some of which may be inhibitors or enhancers

of genotoxic activity. The assay of urine samples measures the net
effect of the chemicals present together, taking into consideration
the synergistic or antagonistic interactions that may be significant.

Another advantage of analyzing human urine is the accessibility
of the samples. Urine collection procedures are non-invasive and
can be conducted on a repeated basis. In addition, the analysis of
urine for genotoxicity may be coupled with quantitative chemical
analysis. Overall, the analysis of urine samples is simple and rapid.

Urine monitoring is most useful in evaluating human exposure to
multiple agents. Rarely is an individual ever exposed to a single
agent. In the majority of cases, the extent of exposure or the route
(e.g., dermal, respiratory, ingestion) will not be known. For
example, in our investigation, most sprayers were exposed to a
variety of pesticides, and it was unknown whether this mixture would
be genotoxic *in vivo*. This question can be answered by urine genotoxicity assays. The actual presence of genotoxic activity coinci-
ding with the time of exposure to the suspected genotoxin serves as
evidence that exposure had occurred, and that cells in various organs
were thus at risk for genetic damage while the chemicals were being
systematically distributed throughout the body. Thus the bioassay
of urine is useful for identifying carcinogenic and mutagenic risks
associated with various work environments.

However, the analysis of urine for genotoxicity is not without
its limitations. Unlike chemical analysis, there is a lack of
sensitivity for specific chemicals (46). As demonstrated in this
study, although clastogenic activity was observed with pesticide
usage, the identity of the clastogens remains unknown. Because of
the unknown nature of the compounds, the assay results can only be
interpreted in a qualitative manner in terms of exposure assessment.
To gain more useful information (quantitative assessment), chemical
techniques (e.g., analytical high-pressure liquid chromatography)
must be employed in conjunction with the examination for urine
genotoxicity.

Moreover, our studies and those of others (2,47,48) show that
urine analysis may be useful only for monitoring recent exposures.
Cumulative exposures cannot be detected (49). Depending on the
xenobiotic, metabolites may be eliminated into the urine within one
to perhaps two days. Beyond this period, the levels of metabolites
in the urine may be too low for detection. Thus it is necessary to
either determine the excretion kinetics of the metabolites or to
obtain multiple urine samples after exposure to an agent. Since both
choices are likely to be impractical, the collection of urine a few
hours after exposure or late in the evening may be a reasonable
alternative. Kriebel et al. (50) found that an evening urine sample
provided a good estimation of the mutagen concentrations of a 24-hour
urine sample. Nevertheless, regardless of the sampling schedule
used, the collection of urine samples far beyond the optimal metabolite excretion period will result in levels of genotoxic activity
undistinguishable from normal background values.

Decomposition of urinary clastogens may present a problem in the
analysis of urine. Some metabolites are short-lived and may never be
detected in the urine. Only those metabolites with long half-lives
can be assayed. Even storage at -20°C does not ensure the stability
of the extract components. A few individuals have investigated the
stability of urine concentrates. Putzrath et al. (51) observed the

loss of genotoxic activity of a few urine concentrates with storage.
Beek et al. (52) also noted decreased genotoxic activity with re-used
urine extracts. In both cases, the authors attributed the loss of
activity to repeated freezing and thawing of the urine extracts.
    Genotoxins may also be lost through the extraction and concen-
tration procedures. For example, with our methods, volatile compounds (e.g., nitrosamines) may be lost through the rotary evaporation or freeze-drying process. Loss of activity may also occur
through limitations in the extraction procedures. Because of the
presence of high salt concentrations in the urine, hydrophilic
materials are difficult to isolate. Toxicity of the salts to
mammalian cells also makes it impossible to test hydrophilic components in urine. This toxicity problem was evident when freeze-dried
unconcentrated urine was assayed for genotoxic material. New
procedures must be developed to extract polar organic compounds in
urine.
    Finally, caution must be used in the interpretation of geno-
toxicity data. The absence of genotoxicity in some cases does not
always necessarily indicate a lack of exposure. Metabolites may be
present in concentrations below the detectable limits of the assay
system. In addition, compounds excreted through routes other than
urine (e.g., lungs, feces, sweat) may never be detected by urine
assays. Some chemicals may also be biotransformed into products that
cannot be reactivated *in vitro* (53). Glucuronide and sulfate conjugates may be readily cleaved by the inclusion of β-glucuronidase
and sulfatase enzymes in the assay system (1,2). In contrast,
chemicals conjugated to glutathione cannot be easily cleaved to yield
the compound in its original form. Instead, glutathione conjugates
are likely to be metabolized such that the glutathione-metabolite
linkage is retained (54). This class of metabolites is not detectable in urine clastogenicity or mutagenicity tests (55). Other
methods such as those that assay for mercapturic acids and other
thioethers must be used to detect glutathione conjugates (56).
Another factor to consider is that although absorption of the compound by the body may have occurred, the suspected agent may not have
yet been metabolized. This pertains, in particular, to lipophilic
substances that persist in the body for a long period of time. The
slow release of these compounds from tissue stores will make their
detection quite difficult.

Confounding Factors Affecting the Urine Clastogenicity Assay. The
presence of genotoxic activity in urine from cigarette smokers has
been demonstrated in several studies (2,4,45,51,57,58). Findings of
increased urine mutagenicity related to passive smoking have been
reported (2,3,59). Certainly, these results illustrate the importance of restricting urine studies to non-smokers when attempting to
demonstrate occupational exposure to environmental chemicals other
than cigarette smoke. Smokers should only be used as a positive
control population.
    Low levels of urinary clastogenic activity were detected in many
subjects in the present study, despite the absence of exposure to
pesticides or cigarette smoke. Similar findings of low levels of
urine mutagenicity unrelated to occupation or smoking have been
reported (45,52,60,61). Recently, various dietary factors affecting
the urine mutagenicity assay have been discovered, such as ingestion

of a fried beef meal (48) or a fried pork or bacon meal (5), but not microwaved meat (48). Urine mutagenicity was also increased in another study where subjects were restricted to a vegetarian diet consisting of soy products, nuts, fruits and vegetables (6). These studies demonstrate that consumption of mutagen-containing foods may be partly responsible for the presence of urine genotoxicity.

The use of medication may also be a contributing factor. Patients treated with the antitumour drug, cyclophosphamide (62), and with the antischistosomal drugs, niridazole and metronidazole (63), and psoriatic patients receiving crude coal tar therapy have exhibited mutagenic activity in the urine (12). Some drugs may synergize the mutagenic activity of urine in combination with other agents. For example, Recio et al. (64) noted that the use of an arthritic drug (Ascription A.D.) increased the mutagenic activity of the urine of a cigarette smoker fivefold above that of urine of other smokers. However, the potential confounding effects of drugs, as illustrated by the above studies, do point to the need to exercise caution in the interpretation of results. Finally, the appearance of low levels of clastogenic activity may be the result of unknown exposure to environmental contaminants such as automobile exhaust (65). In any urine study, it is virtually impossible to control for exposure to such environmental substances. The only solution would be to analyze repeated urine samplings to establish a baseline to account for interfering exposures.

The Micronucleus Test on Exfoliated Human Cells. Although this study demonstrates the presence of clastogenic activity in urine extracts from orchardists during the spraying season, the question arises as to whether the compounds causing this clastogenic activity with *in vitro* cultures would act *in vivo* to induce genotoxic damage. A whole organism may possess activation/inactivation mechanisms which would provide protection from such genotoxic components. In an effort to answer this question, exfoliated epithelial cells were isolated from the urine of pesticide sprayers and examined for the frequency of micronuclei. Unfortunately, few of the examined urine samples contained sufficient cells to permit an accurate assessment of damage. However, samples with sufficient cells did show a significant increase in micronucleated cells. Future studies with this procedure should involve repeated sampling of each examined individual (e.g., 2-3 successive days). Isolated cells would be stored in ethanol and pooled just prior to dropping them onto slides.

The combination of analysis of biological fluids for genotoxic activity and the concurrent assessment of exposed epithelial cells for *in vivo* damage is highly promising. This approach has been used previously to elucidate the relationship between exposure to genotoxins and the induction of genetic damage in target tissues. One such group assayed were tobacco/betel quid chewers in the Philippines and India, a group at elevated risk for oral cancer. Saliva samples taken from individuals during chewing were found to contain genotoxic agents, a portion of which have been identified as tobacco-specific nitrosamines (66-68). Oral smears of exfoliated cells from these chewers showed a significant elevation in micronucleus frequencies. Subsequently, a combination of the two approaches was used to identify components which would act in these populations to increase (e.g., cigarette or alcohol usage) or reduce (chemopreventive agents such as beta-carotene) genotoxic damage (69). A similar approach could be used to study genotoxins in the urine of carcinogen-exposed individuals.

We would be remiss at this point if we did not insert a note of caution in the use of the micronucleus test on exfoliated cells to monitor populations such as pesticide sprayers. Prior to this study, all of the examined population groups had been more or less chronically exposed to carcinogenic agents. All of the populations at risk for oral cancer consisted of tobacco users with a chronic usage of either chewing tobacco or cigarettes. Bilharziasis patients at risk for urinary bladder cancer may be exposed for several years to carcinogenic agents in the urine (16). A similar situation exists for the second population in which an elevated micronucleus frequency was observed in urinary sediments (cigarette smokers in British Columbia) (15). In the case of acute exposure to a genotoxic agent, such as in this study, a temporary elevation in micronucleus frequencies could be missed if only a single sampling is made. Our experience with periodic samples of cancer patients receiving radiation to the pelvic region encompassing the urinary bladder is that the frequency of micronucleated cells in urine samples increases 10-12 days after treatment begins, and declines within a week after treatment is terminated, reflecting the time required for damage in the dividing cells of the basal layers of the epithelium to produce micronuclei in daughter cells, and for these cells to reach the surface of the epithelium and be exfoliated. These kinetics should be kept in mind when examining individuals receiving acute exposure to an agent, and a repeated sampling procedure over these time intervals should be employed.

In conclusion, this study indicates that the examination of extracted urine samples for clastogenic activity in *in vitro* cell cultures may be a valuable indicator of exposure of pesticide workers to genotoxic agents. More studies are required prior to judging the suitability of employing the exfoliated cell micronucleus test as a routine monitor of *in vivo* genotoxic damage in such workers.

Literature Cited

1. Legator, M.S.; Bueding, E.; Batzinger, R.; Connor, T.H.; Eisenstadt, E.; Farrow, M.G.; Ficsor, G.; Hsie, A.; Seed, J.; Stafford, R.S. Mutation Res. 1982, 98, 319-74.
2. Yamasaki, E.; Ames, B.N. Proc. Natl. Acad. Sci. USA 1977, 74, 3555-59.
3. Sorsa, M.; Einisto, P.; Husgafvel-Pursiainen, K.; Jarventaus, H.; Kivisto, H.; Pettonen, Y.; Tuomi, T.; Valkonen, S. J. Toxicol. Environ. Health 1985, 16, 523-34.
4. Dunn, B.P.; Curtis, J.R. Mutation Res. 1985, 147, 179-88.
5. Baker, R.; Arlauskas, A.; Bonin, A.; Angus, D. Cancer Lett. 1982, 16, 81-9.
6. Sasson, I.M.; Coleman, D.T.; Lavoie, E.J.; Hoffmann, D.; Wynder, E.L. Mutation Res. 1985, 158, 149-57.
7. McCoy, E.C.; Hankel, R.; Rosenkranz, H.S.; Giuffida, J.G.; Bizzari, D.V. Environ. Health Perspect. 1979, 21, 221-3.
8. Falck, K.; Grohn, P.; Sorsa, M.; Vainio, H.; Heinonen, E.; Holsti, L.R. Lancet 1979, I, 1250-1.

9. Pasquini, R.; Monarca, S.; Sforzolini, G.S.; Conti, R.;
    Fagioli, F. Int. Arch. Occup. Environ. Health 1982, 50, 387-95.
10. Kriebel, D.; Commoner, B.; Bollinger, D.; Bronsdon, D.; Gold,
    J.; Henry, J. Mutation Res. 1983, 108, 67-79.
11. Legator, M.S.; Truong, L.; Connor, T.H. In Chemical Mutagens:
    Principles and Methods for Their Detection; Hollaender, A.;
    de Serres, F.J., Eds.; Plenum: New York, 1978; Vol. 5, pp 1-23.
12. Wheeler, L.A.; Saperstein, M.D.; Lowe, N.J. J. Invest Dermatol.
    1981, 77, 181-85.
13. Wang, C.Y.; Benson, R.C., Jr; Bryan, G.T. J. Natl. Cancer Inst.
    1977, 58, 871-3.
14. Curtis, J.R.; Dunn, B.P. Mutation Res. 1985, 147, 171-7.
15. Stich, H.F.; Rosin, M.P. Cancer Lett. 1984, 22, 241-53.
16. Raafat, M.; El-Gerzawi, S.; Stich, H.F. J. Egypt. Natl. Cancer
    Inst. 1984, 1, 63-73.
17. Stich, H.F.; San, R.H.C.; Rosin, M.P. Ann. N.Y. Acad. Sci.
    1983, 407, 93-105.
18. Iosefsohn, M. In Selected Methods for the Small Clinical
    Laboratory; Faulkner, W.R.; Meites, S., Eds.; American Associa-
    tion for Clinical Chemistry: Washington D.C., 1982; pp 201-5.
19. Stich, H.F.; San, R.H.C. Mutation Res. 1970, 10, 389-404.
20. Stich, H.F.; Stich, W.; Parida, B.B. Cancer Lett. 1982, 17,
    125-34.
21. Heddle, J.A.; Salamone, M.F. In Short-Term Tests for Chemical
    Carcinogens; Stich, H.F.; San, R.H.C., Eds.; Springer: New York,
    1981; pp 243-9.
22. Heddle, J.A.; Raj, A.S.; Krepinsky, A.B. In Short-Term Tests for
    Chemical Carcinogens; Stich, H.F.; San, R.H.C., Eds.; Springer:
    New York, 1981; pp 250-4.
23. Zar, J.H. In Biostatistical Analysis; Prentice-Hall: Englewood
    Cliffs, N.J., 1984; 2nd ed.
24. Alam, M.T.; Corbeil, M.; Chagnon, A.; Kasatiya, S.S. Chromosoma
    1974, 49, 77-86.
25. Kappas, A.; Green, M.H.L.; Bridges, B.A.; Rogers, A.M.; Muriel,
    W.J. Mutation Res. 1976, 40, 379-82.
26. Bridges, B.A. Mutation Res. 1975, 32, 3-34.
27. Ishidate, M.; Odashima, S. Mutation Res. 1977, 48, 337-54.
28. Moriya, M.; Ohta, T.; Watanabe, K.; Miyazawa, K.; Shirasu, K.
    Mutation Res. 1983, 116, 185-216.
29. Matsuoka, A.; Hayashi, M.; Ishidate, M., Jr. Mutation Res.
    1979, 66, 277-90.
30. Van Bao, T. Humangenetik 1974, 24, 33-57.
31. Carere, A.; Ortali, V.A.; Cardamone, G.; Torracca, A.M.;
    Raschetti, R. Mutation Res. 1978, 57, 277-86.
32. Fahrig, R. In Chemical Carcinogenesis Essays; Montesano, R.;
    Tomatis, L., Eds.; International Agency for Research on Cancer:
    Lyon, 1974; IARC Sci. Publ. No. 10, pp 161-81.
33. Parry, J.M. Mutation Res. 1973, 21, 83-91.
34. Tomkins, D.J.; Grant, W.F. Mutation Res. 1976, 36, 73-84.
35. Kobayashi, H.; Hayatsu, H. Jap. J. Cancer Res. 1984, 75, 489-93.
36. Yoder, J.; Watson, M.; Benson, W. Mutation Res. 1973, 21,
    335-40.
37. Crossen, P.E.; Morgan, W.F.; Horan, J.J.; Stewart, J. N.Z. Med.
    J. 1978, 88, 192-5.

38. Dulout, F.N.; Pastori, M.C.; Olivero, O.A.; Gonzalez Cid, M.; Loria, D.; Matos, E.; Sobel, N.; de Bujan, E.C.; Albiano, N. Mutation Res. 1985, 143, 237-44.
39. Rabello, M.N.; Becak, W.; De Almeida, W.F.; Pigati, P.; Ungaro, M.T.; Murata, T.; Pereira, C.A.B. Mutation Res. 1975, 28, 449-54.
40. Hogstedt, B.; Kolnig, A-M.; Mitelman, F.; Skerfving, S. Hereditas 1980, 92, 177-8.
41. de Cassia Stocco, R.; Becak, W.; Gaeta, R.; Rabello-Gay, M.N. Mutation Res. 1982, 103, 71-6.
42. Steenland, K.; Carrano, A.; Clapp, D.; Ratcliffe, J.; Ashworth, L.; Meinhardt, T. J. Occup. Med. 1985, 27, 729-32.
43. Franklin, C.A.; Fenske, R.A.; Greenhalgh, R.; Mathieu, L.; Denley, H.V.; Leffingwell, J.T.; Spear, R.C. J. Toxicol. Environ. Health 1981, 7, 715-31.
44. Barnes, W.S.; Weisburger, J.H. Mutation Res. 1984, 156, 83-91.
45. Guerrero, R.R.; Rounds, D.E.; Hall, T.C. J. Natl. Cancer Inst. 1979, 62, 805-9.
46. Brusick, D.; de Serres, F.J.; Everson, R.B.; Mendelsohn, M.L.; Neel, J.V.; Shelby, M.D.; Waters, M.D. In Guidelines for Studies of Human Populations Exposed to Mutagenic and Reproductive Hazards; Bloom, A.D., Ed.; March of Dimes Birth Defects Foundation: White Plains, N.Y., 1981; pp 111-40.
47. Kado, N.Y.; Manson, C.; Eisenstadt, E.; Hsieh, D.P.H. Mutation Res. 1985, 157, 227-33.
48. Sousa, J.; Nath, J.; Tucker, J.D.; Ong, T. Mutation Res. 1985, 149, 365-74.
49. Vainio, H.; Sorsa, M.; Falck, K. In Monitoring Human Exposure to Carcinogenic and Mutagenic Agents; Berlin, A.; Draper, M.; Hemminki, K.; Vainio, H., Eds.; International Agency for Research on Cancer: Lyon, 1984; IARC Sci. Publ. No. 59, pp 247-58.
50. Kriebel, D.; Gold, H.J.; Bronsdon, A.; Commoner, B. J. Environ. Pathol. Toxicol. 1985, 6, 157-69.
51. Putzrath, R.M.; Langley, D.; Eisenstadt, E. Mutation Res. 1981, 85, 97-108.
52. Beek, B.; Aranda, I.; Thompson, E. Mutation Res. 1982, 92, 333-60.
53. Falck, K. In Mutagens in Our Environment; Sorsa, M.; Vainio, H., Eds.; Alan R. Liss: New York, 1982; pp 387-400.
54. Dorough, H.W. J. Toxicol. Clin. Toxicol. 1983, 19, 637-59.
55. Ramel, C. In Individual Susceptibility to Genotoxic Agents in the Human Population; de Serres, F.J.; Pera, R.W., Eds.; Research Triangle Park, N.C., 1984; pp 293-303.
56. van Doorn, R.; Leijdekkers, C.M.; Bos, R.P.; Brouns, R.M.E.; Henderson, P.T. Ann. Occup. Hyg. 1981, 24, 77-92.
57. Aeschbacher, H.U.; Chappuis, C. Mutation Res. 1981, 89, 161-77.
58. Caderni, G.; Dolara, P. Pharmacol. Res. Commun. 1983, 5, 775-82.
59. Bos, R.P.; Theuws, J.L.G.; Henderson, P.T. Cancer Lett. 1983, 19, 85-90.
60. Barale, R.; Sozzi, G.; Toniolo, P.; Borghi, O.; Reali, D.; Loprieno, N.; Della Porta, G. Mutation Res. 1985, 157, 235-40.
61. Everson, R.B.; Ratcliffe, J.M.; Flack, P.M.; Hoffman, D.M.; Watanabe, A.S. Cancer Res. 1985, 45, 6487-97.
62. Siebert, D.; Simon, U. Mutation Res. 1973, 21, 257-62.

63. Legator, M.S.; Connor, T.H.; Stoeckel, M. Science 1975, 188, 1118-9.
64. Recio, L.; Enoch, H.; Hannan, M.A. J. Appl. Toxicol. 1982, 2, 241-6.
65. Ohnishi, Y.; Kachi, K.; Sato, K.; Tahara, I.; Takeyoshi, H.; Tokiwa, H. Mutation Res. 1980, 77, 229-40.
66. Stich, H.F.; Rosin, M.P. Mutation Res. 1985, 150, 43-50.
67. Stich, H.F.; Rosin, M.P.; Brunnemann, K.D. Cancer Lett. 1986, 31, 15-25.
68. Stich, H.F. In Mechanisms in Tobacco Carcinogenesis; Hoffmann, D.; Harris, C.C., Eds.; Cold Spring Harbor Laboratory: Cold Spring Harbor, N.Y., 1986; Banbury Report 23, pp 99-111.
69. Stich, H.F.; Stich, W.; Rosin, M.P.; Vallejera, M.O. Int. J. Cancer 1984, 34, 745-50.

RECEIVED March 15, 1988

Chapter 9

Neuropathy Target Esterase in Blood Lymphocytes

Monitoring the Interaction of Organophosphates with a Primary Target

Marcello Lotti

Istituto di Medicina del Lavoro, Università degli Studi di Padova, Via Facciolati 71, 35127 Padova, Italy

Selective toxicity is initiated by specific interactions of the toxin with primary targets. The identification of such targets and their accessibility in human fluids will allow an evaluation of dose-effect relationships at a molecular level. Inter- and intra-individual variations of dose response relationships may then be rationalized and acceptable thresholds properly set. However, the assumption is made that the ultimate toxin is equally delivered to the accessible target and to where toxicity takes place. Some organophosphorus (OP) pesticides cause a rare selective toxicity called organophosphate-induced delayed polyneuropathy (OPIDP). The initiation of this toxicity involves specific interactions of a protein in the nervous system called Neuropathy Target Esterase (NTE). This protein is present in blood lymphocytes and its measurement after exposure to certain OP pesticides has been suggested as a biomonitor for OPIDP. NTE inhibition in blood lymphocytes predicts the development of OPIDP in man. However dose-response relationships are not available for man and a threshold is not yet established. Human lymphocytic NTE shows large interindividual variation, suggesting the need for an individual baseline to evaluate occupational exposures. An attempt to monitor occupational exposures showed a substantial effect on lymphocytic NTE not followed by toxicity. A likely explanation is that the assumption on the delivery previously made was incorrect. Furthermore the turnover of NTE in the target organ might be faster than in the monitored one and thus the effect of exposure overestimated.

0097–6156/89/0382–0117$06.00/0
© 1989 American Chemical Society

Biological monitoring of occupational and environmental exposures
to chemicals will become more meaningful for risk assessment when
the mode of action of the chemical is understood (1).
When the molecular target of toxicity for a given chemical is
identified, dose-response studies are possible (2). If the target
is accessible, such studies occupy a unique position in biological
monitoring because they deal directly with adverse effects
produced by chemicals. In addition, they supply integrated
information on exposure, absorption, distribution, and response
(3). A good example of an accessible target that predicts toxic
effects at an inaccessible site is the acetylcholinesterase enzyme
in the red blood cells which predicts neuronal cholinesterase
activity (4). The purpose of this paper is to report another type
of test to monitor a different toxicity caused by some
organophosphorus pesticides, the organophosphorus induced delayed
polyneuropathy (OPIDP).

OPIDP is a syndrome distinct from acute cholinergic toxicity
and is caused by some but not all OP pesticides. Symptoms and
signs of a peripheral polyneuropathy, axonal in type, are delayed
2-5 weeks after a single exposure and less predictably after
repeated exposures (5). The central nervous system might also be
involved (6). Several commercial pesticides have produced OPIDP in
man, including trichlorphon, trichlornate, methamidophos, and
chlorpyrifos (7).

The mechanism of initiation of OPIDP was elucidated by M.K.
Johnson and reviewed several times (5,8,9,10,11), as well as the
consequent practical gains for human OPIDP biomonitoring
(12,13,14). This paper gives a brief account of these studies and
discusses some limitations of the biomonitoring test which is now
available.

The molecular target for OPIDP is a protein with esteratic
activity called Neuropathy Target Esterase (NTE). OPs which cause
OPIDP phosphorylate more than 70% of NTE of the target axons soon
after dosing in the hen (10, 15). A further step, called aging of
the phosphoryl enzyme complex, leads to a negatively charged
complex and binding of the alkyl group lost during this process to
membranes. This two step reaction usually takes place within hours
after dosing and correlates with the development of OPIDP three
weeks later. Recently another aspect of the pathogenesis has been
identified: a marked reduction of retrograde axonal transport
occurs 3-5 days after dosing in peripheral nerves which eventually
degenerate (16). OPs and related inhibitors which produce a
non-ageable NTE complex do not cause OPIDP and also protect from a
subsequent challenging dose of an effective OP.

Dudek and Richardson reported the presence of NTE activity in
the hen lymphatic system (17), and this finding was confirmed in
man (18). The question was raised whether measurements of NTE
activity in blood lymphocytes after exposure to OPs causing OPIDP
can be used to monitor this toxic effect in humans. Validation of
this test in humans proceeds, for obvious reasons, rather slowly.
Nevertheless, some data have been accumulated so far and their
significance recently discussed (14). Briefly, a case of death due
to the organophosphate dimethoate (phosphorodithioic acid,
0,0-dimethyl S- (2-methylamino)- 2 - oxoethyl ester) validates the

animal data on the negligible potential of this OP to cause OPIDP, i.e. dimethoate does not inhibit NTE in either animals or man at doses far above the lethal ones (19). In a suicide case with chlorpyrifos (0,0 - diethyl - 0 - 3,5,6,-trichloro - 2- pyridyl phosphorothioate), inhibition of lymphocytic NTE correlates with that in peripheral nerve (20). After a large dose of the same chemical to man, substantial inhibition of lymphocytic NTE predicted the development of OPIDP when measured several days before the onset of symptoms (21). All the evidence collected so far, however, leaves the key question open about the threshold of NTE inhibition/aging required to trigger the toxic response in man. As more data become available, also with a larger use of the lymphocytic NTE test, the question will probably be answered.

NTE activity as studied in peripheral lymphocytes of an unexposed population reveals a large interindividual variation (22). To ascertain that low lymphocytic NTE activity represents an effect of occupational exposure, the accurate measurement of baseline values is necessary.

It is possible that "false positive" or "false negative" results maybe occur when lymphocytic NTE is used to monitor OPIDP. Table 1 lists some situations where inhibition of NTE in peripheral lymphocytes might not be related to OPIDP (false positives).

As clarified by mechanistic studies, NTE inhibitors like phosphinates, carbamates and sulphonates do not cause OPIDP. To my knowledge however, none of these protective NTE inhibitors are commercial pesticides. The second situation where "false positive" results might arise is when inhibited NTE ages slowly. Usually, whenever routine tests using NTE assay are performed, it is assumed that the aging process, if formally possible, is very rapid (23,24). This assumption ignores the possibility of slow aging of inhibited NTE, and recent evidence has modified this view. Several OPs exist in steroisomeric forms and studies with chiral isomers have revealed a high degree of stereoselectivity in enzyme reactions with inhibitors and substrates and in biological activities (25).

It is known that racemic EPN (0-ethyl 0-(4-nitrophenyl) phenylphosphonothioate) and its L(-)-EPN isomer cause OPIDP in the hen (26), but not the D(+)-EPN isomer (27). In repeated dosing experiments L(-)-EPN caused OPIDP in the hen, whereas D(+)-EPN had very marginal effects (28). Some years ago we were puzzled by results obtained in vitro with NTE and AChE when challenged with the resolved optical isomers of EPNO (EPN-oxon), because it had been suggested that the ratio AChE I_{50}/NTE I_{50} in vitro is predictive of the likelihood for a given OP to cause OPIDP in vivo (29). Both EPNO isomers showed the same ratio of 0.01, suggesting an identical potency in causing OPIDP (Lotti M.; Johnson M.K. Unpublished results, 1978). The solution came years later when it was demonstrated that the phosphonyl-NTE complex, when formed by L(-)-EPNO, ages quickly, while that formed by D(+)-EPNO ages very slowly (30). The same effects on NTE occur in vivo either with EPA or EPNO isomers and the development of OPIDP is correlated with the rapid aging of phosphonylated NTE (31). The unaged phosphonylated NTE also protects the animal from a subsequent challenging dose of an effective OP. In such cases of slow aging OP isomers, we might therefore observe inhibition of NTE without the clinical correlate.

TABLE 1:   "False Positive" Results When Measuring Lymphocyte NTE Activity for OPIDP Biomonitoring

---

a.   non-aging inhibited NTE (example: phosphinylated, carbamylated and sulphonylated NTE) (8).

b.   slow-aging inhibited NTE (example: D-(+)-EPN phosphinylated NTE) (32).

c.   different access of the inhibitor to lymphocytes and nervous system (example: highly reactive metabolites, perhaps DEF metabolites) (33).

d.   different sensitivity to OPIDP because of interindividual variations of the threshold (?).

e.   the turnover of inhibited NTE is different in the nervous system (permanent cells) and in blood lymphocytes (variable pool) (?).

Number in brackets indicate references. (?) data not available

Another possibility is when NTE inhibition in the predictive organ does not correlate with that in the target organ. This may have been the case when a substantial inhibition of lymphocytic NTE was observed in an occupational exposure to the cotton defoliants DEF (S,S,S – tributylphosphorotrithioate) and Merphos (tributyl phosphorotrithioite) (32). Parallel to enzyme measurements, electrophysiological tests performed on exposed workers, indicated no exposure-related effects on peripheral nervous system functions. The hypothesis is that the active metabolite(s) of these chemicals as formed in the liver (?), is highly reactive and preferentially inhibits NTE in lymphocytes rather than in the nervous system. However, the possibility that NTE was inhibited below the threshold cannot be ruled out.

Once the threshold of NTE inhibition/aging without toxic response is known, possible interindividual variations in sensitivity might also be detectable.

In repeated exposures to OPs capable of causing OPIDP, another possibility of misleading results should be taken into account: that the turnover of inhibited NTE is different in lymphocytes and in the brain leading to either higher or lower inhibition in one organ as compared to the other. This is because the nervous cell population is stable, whereas the pool of circulating lymphocytes is highly variable.

TABLE II: "False Negative" Results When Measuring Lymphocyte NTE
            Activity for OPIDP Biomonitoring

---

a.   delayed inhibition/aging of NTE (example: peak NTE inhibition
     several days after chlorpyrifos) (33).

b.   different sensitivity to OPIDP because of interindividual
     variations of the threshold (?).

c.   the turnover of inhibited NTE is different in the nervous
     system (permanent cells) and in blood lymphocytes
     (variable pool) (?).

Numbers in brackets indicate references.   (?) data not available

Measurements of lymphocytic NTE activity might also give
"false negative" results (Table II).   This might occur when the
timing of measurement is not carefully selected.   We suspected such
"false negative" results in a patient who attempted suicide by
ingesting a large amount of chlorpyrifos (21).   Surprisingly,
lymphocytic NTE was still inhibited more than 20 days after the
poisoning; however, the usual delay between high NTE inhibition and
the clinical onset of OPIDP was maintained (2-3 weeks).   As a
result of this observation some experiments with hens were
performed to clarify this and other discrepancies observed in the
poisoning case.   Chlorphyrifos caused OPIDP in hens but the effect
did not correlate with the inhibition of NTE in the nervous system
24 hours after dosing, as it usually occurs.   At that time, the
inhibition of nervous system NTE was below the threshold (about
50%) and the peak occurred 4-5 days later (33).   It is concluded
therefore that for certain OPs, the usual 24 hour interval after
exposure might not be appropriate to observe the maximal effect on
NTE.
     In conclusion, the understanding of the mechanism of action of
certain OPs in causing OPIDP and the identification of the
molecular target led to the development of a specific test to be
used in human biomonitoring.   Further mechanistic studies and
clinical observations are leading to a better appreciation of the
limits of this test.

Acknowledgments

I wish to thank Mrs. C. Drace-Valentini for her help in preparing
the manuscript.   Supported in part by Grants from CNR
(85.00581.56,SP5), Italian Ministry of Education and Regions
Veneto.

Literature Cited

1.   Aldridge W.N. Ann. Rev. Pharmacol. Toxicol. 1986, 26, 39.
2.   World Health Organization; Report of Planning Meeting.
     International Program on Chemical Safety. ICS/87.17, 1987.
3.   Foa' V.; Emmett E.A.; Maroni M.; Colombi A. (Eds.)
     Occupational and Environmental Chemical Hazards, Cellular and
     Biochemical Indices for Monitoring Toxicity. Ellis Horwood
     Publ., Chichester, U.K., 1987.
4.   Derache R. (Ed.) Organophosphorus Pesticides, Criteria
     (dose/effect relationships) for Organophosphorus Pesticides.
     CEE. Pergamon Press, Oxford, New York, 1977.
5.   Lotti M.; Becker C.E.; Aminoff M.J. Neurology 1984, 34, 658.
6.   Vasilescu C. J. Neurol, Neurosurg. Psychiat. 1982, 45, 942.
7.   World Health Organization; Organophosphorus Insecticides: A
     General Introduction. Environmental Health Criteria 63.
     Geneva, 1986.
8.   Johnson M.K. CRC Crit. Rev. Toxicol. 1975, 3, 289.
9.   Davis C.S.; Richardson R.J. In: Experimental and Clinical
     Neurotoxicology; Spencer P.S.; Schaumburg H.H., Eds.; Williams
     & Wilkins, Baltimore, 1980; pp. 527-544.
10. Johnson M.K. In: Rev. Biochem. Toxicol. vol. 4; Hodgson E.;
     Bend J.R.; Philpot R.M., Eds.; Elsevier, 1982; pp. 141-212.
11. Johnson M.K. Trends Pharmacol. Sci. 1987, 8, 174.
12. Lotti, M. Advances in Biosciences vol. 46; Gilioli R.;
     Cassitto M.G.; Foa' V., Eds; Pergamon Press, Oxford and New
     York, 1983; pp. 101-108.
13. Lotti M. Toxicol. Lett. 1986, 33, 167.
14. Lotti M. Trends Pharmacol. Sci. 1987, 8, 176.
15. Lotti M.; Caroldi E.; Moretto A.; Johnson M.K.; Fish C.;
     Gopinath G.; Roberts N.L. Toxicol. Appl. Pharmacol. 1987,
     88, 87.
16. Moretto A.; Lotti M.; Sabri M.I.; Spencer P.S. J. Neurochem.
     1987, 49, 1515.
17. Dudek B.R.; Richardson R.J. Biochem. Pharmacol. 1982, 31,
     1117.
18. Moretto A; Fassina A; Lotti M. Proc. 2nd International
     Meeting on Cholinesterases, 1983, p. 171.
19. Lotti M.; Ferrara S.D.; Caroldi S.; Sinigaglia F. Arch.
     Toxicol. 1981, 48, 265.
20. Osterloh J.; Lotti M.; Pond S. J. Analyt. Toxicol. 1983, 7,
     125.
21. Lotti M.; Moretto A.; Zoppellari R.; Dainese R.; Rizzuto N.;
     Barusco G. Arch. Toxicol. 1986, 59, 176.
22. Bertoncin D.; Russolo A.; Caroldi S.; Lotti M. Arch. Environ.
     Health 1985, 40, 139.
23. Clothier B.; Johnson M.K. Biochem. J. 1979, 177, 549.
24. Clothier B.; Johnson M.K. Biochem. J. 1980, 185, 739.
25. Ohkawa H. In: Insecticide Mode of Action; Coats J.R.; Ed.;
     Academic Press, NY, London, 1982; pp. 163-185.
26. Aldridge W.N.; Barnes J.M. Biochem. Pharmacol. 1966, 15, 541
     and 549.
27. Ohkawa H.; Mikami N.; Okuno Y.; Miyamoto J. Bull. Envir.
     Contam. Toxicol. 1977, 18, 534.

28. Abou-Donia M.B.; Graham D.G.; Komeil A.A.; Nomeir A.A.; Dauterman W.C. In: Advances in Neurotoxicology; Manzo L., Ed.; Pergamon Press, Oxford, 1980; pp. 237-248.
29. Lotti M.; Johnson M.K. Arch. Toxicol. 1978, 41, 215.
30. Johnson M.K.; Read D.J.; Yoshikawa H. Pest. Biochem. Physiol. 1986, 25, 133.
31. Johnson M.K.; Read D.J. Toxicol. Appl. Pharmacol. 1987, 90, 103.
32. Lotti M.; Becker C.E.; Aminoff M.J.; Woodrow J.E.; Seiber J.N.; Talcott R.E.; Richardson R.J. J. Occup. Med. 1983, 25, 517.
33. Lotti M., In: Occupational and Environmental Chemical Hazards. Cellular and Biochemical Indices for Monitoring Toxicity; Foa' V.; Emmett E.A.; Maroni M.; Colombi A., Eds; Ellis Horwood Publ.; Chichester, U.K., 1987; pp. 499-507.

RECEIVED March 15, 1988

PERCUTANEOUS ABSORPTION AFTER PESTICIDE EXPOSURE

Percutaneous Absorption of Pesticides

It has been shown that percutaneous absorption is the primary route of exposure to users of pesticides (1). For certain pesticides, notably the fumigants, the inhalation route may predominate. The oral route is not considered to be significant relative to the others in the occupational situation.

The risk associated with the use of a pesticide depends on the nature of adverse effects, its potency, the susceptibility of the exposed individuals and the level of exposure. The nature of effects, the potency and susceptibility can be assessed in experimental animals. By exposing animals from different species to a range of doses of the chemicals, a dose-response curve that includes the highest dose at which no effects are observed (NOEL), and the lowest dose at which effects are seen (LOEL) can then be drawn. If the level of human exposure is known, then the dose-response curve from the animal data can be used to predict whether adverse health effects will be seen in humans. When the route of exposure in the test animals and in humans is the same, it has been assumed that dose and exposure are analogous. Uncertainty arises when the routes are dissimilar since absorption can vary considerably from one route to another. Since it may be possible to calculate the internal dose of a pesticide to a worker by multiplying the dermal contact exposure times the percutaneous absorption, attention has focussed on estimating absorption.

The skin is one of the largest organs in the body and its primary functions are to protect the organism from the environment by contributing to the balancing of water loss and retention, the regulation of body temperature and the prevention of entry of xenobiotics into the body. The stratum corneum is the outermost layer of the skin and appears to be the major barrier to penetration (2).

The fact that some chemicals are almost completely absorbed through the skin while others are not has been utilized by the pharmaceutical industry in designing modes of delivery for topical and systemic drug preparations. Although the mechanism of absorption is not well understood, there are many factors that are known to influence it: structure of the stratum corneum (thickness, integrity, previous contact with solvents, temperature and hydration); anatomic site; skin characteristics (age, sex); species variation; solvent effects; occlusion of test site; quantity and frequency of dosing and skin metabolism are some of them.

One widely used method for estimating percutaneous absorption in vivo is based on excretion of radioactivity following topical application of the labelled compound (3,4,5). This is an indirect method consisting of two steps. In the first one, the compound is administered parenterally (intravenously or intramuscularly) and the urine and feces are collected until radioactivity is no longer detectable. If 100% of the activity appears in the urine and feces it suggests that the compound is not stored in the body or exhaled. If only 50% is excreted it suggests that the remaining 50% is retained in the body or exhaled. The second step is to apply a known dose to the skin and collect urine and feces until there is no detectable radioactivity. The application is often about 4 μg/cm^2 and the dose contains approximately 1 μCi specific activity. Lipophilic chemicals are applied in acetone and hydrophilic ones in aqueous solutions with a contact time of 24 hours. The application site is then washed, but urine and feces collected until activity is not detectable. The excretion from the second step can be corrected for incomplete excretion using the value obtained in the first step (parenteral correction).

This method has proven to be extremely useful in obtaining an estimate of the total amount of pesticide that is absorbed (6). Using this method, it has been shown that the amount of chemical absorbed can vary depending on the anatomic site of application (7). Penetration through skin on the forehead can be more than twice as high as on the forearm (8,9), two sites that are frequently contaminated on pesticide applicators (10). Other in vivo methods are discussed in a report by Wester and Maibach (11).

One question that is frequently asked is what is the effect of concentration of dosing solutions on dermal absorption. For testosterone, hydrocortisone and benzoic acid, increasing the dose (4-4,000 μg/cm^2) in humans decreased the relative efficiency of absorption (12, 13). The results with pesticides have varied. Again in humans, penetration of parathion over a dose range of 4 to 4,000 μg/cm^2 was consistently around 9%; penetration of lindane decreased from 9 to 4% over a similar dose range (5). Azinphos methyl was shown to penetrate consistently at approximately 100% in rats over a dose range of 100 to 400 μg/cm^2 (14). In humans, preliminary data suggest that the absorption from the forehead was about 50% at 500 and 1,000 μg/cm^2 and dropped off to 17% and 27% at 4,000 and 6,000 μg/cm^2 respectively (15). These data as well as others discussed in the paper presented in this section by Wester and Maibach (16) suggest that percutaneous penetration may not always be linear, particularly in the high dose region. Noonan and Wester (17) have also shown that increasing the surface area on which the chemical is applied increases the absorption. The contact time can also increase the absorption as well as repeated dosing and dividing the doses. Another factor which may have considerable importance for some products is the metabolism in the skin which is not well understood except for a few chemicals.

A major factor in the estimation of percutaneous penetration is the animal model. It has been shown that absorption in the pig and monkey (rhesus and squirrel) is similar to that in humans whereas the rat and especially the rabbit have significantly more penetrable skin (9,18,19).

All of these factors mentioned above have to be taken into consideration before a given penetration estimate should be used to convert a dermal contact exposure into an absorbed dose estimate.

In vitro methods have also been used to estimate percutaneous penetration. These appear to be based on the premise that absorption is a passive diffusion process and that metabolism would not affect the rate of entry into the skin (20). There are several advantages to in vitro methods including the possibility of using human skin, the fact that the procedure is less time consuming and it is less expensive, allowing more chemicals to be screened. The two methods that appear to be most widely used are the static cell (21) and the flow through cell systems (22). These procedures use dermatome preparations of human skin at a thickness of 350 μm. The thinner skin of mouse and rabbit can be used whole.

There is considerable controversy over the validity of the in vitro method. Some researchers feel that "the relevance of in vitro percutaneous absorption can only be justified with in vivo data" (7). However, the flow through method seems to give an estimate that is closer to in vivo methods (23). Other authors have found fairly good concordance between the two methods for at least a few compounds (20). Hydrophobic compounds appear to pose problems in in vitro systems because the receiving fluid in the cells is generally aqueous. Bronaugh (20) discusses this issue and presents data on a variety of receptor fluids which look promising and may solve some aspects of this problem.

Unfortunately, there are only a few chemicals for which there are properly conducted in vivo and in vitro studies, and it is difficult to generalize about the predictive capability of the in vitro cell methods. Some data suggest that they can be used effectively (20). In a paper presented in this section (24), data are presented which suggest that an in vitro system can accurately predict the in vivo penetration of cypermethrin and carbaryl.

Although there are many more data available now on the percutaneous penetration of pesticides from both in vivo and in vitro models, there are still many uncertainties. These issues are discussed in the chapters in this section. The in vivo methods which estimate the total amount of pesticide that is excreted following a 24 hour contact exposure (3,4,5) provide an estimate of the total bioavailable dose. However, the kinetics of distribution, metabolism and excretion are not known generally. Similarly the in vitro methods provide data on the passive diffusion of the chemicals through the barrier layer but lack the rest of the physiological processes that may have an impact on dermal penetration.

There is a definite need for studies conducted both in vivo and in vitro for many compounds to adequately resolve these questions. Nevertheless, despite the shortcomings of both methods, they do provide a means of estimating the internal dose and bring us one step closer to the correct answer.

Literature Cited

1. Durham, W.F.; Wolfe, H.R.; Elliot, J.W. Arch. Environ. Hlth. 1972, 24, 381-387.
2. Menczel, E.; Bucks, D.A.W.; Wester, R.C.; Maibach, H.I. In Percutaneous Absorption; Bronaugh, R.L.; Maibach, H.I., Eds.; Marcel Dekker: N.Y., 1985; pp. 43-56.
3. Feldmann, R.J.; Maibach, H.I. J. Invest. Dermatol. 1969, 52, 89-94.
4. Feldmann, R.J.; Maibach, H.I. J. Invest. Dermatol. 1969, 54, 339-404.
5. Feldmann, R.J.; Maibach, H.I. Toxicol. Appl. Pharmacol. 1974, 28, 126-132.
6. Wester, R.C.; Maibach, H.I. In Percutaneous Absorption; Bronaugh, R.L.; Maibach, H.I., Eds.; Marcel Dekker: N.Y., 1985; pp. 245-266.
7. Feldmann, R.J.; Maibach, H.I. J. Invest. Dermatol. 1967, 48, 181-183.
8. Franklin, C.A., In Dermal Exposure Related to Pesticide Use; Honeycutt, R.C.; Zweig, G.; Ragsdale, N.N.; Eds.; ACS Symposium Series No. 273; American Chemical Society: Washington, D.C., 1985; pp. 429-444.
9. Moody, R.P.; Franklin, C.A. J. Toxicol. Environ. Hlth. 1987, 20, 209-218.
10. Franklin, C.A.; Fenske, R.A.; Greenhalgh, R.; Mathieu, L.; Denley, H.V.; Leffingwell, J.T.; Spear, R.C. J. Toxicol. Environ. Hlth. 1981, 7, 715-731.
11. Wester, R.C.; Maibach, H.I. In Dermatotoxicology; Marzulli, F.N.; Maibach, H.I., Eds; Hemisphere: Washington, D.C., 1987; pp. 135-152.
12. Maibach, H.I.; Feldmann, R.J. J. Invest. Dermatol. 1969, 52, 382.
13. Wester, R.C.; Maibach, H.I. J. Invest. Dermatol. 1976, 67, 518-520.
14. Franklin, C.A.; Greenhalgh, R.; Maibach, H.I. In IUPAC Pesticide Chemistry, Human Welfare and the Environment; Miyamoto, J. et al. Eds.; Pergamon Press: Oxford 1983; pp. 221-226.
15. Franklin, C.A.; Muir, N.J.; Moody, R.P. Toxicol. Lett. 1986, 33, 127-136.
16. Wester, R.C.; Maibach, H.I. In Biological Monitoring of Pesticide Exposure, Wang, R.G.H.; Franklin, C.A.; Honeycutt, R.C.; Reinert, J.C. Ed.; ACS Symposium Series Chpt. 10, This book.
17. Noonan, P.K.; Wester, R.C., J. Pharm. Sci. 1980, 69, 365-366.
18. Sidon, E.; Moody, R.P.; Franklin, C.A. J. Toxicol. Environ. Hlth. 1988, 23, 207-216.
19. Bartek, M.J.; La Budde, J.A.; Maibach, H.I. J. Invest. Dermatol. 1970, 54, 114-123.
20. Bronaugh, R.L. In Percutaneous Absorption; Bronaugh, R.L.; Maibach, H.I., Eds.; Marcel Dekker: N.Y. 1985; pp. 267-279.
21. Franz, T.J. J. Invest. Dermatol. 1975, 64, 190-195.
22. Bronaugh, R.L., Stewart, R.F. J. Pharm. Sci. 1985, 74, 64-67.

23. Wester, R.C., Maibach, H.I.; Surinchak, J.; Bucks, D.A.W. In Percutaneous Absorption; Bronaugh, R.L.; Maibach, H.I.; Eds; Marcel Dekker: N.Y. 1985; pp. 223-226.
24. Scott, R.C. In Biological Monitoring of Pesticide Exposure, Reinert, J.C. Eds.; ACS Symposium Series Chpt. 13, This book.

Claire A. Franklin
Environmental and Occupational Toxicology Division
Environmental Health Directorate
Tunney's Pasture
Ottawa, Ontario K1A 0L2
Canada

RECEIVED June 1, 1988

Chapter 10

Percutaneous Absorption and Inherent Toxicity

Ronald C. Wester and Howard I. Maibach

Department of Dermatology, University of California School of Medicine, San Francisco, CA 94143–0989

The aim of a toxicological study is to determine the inherent activity of some chemical relative to a target tissue. This process requires delivery to the target tissue -- usually described as bioavailability. With topical products, bioavailability is the process of percutaneous absorption and it is as important as the inherent activity of the chemical. Failure of a patch test system to deliver chemical into skin will produce false negative results. In the skin, the amount of chemical present can correlate with erythema response and epidermal tumors. The skin also has metabolic potential and can alter chemical to more reactive metabolites.

Relationship: Percutaneous Absorption and Inherent Toxicity

The skin is recognized both as a barrier to absorption and as a primary route to the systemic circulation. The skin's barrier properties are often, but not always, impressive. Fluids and electrolytes are reasonably well retained within the body, while at the same time many foreign chemicals are partially restricted from entering the systemic circulation. Despite these barrier properties, the skin is the route by which many chemicals enter the body. In most instances, the toxicology of the chemical is slight, and/or the bioavailability (rate and amount of absorption) of the chemical is too low to cause an immediate response. However, some chemicals applied to the skin have the potential to produce toxicity.

It is now recognized that local and systemic toxicity depend on a chemical penetrating the skin. Table I shows the relationship of percutaneous absorption to toxicologic activity. A local or systemic effect cannot occur unless the chemical has inherent toxicity and the chemical is able to overcome the barrier properties of skin and enter a biologic system (local skin and/or systemic circulation (1). This chapter explores this concept of percutaneous absorption and inherent toxicity.

0097–6156/89/0382–0131$06.00/0

© 1989 American Chemical Society

Table I. Relationship of Percutaneous
Absorption to Toxicologic Activity

Property of Chemical		Local or systemic effect
Absorption through skin	Inherent toxicity	
−	−	None
+	−	None
−	+	None
+	+	Reaction

Patch Test Systems

The development of topical drug products requires testing for skin
toxicology reactions. A variety of patch test systems are available
with which chemicals are applied to skin. The purpose of this study
was to determine the skin absorption of the allergen paraphenyl-
enediamine (PPDA) from a variety of patch testing systems. [14C]-
PPDA (1% in petrolatum,USP) was placed in a variety of patch test
systems at a concentration normalized to equal surface area
(2 mg/mm2). Skin absorption was determined in the guinea pig by
urinary excrtion of 14C. There was a six-fold difference in the
range of skin absorption (p Ñ 0.02) (Figure 1).   In decreasing
order, percent skin absorptions from various patch test systems were
Hill Top Chamber (53.4 + 20.6),   Teflon Control Patch (48.6 + 9.3),
Small Finn Chamber with paper disc insert (34.1 + 19.8), Small Finn
Chamber (29.8 + 9.0), Large Finn Chamber (23.1 + 7.3),   AL-Test
Chamber (8.0 + 0.8). Thus, the choice of patch system could produce
a false negative error if the system inhibits skin absorption, and
subsequent skin toxicology reaction (2).
    The highest efficiency of skin absorption was with the Hill-Top
Chamber. Polikandritou and Conine (3) performed comparative studies
using the Hill-Top chamber system and Webril patch system to compare
delayed contact hypersensitivity. Reactions were induced at
significantly lower concentrations for samples tested with the
Hill-Top Chamber. The reason for this may have been higher skin
absorption.

Metabolic Production of Cutaneous Carcinogens

Much attention has been focused on polycyclic aromatic hydrocarbons
because they produce skin carcinomas. Metabolic activation of these
compounds is usually the first step toward the induction of skin
cancers. The metabolites of benz[a]pyrene (BP) generally fall into
three classes: phenols, quinones, and dihydrodiols. It is the

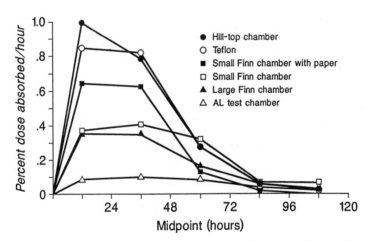

Figure 1. Skin absorption of *p*-phenylenediamine, measured by using various patch-testing systems.

dihydrodiols that, when metabolized to epoxide diols, become the
more potent carcinogens. The epoxides react with cellular nucleophiles such as DNA, RNA, or proteins. The same is true for other
polycyclic aromatic hydrocarbons such as 3-methylcholanthrene and
benz[a]anthracene derivatives. These compounds induce skin tumors
and this probably is caused by a reactive metabolite (an epoxide).
    Knowledge of the binding of BP metabolites to macromolecules
has reached a higher level of sophistication. Binding of
BP-dihydrodiol epoxides was found to occur with high stereoselectivity. These investigators isolated the polymer adducts that
were formed when [3H]BP was applied to the skin of mice. There are
two stereochemical configurations for the BP-7,8-dihydrodiols, and
they may both be metabolized to the respective 9,10-epoxide. The
epoxide may then react with cellular nucleophiles such as DNA, RNA,
or proteins. For nucleic acids, the in vivo binding occurred
preferentially to guanine at the 2-amino group (in both DNA and
RNA). Both stereoisomers bound cellular components, but isomer A
formed mostg of the covalently bound products (4). Thus, any
compound such as benzo[a]pyrene that penetrates the skin must first
pass into and through the epidermis and would be subject to an
extensive metabolic reaction.

Percutaneous Absorption and Epidermal Tumors

Wester and co-workers (5) determined the effect of frequency of
application on percutaneous absorption of hydrocortisone (Table II).
When material was applied once or three times per day there was a
statistical difference (p 0.05) in the percutaneous absorption of
hydrocortisone. One application per 24-hour exposure gave a higher
percutaneous absorption than if the material was applied at a lower
concentration but more frequently, namely, three times per day.
This was confirmed with a second chemical, testosterone (6).

Table II. Application Frequency and Percutaneous
Absorption of Hydrocortisone

Dose (ug/cm2)	Application (times/day)	Total dose (ug/cm2)	Absorption (ug/cm2)
13.3	1	13.3	0.18
13.3	3	40	0.29
40	1	40	0.84

There is a correlation between frequency of application,
percutaneous absorption, and toxicity of applied chemical. Wilson
and Holland (7) determined the effect of application frquency in
epidermal carcinogenic assays. Application of a single large dose
of a highly complex mixture of petroleum or synthetic fuels to a
skin site increased the carcinogenic potential of the chemical
compared to smaller or more frequent applications (Table III).

This carcinogenic toxicity correlated well with the results of Wester et al (6), where a single applied dose increased the percutaneous absorption of the material compared to smaller or intermittent applications.

Table III.   Shale Oil-Induced Incidence of Epidermal Tumors

Shale oil	Dose (mg)	Frequency (per week)	Total dose per week (mg)	No. of animals with carcino-genic tumors
OCSO No. 6	10	4 x	40	2
	10	2 x	40	4
	40	1 x	40	13
PCSO II	10	4 x	40	11
	30	4 x	40	17
	40	1 x	40	19

Cosmetic Chemicals and Toxicity

Table IV shows the relationship between percutaneous absorption and erythema for several oils used in cosmetics. The authors attempted to correlate absorbability with erythema. The most absorbed oil, isopropyl myristate, produced the most erythema. The lowest absorbing oil, 2-hexyl- decanoxyoctane, produced the least erythema. Absorbability and erythema for the other oils did not correlate (8). The lesson to remember with percutaneous toxicity is that a toxic response required both an inherent toxicity in the chemical and the percutaneous absorption of the chemical. The degree of toxicity will depend on the contribution of both criteria.

Table IV.   Relationship of Percutaneous Absorption and Erythema for Several Oils Used in Cosmetics

Absorbability (greatest to least)	Erythema
Isopropyl myristate	+ +
Glycerol tri(oleate)	−
n −Octadecane	+
Decanoxydecane	+
2-Hexyldecanoxyoctane	−

Ten Steps to Percutaneous Absorption

The preceding examples have shown that two components, namely inherent chemical activity and percutaneous absorption, are

necessary to get a toxicological reaction. It is the rate and
extent that a reactive chemical is delivered to the target tissue
that determines the degree of toxicological response. However,
percutaneous absorption is not a simple act of apply chemical to
skin and then "seeing what happens". Percutaneous absorption is a
complex process consisting of many factors, any of which can affect
the final outcome. Wester and Maibach (9) have summarized the
process in ten steps (our current view, but presumably many steps
remain to be discovered).

Ten Steps to Percutaneous Absorption

1.   Vehicle release
2.   Absorption kinetics
   a. Skin site of application
   b. Individual variation
   c. Skin condition
   d. Occlusion
   e. Drug concentration and surface areas
   f. Multiple-dose application
3.   Excretion kinetics
4.   Effective cellular and tissue distribution
5.   Substantivity (nonpenetrating surface adsorption)
6.   Wash and rub resistance
7.   Volatility
8.   Binding
9.   Anatomic pathways
10.   Cutaneous metabolism

Literature Cited

1.   Wester, R.C.; Maibach, H.I. In Environmental Pathology,
       N.K. Mottet, Ed.; Oxford University Press: New York,
       1985;181–194.
2.   Kim, O.K.; Wester, R.C.; McMaster, J.A., Bucks, D.A.W.;
       Maibach, H.I. Contact Dermatitis 1987 17 (in press).
3.   Polikandriton, M.; Conine, D.L. J. Soc. Cosmetic Chem.
       1985, 36, 159–168.
4.   Noonan, P.K.; Wester, R.C. In Dermatotoxicology, F.N.
       Marzulli and H.I. Maibach, Eds.; Hemisphere Publishing:
       New York, 1983; pp 71–90.
5.   Wester, R.C.; Noonan, P.K.; Maibach, H.I. Arch.
       Dermatol. Res.,1977 113, 620–622.
6.   Wester, R.C.; Noonan, P.K.; Maibach, H.I. Arch.
       Dermatol. Res.1980 267, 229–235.
7.   Wilson, J.S.; Holland, L.M. Toxicology 1982, 24, 45–54.
8.   Suzuki, M.; Asaba, K.; Komatsu, H.; Mockizuki, M.
       J. Soc. Cosmet. Chem. 1978 29, 265–271.
9.   Wester, R.C.; Maibach, H.I. Cutaneous Pharmacokinetics:
       10 Steps to Percutaneous Absorption. Drug Metab.
       Disposition, 1983.

RECEIVED January 25, 1988

Chapter 11

Dinocap Dermal Absorption in Female Rabbits and Rhesus Monkeys

Implications for Humans

Stephen L. Longacre[1], Laura J. DiDonato[1], Ronald C. Wester[2], Howard I. Maibach[2], Susan S. Hurt[1], and Richard D. Costlow[2]

[1]Toxicology Department, Rohm and Haas Company, Spring House, PA 19477
[2]Department of Dermatology, University of California School of Medicine, San Francisco, CA 94143

The dermal absorption of dinocap was determined in female rabbits and rhesus monkeys as part of the risk assessment for Karathane[R] Fungicide/Miticide. ^{14}C-2,4-Dinitro-6-(1-methylheptyl)phenyl crotonate (2,4-DNHPC) was used as the model isomer for dinocap in these studies. In rabbits, the dermal absorption of 25 mg/kg (approximately 2500 ug/cm^2) 2,4-DNHPC was 4-9%, whether 2,4-DNHPC was applied neat (undiluted) or dissolved in acetone, or applied as the wettable powder or liquid concentrate formulation. The total absorption of 13 daily 6-hr dermal doses of 25 mg/kg/day (2500 ug/cm^2/day) of neat 2,4-DNHPC in rabbits was 6%, similar to the percent absorption observed following a single dermal dose. In rhesus monkeys, the dermal absorption of 2,4-DNHPC at 2500 ug/cm^2 (in acetone) was similar to the dermal absorption in rabbits (5%). Dermal absorption of 2,4-DNHPC in monkeys at 40 ug/cm^2 was 16%; this dose approximated a use-dilution. The absorption data for 2,4-DNHPC in rabbits and monkeys support the conclusion that, under expected use conditions, dermal exposure to dinocap does not pose an unreasonable developmental risk to man.

Dinocap (Karathane[R] Fungicide/Miticide) was registered by Rohm and Haas Company in the United States in 1951, and is principally used as a fungicide for control of powdery mildew and as a miticide. Dinocap contains as its active ingredients a mixture of 2,4- and 2,6-dinitrooctylphenyl crotonates in an approximate 2:1 ratio, where "octyl" refers to a mixture of 1-methylheptyl, 1-ethylhexyl,

NOTE: A more detailed version of these data will be published in a toxicology journal.

0097–6156/89/0382–0137$06.00/0
© 1989 American Chemical Society

and 1-propylpentyl isomers (Figure 1). Small amounts of the
corresponding free phenols are also present as active ingredients.

Developmental toxicity studies in New Zealand white rabbits
indicated that oral exposure to dinocap technical during the period
of organogenesis produced terata, which were manifested as hydro-
cephalus and/or malformations of the neural tube and skull (1).
The no-observed effect level (NOEL) and the minimum effect level
(MEL) for dinocap oral developmental toxicity in rabbits were
judged to be 0.5 and 3 mg/kg/day, respectively (1).

Residues of dinocap on crops are such that the risk of dinocap
to humans by the oral route is negligible. To ascertain the
possible risk of dinocap to agricultural workers, several studies
were performed. These studies included a dinocap dermal/oral
absorption study in rabbits, and a dinocap dermal absorption study
in rhesus monkeys. Our objectives in these absorption studies were
a) to compare the percent dermal absorption of dinocap in the
rabbit and rhesus monkey at dose levels used in rabbit dinocap
toxicology studies, and b) to determine the percent dermal
absorption in the rhesus monkey at potential worker exposure
concentrations. To facilitate the interpretation of the data, the
absorption studies were performed using ^{14}C-2,4-dinitro-6-
(1-methylheptyl)-phenyl crotonate (2,4-DNHPC) as the model compound
for the alkyl substituted isomers of dinocap (Figure 2).

Materials and Methods

Test Compounds. ^{14}C-2,4-DNHPC (7.58 mCi/g; radiopurity = 96.5%;
molecular weight = 256 g/mole), and nonradiolabeled 2,4-DNHPC
(purity = 97%) used to dilute the specific activity of the
^{14}C-2,4-DNHPC, were both synthesized at Rohm and Haas Company
(Spring House, PA). The test compounds were light amber colored
oils.

Animals. Female New Zealand white rabbits (34-42 weeks old;
2.9-3.9 kg; Hazleton Dutchland; Denver, PA), and female rhesus
monkeys (5.4-10.7 kg; University of California at Davis Primate
Center; Davis, CA) were used in these studies (3 or 4 animals per
group).

Rabbit Intravenous Study. ^{14}C-2,4-DNHPC, dissolved in dimethyl
sulfoxide (DMSO), was administered in the jugular vein (0.1 ml/kg)
at 3 mg/kg (3 uCi/kg). Urine and feces were collected at intervals
up to 4 days after dosing and analyzed for total ^{14}C-label. All
rabbits were humanely killed by an intracardiac injection of
euthanasia solution (T-61^R; American Hoechst Corp., Somerville,
NJ).

Rabbit Oral Studies. ^{14}C-2,4-DNHPC, suspended in aqueous 1% gum
tragacanth, was administered by gavage (5 ml/kg) at 0.5, 3, or
25 mg/kg (3-17 uCi/kg). Urine, feces, and plasma were collected
at intervals up to 4 days after dosing and analyzed for ^{14}C-label.

Rabbit 6 Hr Dermal Exposure Studies. The fur on the dorsal side
of each rabbit was clipped to expose an area of approximately 280
cm^2 1-3 days prior to dosing. Plastic collars were placed on each
rabbit to prevent preening of the application site. ^{14}C-2,4-DNHPC
(23-31 uCi/kg) was applied directly onto a 5 x 8 cm^2 area of the

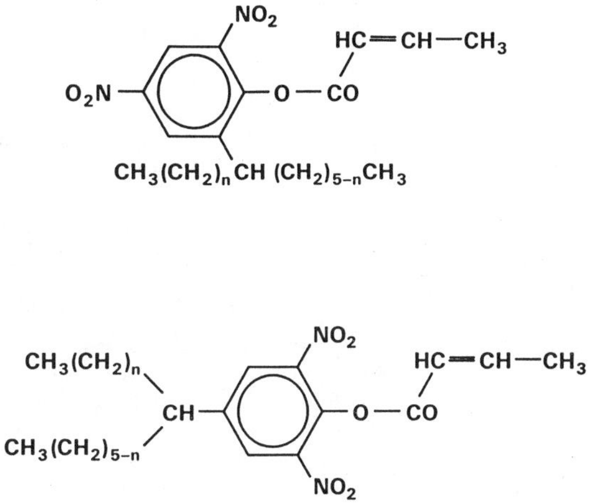

Figure 1. Structural formulae of the active ingredient components of dinocap [2,4-dinitrooctylphenyl crotonates (top) and 2,6-dinitrooctylphenyl crotonates (bottom)]; "n" equals 0, 1, and 2.

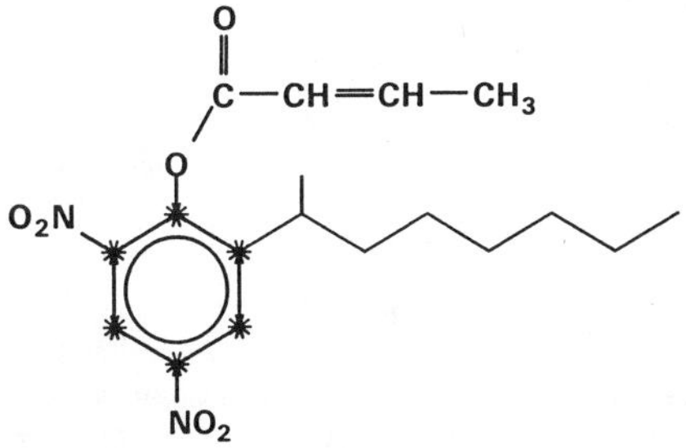

Figure 2. Structural formula of ^{14}C-2,4-DNHPC; the asterisks indicate location of the ^{14}C-label.

clipped dorsal site as a) the neat (undiluted) material at 25 (2.2), 100 (8.3), and 220 mg/kg (18.3 mg/cm^2); b) the wettable dust (WD) formulation at 25 mg ai/kg (2.4 mg/cm^2) applied as a 20.4% ai paste (1:1.3 paste:water) at 0.28 g paste/kg; c) the liquid concentrate (LC) formulation at 25 mg ai/kg (2.5 mg/cm^2 applied as a 39.8% ai solution (0.06 ml/kg); or d) in acetone at 25 mg/kg (2.2 mg/cm^2) applied as a 39.8% ai solution (0.06 ml/kg).

Six (6) hr after dose application, the application sites were wiped with gauze pads soaked with aqueous 95% ethanol, followed by wiping with pads saturated with water. Application sites of rabbits treated with the ^{14}C-2,4-DNHPC-WD formulation were wiped with distilled water only. The wipes were extracted with acetone and analyzed for total ^{14}C-label. Urine, feces, and plasma were collected at intervals up to 7 days and analyzed for ^{14}C-label. At termination, the application site skins were collected, dissolved in tissue solubilizer (Unisol^R; Isolab Inc.; Akron, OH), and analyzed for total ^{14}C-label.

Rabbit 7 Day (Leave-On) Dermal Exposure Study. ^{14}C-2,4-DNHPC was applied dermally as the neat material at 25 mg/kg (2.1 mg/cm^2; 30 uCi/kg), and was left on for 7 days. Urine, feces, and plasma were collected at intervals over the 7-day period and analyzed for ^{14}C-label. At termination, the application site skins were collected and analyzed for ^{14}C-label. The application sites were not wiped prior to ^{14}C-analysis of the skin, since a large amount of fur had grown back.

Rabbit Multiple Dermal Dose Study. Neat ^{14}C-2,4-DNHPC was applied as 13 daily 6 hr doses at 25 mg/kg/day. The 5 x 8 cm^2 application area was rotated among 7 sites such that consecutive doses were not applied to the same or adjacent sites. The application sites were wiped 6 hr after each ^{14}C-dose application, and the wipes were analyzed for ^{14}C-label. Urine, feces, and plasma were collected at intervals during the 13 day dosing phase and for up to 10 days after the last dose, and analyzed for ^{14}C-label. Rabbits were killed 10 days after the last dose, and the application sites were collected and analyzed for ^{14}C-label.

Monkey Intravenous Study. ^{14}C-2,4-DNHPC dissolved in DMSO, was administered in the femoral vein (0.1 ml/kg) at 0.2 mg/kg (0.15 uCi/kg). Plasma was collected at intervals up to 2 days after dosing, while urine and feces were collected at intervals up to 4 days after dosing and analyzed for ^{14}C-label. Fecal samples were pooled prior to analysis. These animals were used in subsequent dermal studies once it was determined that plasma and urine contained no residual ^{14}C-label.

Monkey Percutaneous Study (40 ug/cm^2). ^{14}C-2,4-DNHPC, dissolved in 400 ul acetone, was applied to 40 cm^2 of abdominal skin at 40 ug/cm^2 (1.6 mg/monkey; approximately 0.2 mg/kg; 12 uCi/monkey). The animals were restrained in metabolic chairs during the dermal exposure period, and were returned to metabolic cages immediately following the dose wipe-off. The application sites were wiped with cotton balls ladened with water, or with aqueous 95% ethanol followed by a water rinse 6 hr after application; the wipes were analyzed for ^{14}C-label. Plasma was collected at intervals up to 2 days, while urine and feces were collected at intervals up to 4 days and analyzed for ^{14}C-label.

Monkey Percutaneous Study (2500 ug/cm^2). ^{14}C-2,4-DNHPC dissolved in 14 ul acetone, was applied to 0.64 cm^2 of abdominal skin at 2500 ug/cm^2 (1.6 mg/monkey; approximately 0.2 mg/kg; 12 uCi/monkey). The application sites were wiped with aqueous 95% ethanol, followed by water, 6 hr after dose application; the wipes were analyzed for ^{14}C-label. Plasma was collected at intervals up to 2 days, while urine and feces were collected at intervals up to 4 days and analyzed for ^{14}C-label.

Percent Absorption. The fraction of an oral or dermal dose of ^{14}C-2,4-DNHPC absorbed represented the urinary ^{14}C-excretion after oral or dermal administration divided by the urinary ^{14}C-excretion after iv administration (2, 3).

Results

Rabbit Intravenous Study. Most (58-85%) of an iv dose of ^{14}C-2,4-DNHPC was excreted from rabbits within 24-48 hr (Figure 3). Urinary ^{14}C-excretion was 5-fold greater than fecal excretion; 73% of the dose was recovered in the urine by 96 hr.

Rabbit Oral Studies. The percent absorption of an oral dose of ^{14}C-2,4-DNHPC (0.5-25 mg/kg) was 60-69% (Table I).
    Practically all of an oral dose of ^{14}C-2,4-DNHPC was eliminated in the excreta of rabbits within 48 hr (Figure 3). The percent cumulative urinary and fecal ^{14}C-excretion were each similar among the three oral dose groups. Fecal ^{14}C-excretion (57-72% of dose) was slightly greater than urinary ^{14}C-excretion (35-51% of dose) by 96 hr.
    ^{14}C-2,4-DNHPC-derived ^{14}C-label was rapidly absorbed after oral administration, reaching peak plasma ^{14}C-concentrations within 1-3 hr (Table II). Peak plasma ^{14}C-concentration was proportional to dose (Table II). Elimination of ^{14}C-label was biphasic for all groups; a rapid elimination phase (t 1/2 = 2.2-3.8 hr), lasting approximately 24 hr after dosing, preceded a slower terminal elimination phase (t 1/2 = 33.3-55.1 hr).

Rabbit 6 Hr Dermal Exposure Studies. The percent absorption of a 6 hr dermal exposure of ^{14}C-2,4-DNHPC was 4-9%, regardless of the dose or the formulation/vehicle (Table I).
    A majority of the applied ^{14}C-2,4-DNHPC (60-95% of dose; 89-95% of recovered ^{14}C-label) was recovered in the 6 hr wipe-off regardless of the dose or the formulation/vehicle (Table III). Little ^{14}C-label (0.02-1% of dose) was recovered in the application site skins at the end of the 7-day in-life phase (Table III).
    A total of 5-12% of a 6 hr dermal exposure of ^{14}C-2,4-DNHPC was eliminated in the excreta within 7 days regardless of the dose or the formulation/vehicle (Table III). Also, the percent cumulative urinary and fecal ^{14}C-excretion were comparable among the dermal groups, regardless of the dose or the formulation/ vehicle. Most of the excreted ^{14}C-label was eliminated within 2-4 days (Figure 3), and was essentially evenly distributed between the urine and feces.

Table I.   Percent Absorption of ^{14}C-2,4-DNHPC
in Female Rabbits and Rhesus Monkeys

Dose mg/kg	Dose ug/cm²	n	Route	Exposure Time	Formulation/ Vehicle	Percent Absorption[a]
Rabbit						
3	--	3	iv	--	DMSO	100 ± 6
0.5	--	4	Oral	--	Gum Trag[b]	69 ± 29
3	--	3	Oral	--	Gum Trag	60 ± 4
25	--	4	Oral	--	Gum Trag	64 ± 6
25	2150	3	Dermal	6 Hr	Neat	4 ± 2
100	8310	3	Dermal	6 Hr	Neat	5 ± 3
220	18,300	3	Dermal	6 Hr	Neat	5 ± 4
25	2390	3	Dermal	6 Hr	WD	9 ± 3
25	2450	3	Dermal	6 Hr	LC	4 ± 1
25	2220	4	Dermal	6 Hr	Acetone	7 ± 2
25	2060	4	Dermal	7 Day	Neat	13 ± 6
25	1850-2313	4	Dermal	6 Hr (x13)	Neat	6 ± 1
Monkey						
0.2	--	4	iv	--	DMSO	100 ± 16
0.2	40	8	Dermal	6 Hr	Acetone	16 ± 7
0.2	2500	4	Dermal	6 Hr	Acetone	5 ± 3

[a] Percent absorption (% of dose); mean ± standard deviation.

[b] One (1) percent gum tragacanth suspension.

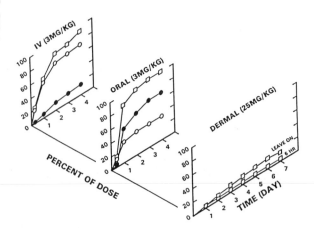

Figure 3.   Cumulative excretion of ^{14}C-label in the urine (O),
feces (●), and combined urine and feces (□) of female rabbits
administered an iv, oral, 6 hr dermal, or 7-day (leave-on)
dermal dose of ^{14}C-2,4-DNHPC.

Table II. Peak Plasma ^{14}C-Concentration in Female Rabbits and Rhesus Monkeys Administered ^{14}C-2,4-DNHPC

Dose mg/kg	ug/cm^2	Route	Exposure Time	Formulation/ Vehicle	n	Peak Plasma ^{14}C-Concentration[a] (ppm)	(hr)
Rabbit							
0.5	--	Oral	--	Gum Trag[b]	4	0.29 ± 0.04	1
3	--	Oral	--	Gum Trag	3	1.26 ± 0.42	3
25	--	Oral	--	Gum Trag	4	14.55 ± 6.62	3
25	2150	Dermal	6 Hr	Neat	3	0.15 ± 0.05	6
100	8310	Dermal	6 Hr	Neat	3	0.47 ± 0.10	6
220	18,300	Dermal	6 Hr	Neat	3	1.51 ± 1.12	24
25	2390	Dermal	6 Hr	WD	3	0.19 ± 0.03	24
25	2450	Dermal	6 Hr	LC	3	0.24 ± 0.07	6
25	2220	Dermal	6 Hr	Acetone	4	0.28 ± 0.00	24
25	2060	Dermal	7 Day	Neat	4	0.24 ± 0.19	6
25 (x13)	1850-2313	Dermal	6 Hr (x13)	Neat	4	0.89 ± 0.33	318
Monkey							
0.2	40	Dermal	6 Hr	Acetone	4	ND[c]	-
0.2	2500	Dermal	6 Hr	Acetone	4	ND	-

[a] Plasma concentration of ^{14}C-label as ug 2,4-DNHPC equivalents/ml (ppm); mean ± standard deviation.

[b] One (1) percent gum tragacanth suspension.

[c] ND: Not detected. Plasma ^{14}C-concentrations were in the range of background to twice background.

Table III.   Recovery of 14C-Label from Female Rabbits and Rhesus Monkeys Administered ^{14}C-2,4-DNHPC[a]

Dose mg/kg ug/cm²	Route	Exposure Time	Formulation/ Vehicle	n	Urine	Feces	Total Excreta	Wipe	Application Site Skin	Total
						Rabbit				
3 --	iv	--	DMSO	3	73 ± 4	17 ±11	90 ± 7			90 ± 7
0.5 --	Oral	--	Gum Trag[b]	4	51 ±21	72 ±10	122±17			122±17
3 --	Oral	--	Gum Trag	3	44 ± 3	68 ± 8	111± 6			111± 6
25 --	Oral	--	Gum Trag	4	46 ± 4	57 ± 8	104± 7			104± 7
25 2150	Dermal	6 Hr	Neat	3	3 ± 1	3 ± 1	5 ± 2	68 ±11	0.02±0.01	73 ±11
100 8310	Dermal	6 Hr	Neat	3	4 ± 2	2 ± 1	5 ± 2	74 ± 6	0.3±0.3	79 ± 8
220 18,300	Dermal	6 Hr	Neat	3	4 ± 3	3 ± 2	7 ± 5	67 ±24	0.2±0.3	67 ±24
25 2390	Dermal	6 Hr	WD	3	7 ± 2	5 ± 2	12 ± 2	102±12	1 ± 1	115±14
25 2450	Dermal	6 Hr	LC	3	3 ± 1	2 ±0.1	5 ± 1	95 ± 3	0.2±0.1	100± 3
25 2220	Dermal	6 Hr	Acetone	4	5 ± 2	3 ± 2	9 ± 3	73 ± 6	0.07±0.03	82 ± 8
25 2060	Dermal	7 Day	Neat	4	10 ± 4	7 ± 1	16 ± 5	39 ± 8[c]		55 ± 9
25 1850-(x13) 2313	Dermal	6 Hr (x 13)	Neat	4	5 ± 1	3 ± 1	8 ± 1	82 ± 2	0.1±0.1	89 ± 3
						Monkey				
0.2 --	iv	--	DMSO	4	49 ± 8	35 ± 8	85 ± 5			85 ± 5
0.2 40	Dermal	6 Hr	Acetone	8	8 ± 4	6 ± 3	13 ± 3	29 ±13		42 ± 4
0.2 2500	Dermal	6 Hr	Acetone	4	3 ± 1	2 ± 1	4 ± 2	75 ± 7		79 ± 8

a values represent percent of administered dose; mean ± standard deviation.

b One (1) percent gum tragacanth suspension.

c Application site skins were not wiped prior to ^{14}C-analysis.

^{14}C-2,4-DNHPC-derived ^{14}C-label was moderately to slowly absorbed following a 6 hr dermal exposure; peak plasma ^{14}C-concentrations were achieved within 6-24 hr (Table II). Peak plasma ^{14}C-concentration following application of the neat material was proportional to dose (Table II). Similar peak plasma ^{14}C-concentrations were achieved when ^{14}C-2,4-DNHPC was applied as the WD or LC formulation, or dissolved in acetone compared to an equivalent dermal dose of the neat material (Table II). Elimination of ^{14}C-label was biphasic for all 6 hr dermally exposed groups; a rapid elimination phase (t 1/2 = 7.9-21.8 hr), lasting approximately 2-3 days after dosing, preceded a slow terminal elimination phase (t 1/2 = 119-369 hr).

The peak plasma ^{14}C-concentration (0.15-0.28 ppm) following a 6 hr dermal exposure of 25 mg/kg ^{14}C-2,4-DNHPC was 52- to 97-fold less than the peak plasma ^{14}C-concentration of an equivalent oral dose of ^{14}C-2,4-DNHPC (14.55 ppm).

Rabbit 7 Day (Leave-On) Dermal Study. The percent absorption of a 7-day leave-on dermal dose of ^{14}C-2,4-DNHPC was 13% (Table I).

Most of the recovered ^{14}C-label (71%; 39% of applied dose) was present in or on the application site skin at the end of the 7-day in-life phase (Table III). A total of 17% of the dose had been eliminated in the excreta by 7 days (Figure 3). The excreted ^{14}C-label was eliminated in a linear fashion at a rate of 1.4 and 1.0% of the dose excreted per day from the urine and feces, respectively.

^{14}C-2,4-DNHPC-derived ^{14}C-label was moderately to slowly absorbed following application of a leave-on dermal dose of ^{14}C-2,4-DNHPC, similar to 6 hr dermally exposed rabbits. Also, 7-day exposed animals achieved a similar peak plasma ^{14}C-concentration by 6 hr compared to 6 hr dermally exposed animals (Table II). The 7-day exposed animals exhibited a short rapid elimination phase (t 1/2 = 3.3 hr), which preceded a steady state phase; the latter persisted for the remainder of the in-life phase.

Rabbit Multiple Dermal Dose Study. Six (6)% of 13 daily 6 hr dermal doses of 25 mg/kg/day ^{14}C-2,4-DNHPC was absorbed (Table I).

Most of the multiple dermal doses was recovered in the daily 6 hr wipe-offs (82% of dose; 92% of recovered ^{14}C-label); 0.1% of the total dose was recovered in the application site skins 10 days after the last (13th) dose (Table III). ^{14}C-Excretion was greatest between 6 and 48 hr after the initial dose; excretion then slowed for the remainder of the in-life phase (Figure 4). Only 8% of the multiple doses had been eliminated in the excreta by the end of the 10-day post-dose phase (Table III).

Plasma ^{14}C-concentration increased approximately 6-fold from 0.16 ppm 6 hr after the first dose to a peak plateau ^{14}C-concentration of 0.89 ppm 6 hr after the 13th (last) dose (Table II). The elimination of ^{14}C-label from the plasma following completion of the dosing phase (t 1/2 = 131 hr) was comparable to the terminal elimination rate following a single 6 hr dermal exposure of ^{14}C-2,4-DNHPC.

Monkey Intravenous Study. A total of 49 and 35% of the dose was excreted in the urine and feces, respectively, within 4 days. Urinary ^{14}C-excretion was essentially completed within 24 hr. ^{14}C-2,4-DNHPC-derived ^{14}C-label was rapidly eliminated from

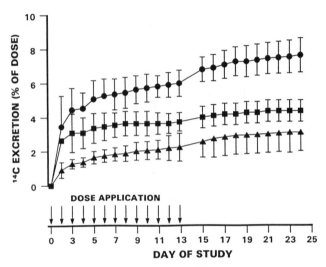

Figure 4. Cumulative excretion of ^{14}C-label in the urine (▲), feces (■), and combined urine and feces (●) following 13 daily 6 hr dermal doses of 25 mg/kg/day ^{14}C-2,4-DNHPC applied as the neat material. Data points represent the mean ± standard deviation.

the plasma in a biphasic manner; a rapid elimination phase (t 1/2 = 1.4 hr) lasting approximately 10 hr preceded a slower elimination phase (t 1/2 = 24 hr).

Monkey 6 Hr Dermal Exposure Studies. The percent dermal absorption of 40 and 2500 ug/cm^2 in monkeys was 16 and 5%, respectively Table I).
    Most of a dermal dose of ^{14}C-2,4-DNHPC was recovered in the 6 hr wipe-off [69 and 95% of the recovered ^{14}C-label (29 and 75% of the applied dose) following 40 and 2500 ug/cm^2, respectively]. A total of 13 and 4% of the applied dose was eliminated in the excreta within 7 days following 40 and 2500 ug/cm^2, respectively (Table III). The excreted ^{14}C-label was eliminated at a fairly linear rate over most of the 4-day in-life phase, especially from the 40 ug/cm^2 dosed animals (Figure 5). The excreted ^{14}C-label was essentially evenly distributed between the urine and feces, similar to the ^{14}C-excretion pattern observed for 6 hr dermally exposed rabbits.
    Plasma ^{14}C-concentrations were in the range of background to twice background (limit of sensitivity $\cong$ 0.002 ppm) following dermal application of ^{14}C-2,4-DNHPC (Table II).

Discussion

A concurrently performed study indicated that dinocap technical did not produce developmental toxicity in rabbits following dermal application of 25, 50, and 100 mg/kg/day (1). Dinocap did cause irritation at all dose levels, however. Because of the severity of the irritation, 100 mg/kg/day was the highest dose studied. Even at that, the application site needed to be rotated among 7 sites such that consecutive doses were not applied to the same or adjacent sites. Maternal toxicity, manifested by reduced feed consumption and reduced weight gain, was produced at 100 mg/kg/day. The NOEL for dinocap-induced developmental toxicity by the dermal route was $\geq$ 100 mg/kg/day. Results of the absorption studies support the conclusion that dinocap does not cause developmental toxicity in rabbits by the dermal route in that a) the dermal absorption of dinocap is significantly less than the oral absorption, b) peak plasma ^{14}C-levels are much less after dermal application compared to oral administration of an equivalent dose, and c) dinocap does not accumulate upon multiple dermal dose administration.
    The rabbit oral and dermal absorption studies described here were designed to simulate the designs of the oral and dermal developmental toxicity studies. The oral doses in the absorption study included the NOEL and MEL doses of the oral developmental toxicity studies. The dermal doses in the absorption study bracketed those used in the dermal developmental toxicity study; the high dermal dose of 220 mg/kg in the absorption study represented the maximum dose of commercial dinocap LC formulation that physically could be applied to a 40 cm^2 dose area. ^{14}C-2,4-DNHPC was dermally applied as the neat material to simulate the exposure to dinocap technical in the dermal developmental toxicity study. Finally, 13 daily 6 hr dermal doses of

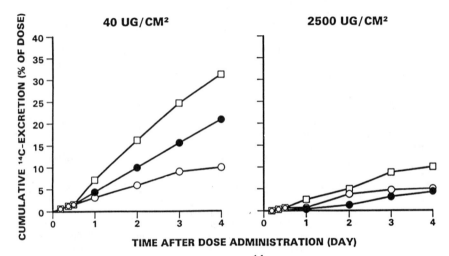

Figure 5. Cumulative excretion of ^{14}C-label in the urine (O), feces (●), and combined urine and feces (□) of female rhesus monkeys following a 6 hr dermal exposure of ^{14}C-2,4-DNHPC in acetone.

[14]C-2,4-DNHPC were applied to 7 rotating application sites to similate the dosing regimen of the developmental toxicity study. Results of the ^{14}C-2,4-DNHPC multiple dermal dose study indicated that dinocap does not accumulate in the skin or alter the barrier function of the skin as to permit greater absorption following multiple dose application compared to single dose application. Similar results have been observed for malathion and several steroids in humans (4, 5).

Additional groups were included in the design of the dermal absorption study to investigate other parameters useful in the risk estimation of dinocap. For example, dinocap is sold commercially as both the WD and LC formulations. The similarity in the dermal absorption and pharmacokinetics of ^{14}C-2,4-DNHPC applied as the WD and LC formulations compared to the neat material strongly suggests that these formulations do not pose any more of a developmental risk in rabbits than does the technical material. The effect of acetone on the dermal absorption of ^{14}C-2,4-DNHPC in rabbits was studied to compare these results to the monkey absorption results. The monkey dinocap dermal study utilized acetone as the vehicle, since a significant data base of human and monkey dermal absorption studies exists which utilized acetone as the vehicle (6-10). It is noteworthy that the dermal absorption of dinocap in rabbits and monkeys was similar, since a number of compounds are known to be more permeable in rabbits than in monkeys and humans (10).

Results indicated that oral and dermal doses of ^{14}C-2,4-DNHPC in rabbits were each handled in a similar (linear) fashion pharmacokinetically. First, the percent absorption was similar for all doses after each route of administration (Table I). Second, the fraction of the excreted ^{14}C-label recovered in the urine or feces was similar for all dose levels for each route of administration (Table III). Third, the peak plasma ^{14}C-concentration was proportional to dose after each route of exposure. Fourth, the elimination of ^{14}C-label from the plasma and the patterns of elimination of ^{14}C-label in the excreta were similar for all doses after each route of administration. Thus, the observed toxicity at the higher dose levels following oral (developmental toxicity) or dermal (maternal toxicity) administration did not appear to alter the absorption, distribution, or elimination of ^{14}C-2,4-DNHPC compared to lower, no-effect doses. The linear pharmacokinetics indicate that extrapolation from high, effect-level doses to lower no-effect level doses may be performed with greater confidence.

The monkey was used as a model to estimate the dermal absorption of dinocap in humans, since the monkey has been shown to be an appropriate model for studying dermal absorption of various xenobiotics in man (10, 11). The dermal absorption of dinocap in monkeys was investigated at two concentrations which approximate potential worker exposure concentrations. The high concentration (2500 ug/cm^2), which was also used in the rabbit dermal developmental and absorption studies, approximates the exposure which might result from contact with undiluted dinocap product (Streelman, D. R., Rohm and Haas Company Inter-Company Communication, 1986). The low concentration (40 ug/cm^2) approximates the exposure which might result from contact with dinocap formulations

at their use dilution. The percent absorption was 3-fold greater
at the low exposure concentration compared to the high concentration (16 versus 5%). A greater efficacy of dermal absorption at
lower exposure concentrations has been observed for a number of
compounds (9, 12). Since different worker exposure situations
(i.e., working with the full concentrate or the use-dilution)
can result in substantially different contact exposures, it is
imperative that the appropriate absorption factors be used when
basing the risk estimation of dinocap on absorbed dose.

Conclusions

The risk assessment for dinocap included a) the determination that
the percent dermal absorption of dinocap in rabbits (a sensitive
species for dinocap-induced developmental toxicity) was similar to
the dermal absorption in monkeys (a non-human primate model), and
b) the measurement of the percent dermal absorption of dinocap at
potential worker exposure concentrations in a non-human primate
model. This approach is both practical and appropriate for use in
evaluating the risk of dinocap to man by the dermal route. Using
this approach, the dermal absorption of full concentrate dinocap
formulations in man is estimated to be 5% of the applied dose. The
dermal absorption of dinocap at its use-dilution in man is
estimated to be 16% of the applied dose. These absorption data, in
conjunction with measured field exposures, support the conclusion
that agricultural uses of dinocap do not pose an unreasonable
developmental risk to man.

Acknowledgments. The authors acknowledge the expert technical help
of Ms. Donna M. Anderson, Mr. Howard L. Tomlinson, and Mr. Thomas
W. Greger of Rohm and Haas Company; Mr. Daniel A. W. Bucks and Mr.
James McMaster of Univ. of California San Francisco; and Mr. Robert
Sarason of the Primate Center of the University of California at
Davis. Dr. Diana D. Bender and Mr. Ronald P. Owen of Rohm and Haas
Company synthesized the ^{14}C-2,4-DNHPC and nonradiolabeled
2,4-DNHPC, respectively.

Literature Cited

1. Costlow, R. D.; Lutz, M. F.; Kane, W. W.; Hurt, S. S.;
    O'Hara, G. P. Toxicologist 1986, 6, 85.
2. Shah, P. V.; Guthrie, F. E. J. Invest. Dermatol. 1983,
    80, 291-293.
3. Wester, R. C.; Maibach, H. I. In Dermatotoxicity, 2nd
    Edition; Marzulli, F. N.; Maibach, H. I., Eds.; Hemisphere
    Publishing Corporation: New York, 1983; pp 131-146.
4. Wester, R. C.; Maibach, H. I.; Bucks, D. A. W.; Guy, R. H.
    Toxicol. Appl. Pharmacol. 1983, 68, 116-119.
5. Bucks, D. A. W.; Maibach, H. I.; Guy, R. H. J. Pharm.
    Sci. 1985, 74, 1337-1339.
6. Feldmann, R. J.; Maibach, H. I. J. Invest. Dermatol.
    1970, 54, 399-404.
7. Bartek, M. J.; LaBudde, J. A.; Maibach, H. I. J. Invest.
    Dermatol. 1972, 58, 114-123.

8. Feldmann, R. J.; Maibach, H. I. Toxicol. Appl. Pharmacol.
    1974, 28, 126-132.
9. Wester, R. C.; Maibach, H. I. J. Toxicol. Environ. Health
    1985, 16, 25-37.
10. Wester, R. C.; Maibach, H. I. In Percutaneous Absorption;
    Bronaugh, R. L.; Maibach, H. I., Eds.; Marcel Dekker, Inc.:
    New York, 1985; Chapter 20.
11. Wester, R. C.; Maibach, H. I. Toxicol. Appl. Pharmacol. 1975,
    32, 394-398.
12. Wester, R. C.; Maibach, H. I. In Percutaneous Absorption;
    Bronaugh, R. L.; Maibach, H. I., Eds.; Marcel Dekker, Inc.:
    New York, 1985; Chapter 26.

RECEIVED December 4, 1987

Chapter 12

Percutaneous Absorption in Rhesus Monkeys and Estimation of Human Chemical Exposure

Ronald C. Wester[1], James McMaster[1], Daniel A. W. Bucks[1], Eugene M. Bellet[2], and Howard I. Maibach[1]

[1]Department of Dermatology, University of California School of Medicine, San Francisco, CA 94143
[2]Chemical Consultants International, Overland Park, KS 66204

Skin absorption estimate is dependent upon animal model for predicting human health hazard for a chemical entering the body through skin. An example is Dinoseb, which, when applied to skin of rats (acetone vehicle; 72 hr exposure) is 90% absorbed. The literature shows absorption through rat skin to be much higher than in man. Dinoseb applied to the skin of rhesus monkeys (Premerge-3; 24 hr exposure) gave absorption of less than 10 percent. Balance in the monkey study accounted for greater than 80 percent of the applied dose, the majority of which was unabsorbed Dinoseb removed from the skin with the post 24 hr soap and water wash. Comparative absorption data for other chemicals show skin absorption in rhesus consistent with man.

Central to the determination of human health hazard effects for skin exposure of chemicals is the estimate for percutaneous absorption. This value estimates the rate and extent that a chemical will penetrate the living human epidermis and becomes systemically available for distribution in the human body. Percutaneous absorption is a complex process involving many variables which can affect the estimate for systemic availability (1). However, the objective is crystal clear; an estimate of percutaneous absorption in vivo in man. Therefore, the study design should minimize variables and include aspects most relevant to man. This paper focuses on the variables of the animal model, and on accountability for applied dose. It is hoped that the conclusions derived from the information presented here will aid in producing relevant study designs and continued relevant data.

Animal Model

The best estimate for human percutaneous absorption would be an in vivo study in man. Factors such as risk, cost, and access to human volunteers necessitate use of an animal model. Cost and access

0097–6156/89/0382–0152$06.00/0
© 1989 American Chemical Society

suggest a small laboratory animal. The historical use of the rat in toxicological studies suggests its use. What may get lost in the choice of animal is the priority of relevance to man for percutaneous absorption.

Table I shows the percutaneous absorption of several chemicals by rat, rabbit, pig and man (2). Questions for relevancy should be if the skin absorption in the animal is the same as in man and, if not the same, then is the skin absorption consistently proportionally different from man? The answer to both questions for rat and rabbit is no. For the pig, the answer is a maybe.

Table I. Percutaneous Absorption of Several Compounds
by Rat, Rabbit, Pig and Man (in vivo)

Penetrant	Percent Dose Absorbed			
	rat	rabbit	pig	man
Haloprogin	95.8	113.0	19.7	11.0
Acetylcysteine	3.5	2.0	6.0	2.4
Cortisone	24.7	30.3	4.1	3.4
Caffeine	53.1	69.2	32.4	47.6
Butter yellow	48.2	100.0	41.9	21.6
Testosterone	47.4	69.6	29.4	13.2

Source: Bartek et al (2)

It is beyond this paper's scope to present all comparative data involving in vivo and in vitro skin absorption in laboratory animals and man. Details are in references (3-7). This paper focuses on the use of the rat and the rhesus monkey as relevant animal models.

Table II shows the comparative in vivo percutaneous absorption of testosterone in several small species. Absorption in the laboratory species (rat, rabbit, guinea pig) are on the upper end of the absorption scale, while those in the pig, rhesus monkey and man are on the lower end of the scale.

Table II. Comparative Percutaneous Absorption
of Testosterone on Several Species

Species	Percent of Dose Absorbed
Rat	47.4
Rabbit	69.6
Guinea pig	34.9
Rhesus monkey	18.4
Man	13.2

Table III summarizes the existing comparative in vivo percutaneous absorption in the rhesus monkey and man. The list includes a variety of chemicals and a broad range of skin absorption estimates. In all cases, the percutaneous absorption in the rhesus monkey is consistent with that found in man.

Table III. In Vivo Percutaneous Absorption
in the Rhesus Monkey and Man

Chemical	Percent Dose Absorbed		Reference
	Rhesus Monkey	Man	
2,4-Dinitrochlorobenzene	52.5 + 4.3	53.5 + 6.2	(8)
Nitrobenzene	4.2 + 0.5	1.5 + 0.3	(8)
Cortisone	5.3 + 3.3	3.4 + 1.6	(9)
Testosterone	18.4 + 9.5	13.2 + 3.0	(10)
Hydrocortisone	2.9 + 0.8	1.9 + 1.6	(10)
Benzoic acid	59.2 + 7.6	42.6 + 16.4	(10)
Resorcinol	0.18 + 0.03	0.08 + 0.03	(11)
P-Phenylendiamine	0.18 + 0.06	0.19 + 0.04	(11)
2-Nitro-PPD	0.55 + 0.10	0.1 4+ 0.04	(11)
HC-Blue #1	0.13 + 0.03	0.15 + 0.12	(11)

Basic to scientific inquiry is the dose response. For skin absorption in man, the percent dose absorbed will be dependent on the applied dose (Table IV, references 10,12). The dose response is similar for the rhesus monkey.

Table IV. Percutaneous Absorption of Increased
Topical Doses of
Several Compounds in the Rhesus Monkey and Man (in vivo)

Penetrant	Dose ug/cm2	Percent of Dose Absorbed	
		Rhesus	Man
Hydrocortisone	4	2.9	1.9
	40	2.1	0.6
Benzoic Acid	4	59.2	42.6
	40	33.6	25.7
	2,000	17.4	14.4
Testosterone	4	18.4	13.2
	40	6.7	8.8a
	250	2.9	
	400	2.2	2.8
	1,600	2.9	
a	4,000	1.4	

a 30 ug/cm2.

Dose Accountability

The preceding section on animal models suggests the possibility of differences in skin absorption and subsequent human health hazard effect estimates dependent upon animal species. The percent skin penetration data from Table V would estimate, based on the rat, that all of the Dinoseb which gets on skin is absorbed. Human health hazard estimates would be prejudiced in this direction. Absorption in the rhesus monkey would suggest that an absorption of no more than ten percent would better estimate human health hazards. The obvious question with the rhesus monkey data is an accountability of the majority of the dose to ensure that nothing peculiar happened during the study. Table VI gives an accountability of the applied Dinoseb dose. The majority of the dose appeared in the 24 hour post application soap and water skin wash, and thus was not absorbed. Thus, the less than ten percent absorption is real and is probably more relevant to man than the complete absorption observed in the rat.

Table V. In Vivo Percutaneous Absorption of
Dinoseb in Rhesus Monkey and Rat[a]

Applied Dose ug/cm2	Percent Skin Penetration	Percent Dose Accountability
	RAT	
51.5	86.4 + 1.1	87.9 + 1.8
128.8	90.5 + 1.1	91.5 + 0.6
643.5	93.2 + 0.6	90.4 + 0.7
	RHESUS MONKEY	
43.6	5.4 + 2.9	86.0 + 4.0
200.0	7.2 + 6.4	81.2 + 18.1
3,620.0	4.9 + 3.4	80.3 + 5.2

[a] Rat = acetone vehicle; 72 hr application
Monkey = Premerge-3 vehicle; 24 hour application
Complete Dinoseb data to be published elsewhere
Reference 13 for rat data

Study Design Objective

A study design should reflect a clear objective. In the case of Dinoseb, the rhesus monkey study was designed to best estimate human skin absorption for a 24 hour exposure period. Dinoseb was applied as its commercially available formulation (Premerge-3), and the doses

Table VI. Percutaneous Absorption and Accountability of
Dinoseb In Vivo Study in the Rhesus Monkey[a]

Disposition Parameter	Applied Dose (ug/cm^2)		
	43.6	200.0	3,620.0
Percent Applied Dose Accountability			
Urine	3.3 ± 1.8	4.4 + 2.39	3.0 ± 2.1
Feces	0.8 ± 0.5	1.0 + 0.6	3.0 ± 1.7
Contaminated solids	0.03 ± 0.02	0.02+ 0.02	0.07± 0.08
Pan wash	0.04± 0.03	0.8 + 1.1	0.4 ± 0.3
Skin wash	81.1± 4.0	75.0 + 22.9	73.8 ± 6.8
Total Accountability	86.0± 4.0	81.2 + 18.1	80.3 ± 5.2

[a] Complete Dinoseb data to be published elsewhere

represent concentrations which human skin would be exposed to. The
rat data was taken out of context, since its objective was to compare
skin absorption of young and old skin for a 72 hour exposure of
Dinoseb when applied to skin in acetone. The comparison of the rat
study extrapolated to a health hazard assessment in humans would be
for human applicators to use Dinoseb, mixed in acetone, continually
for 72 hours without the benefit of a shower or bath for the 3 day
period. This clearly points up the fallacy of using inappropriate
data from animal models in the extrapolation of
health hazard effects to man. The design of a proper study complete
with well though out objectives which are tied in a rational
scientific manner to human health exposure is what is required.

Animal Percutaneous Absorption Data to Estimate Human Exposure

The objective of percutaneous absorption data is to estimate the
amount of chemical which will transfer from the surface of skin
through the epidermis into the systemic circulation. That which gets
into the epidermis or systemic circulation determines the existence
or degree of local or systemic toxicity. Thus, skin absorption is
pivotal and important in estimating potential health hazards for
topical exposure, and relevant information is necessary. Data in
animal models not relevant to man for skin absorption certainly
cannot give a true estimate, and in fact may lead to further
confusion.

The best animal model for estimating percutaneous absorption
relevant to man is man him(her) self. Yet especially with agriculture
chemicals there is continual searching for "relevant" animal data,
when the correct answers can easily be obtained in man. Perhaps when
regulatory and managerial people realize this, the emphasis will
shift to the proper human studies.

Literature Cited

1. Wester, R.C.; Maibach, H.I. Drug Metab. Rev. 1983, 14, 169–205
2. Bartek, M.J.; La Budde, J.A.; Maibach, H.I. J. Invest. Dermatol.1972, 58, 114–23.
3. Wester, R.C.; Noonan, P.K. Int. J. Pharmaceutics, 1980, 7, 99–110.
4. Wester, R.C.; Maibach, H.I. In Models in Dermatology; H.I. Maibach and N.J. Lowe, Eds.; S. Karger: Basel, 1985, 159–169.
5. Wester, R.C.; Maibach, H.I. In Percutaneous Absorption; R.L. Bronaugh and H.I. Maibach, Eds.; Marcel Dekker: New York, 1985; 251–66.
6. Wester, R.C., Maibach, H.I. In Progress in Drug Metabolism; J.W. Bridges and L.F. Chasseaud, Eds.; Taylor and Francis: Philadelphia, 1986; Chapter 3.
7. Wester, R.C.; Maibach, H.I. In Dermatotoxicology; F.N. Marzulli and H.I. Maibach, Eds.; Hemisphere: New York, 1987; 135–52.
8. Bronaugh, R.L. In Percutaneous Absorption; R.L. Bronaugh and H.I. Maibach, Eds.; Marcel Dekker: New York; 1985; 267–279.
9. McMaster, J.; Maibach, H.I., Wester, R.C.; Bucks, D.A.W. In Percutaneous Absorption; R. Bronaugh and H. Maibach, Eds.; Marcel Dekker: New York; 1985; 359–61.
10. Wester, R.C.; Maibach, H.I.; Toxicol. Appl. Pharmacol. 1975, 32; 394–98.
11. Wolfram, L.J. In Percutaneous Absorption; R. Bronaugh and H.I. Maibach, Eds; Marcel Dekker: New York, 1985; 409–22.
12. Wester, R.C.; Maibach, H.I. J. Invest. Dermatol. 1976, 67; 518–20.
13. Shah, P.V.; Fisher, H.L.; Sumler, M.R.; Monroe, R.J.; Chernoff, N.;Hall, L.L. J. Toxicol. Environ. Hlth.; 1987, 353–66.

RECEIVED January 25, 1988

Chapter 13

Percutaneous Absorption

In Vitro Technique as an Alternative to In Vivo Assessments

R. C. Scott

Central Toxicology Laboratory, Imperial Chemical Industries PLC, Alderley **Park, Nr. Macclesfield, Cheshire SK10 4TJ, United Kingdom**

Chemicals, during manufacture and use may come into contact with human skin and have the potential to be absorbed. Hence an integral part of their safety evaluation should involve quantitation of percutaneous absorption. Currently, Regulatory Agencies require in vivo dermal absorption studies for this quantitation. Such in vivo data, obtained using animal skin, are used to predict the potential hazard to man. As the permeability of animal skin and human skin has been shown to be different (for many chemicals) extrapolation is difficult. In the studies reported in this paper in vivo and in vitro absorption data using rat skin have been obtained with two molecules, cypermethrin and carbaryl, which have different physicochemical properties. For both these chemicals the in vitro absorption data which were obtained predicted the in vivo data. In vitro carbaryl absorption data were also obtained with human skin and compared with published in vivo data. Again, the in vitro data predicted the available in vivo results. As in vitro data are more readily obtained and as human skin can be used (thus eliminating any extrapolation step from animal to man) the in vitro system offers a geniune alternative and improvement to in vivo animal experiments.

Safety evaluation of pesticides and their formulations requires an integrated series of toxicity studies. By necessity, animals are used as models for man and the data are then extrapolated to predict the potential hazard to man. Toxicity after the percutaneous absorption of toxic active ingredients, such as pesticides, is assessed currently using in vivo absorption data determined using an animal skin (usually rat or rabbit). This method is used since chemicals with only a limited toxicology data base cannot, for ethical reasons, be tested in man directly.

0097–6156/89/0382–0158$06.00/0
◦ 1989 American Chemical Society

However, once sufficient information has been gathered to enable a fuller understanding of the toxicological profile of an active ingredient, human volunteer studies might then be possible. Inevitably the ability to conduct such studies is determined by considerations of ethical committees who approve protocols. Often pesticides are prepared in many formulations and the problem of, for example, assessing the safety of several novel formulations (ie the formulation which resulted in the lowest absorption rate) with the same active ingredient by the human volunteer experimental route would be a daunting task. In vivo, animal studies are only marginally less complex, although the acquisition of data is facilitated by more ready access to test subjects.

In order to facilitate the development of data on the absorption of pesticides from various formulations, in vitro techniques have been developed to predict in vivo percutaneous absorption.

The major advantage with the in vitro technique is the safe use of human tissue, the best model for man, in addition to a reduction in the use of animals. It is the intention of this paper to show that the percutaneous absorption of pesticides can be measured in vitro with the same degree of certainty and accuracy demanded from in vivo studies. Some of the potential experimental pitfalls for the unwary experimentalist are also discussed and comparisons with in vivo data presented.

The in vivo and in vitro absorption, through rat skin, of a poorly absorbed lipophilic molecule, the insecticide cypermethrin, has been studied (1). In this study 3µl of a potential concentrate field formulation (nominal cypermethrin concentration, 359g/1), or 20µl of an oil-based spray dilution (nominal cypermethrin concentration, 29g/1), was applied to the shorn backs of 4-5 week old rats (Alpk/AP strain, Wistar derived). The application site was left open to the atmosphere but protected by a plastic guard.

To facilitate the determination of absorption, [14C] cypermethrin was added to the formulation. Absorption was assessed after 8 hours. This time period was selected to represent a typical working day period. With the spray dilution the time-course of absorption over a 24 hour contact period was determined.

In both studies, determination of total absorption up to a particular time point required animals to be killed humanely prior to the analysis of the skin site, urine, faeces and various tissues for [14C] content (which was regarded as equivalent to cypermethrin).

During the 8 hour contact period with the concentrate formulation a mean of 1.0% (SEM ± 0.4; n = 3) of the applied radiolabel was detected to have been absorbed. In our experiments we defined the absorbed chemical as that which had passed through the skin, ie entered the circulatory system and, therefore, capable of exerting systemic toxicity. A chemical which is located in the stratum corneum (the outermost layer of the epidermis), although potentially absorbable, cannot exert systemic toxicity, other than local, and so is not regarded as absorbed.

A series of in vitro experiments were done to obtain data for
comparison with that obtained in vivo. The application conditions
of the formulation on the skin in vitro duplicated those in vivo.
The apparatus used for the in vitro experiments was a glass
diffusion cell (Figure 1) in which the skin membrane was sandwiched
between a donor and receptor chamber, with the epidermal surface
adjoining the donor chamber. The donor chamber was open at the top
in order to expose the epidermal surface to ambient atmospheric
conditions and the receptor chamber was placed in a water-bath
maintained at a constant temperature ($30^o \pm 1^oC$). Two variables
were introduced into the experiment. Firstly, whole skin
(epidermis and dermis) or an epidermal membrane (dermis removed)
was used (2). Secondly, several receptor fluids (physiological
saline, 6% VOLPO in saline, 6% PEG in saline, 20% foetal calf serum
and 50% aqueous ethanol) were used with both whole and epidermal
skin membranes. The in vitro data are presented in Table 1.

With whole skin in the diffusion cells no absorption was
detected during the 8 hour contact period into any of the receptor
fluids. These results do not agree with the in vivo data. However,
when epidermal membranes were used, absorption (similar to that
measured in vivo) was detected with 3 of the 5 receptor fluids.
Cypermethrin is essentially insoluble in the 2 receptor fluids
(physiological saline and 6% PEG in saline) into which no
absorption was detected.

These data indicate that the in vivo percutaneous absorption
of a lipophilic molecule can be predicted in vitro by using
epidermal membranes and a suitable receptor fluid in which the
penetrant is soluble. The inability of lipophilic molecules to
penetrate in vitro whole skin (though essentially the dermis) has
been demonstrated previously (2,3). In vivo chemicals must diffuse
through the stratum corneum and viable epidermis, to reach the
systemic circulation, but not the full width of the dermis. Thus
the use of epidermal membranes in vitro mimics the in vivo pathway
to the circulatory system. The need for a receptor fluid in which
the penetrant is soluble, (but which does not alter the overall
integrity of the diffusion barrier) is necessary and has been
reported previously (4) but this is still not appreciated fully.

The technical mistake of using whole skin and an unsuitable
receptor fluid might, in the past, have prejudiced workers in the
investigatory field of percutaneous absorption from using the in
vitro technique. Certainly, the inability to reproduce in vivo
absorption results in vitro would have been a frustrating
experience.

The profiles of in vivo and in vitro cypermethrin absorption
against time, through rat skin, from the oil-based spray dilution
are shown in Figure 2. During the initial 12 hour contact period
there was no difference between the in vivo and in vitro data, but
after this time the data obtained with 6% VOLPO 20 as the receptor
fluid in vitro underestimated the in vivo absorption. The 50%
aqueous ethanol solution again demonstrated that over prolonged
contact periods, the in vitro technique is capable of predicting
the in vivo absorption.

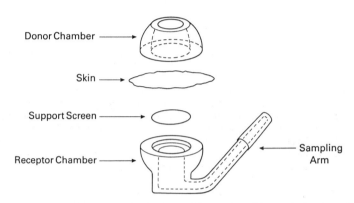

Donor Chamber

Skin

Support Screen

Receptor Chamber

Sampling Arm

Figure 1   Diagram of the glass diffusion cell used in in vitro
percutaneous absorption experiments

Table I.   In vitro Absorption of Cypermethrin through Rat Skin
During 8hr Contact Period from a Concentrate
Field Formulation

% applied dose absorbed									
Whole skin						Epidermis			
Receptor						Receptor			
1	2	3	4	5		1	2	3	4	5
ND	ND	ND	ND	ND		2.7	1.7	ND	2.1	ND
(5)	(5)	(5)	(5)	(5)		±0.4	±0.2		±0.4	
						(4)	(4)		(3)	

Receptor fluids used:
(1) 50% aqueous ethanol
(2) 6% VOLPO 20 in saline
(3) physiological saline
(4) 20% foetal calf serum
(5) 6% PEG in saline

Such an in vivo time course experiment, using this type of protocol, requires the use and sacrifice of many animals (eg. 2-5 per time point), whilst the in vitro technique requires much fewer (3-5 replicates for each receptor fluid with 3-5 skin samples from each rat). The ability to study the effect of altering the concentration, time of skin contact or changes in formulations could be measured in vitro much more efficiently and the effect on in vivo absorption predicted. In such a manner development of less toxic formulations, ie those which cause the least percutaneous absorption, would be facilitated.

A similar degree of accurate prediction of in vivo absorption, using the in vitro method, has also been achieved with a more water soluble and well absorbed pesticide, carbaryl. Initially, animals were given a single intravenous bolus injection of carbaryl and the urine and faeces collected. The proportion of the dose eliminated in the urine was then calculated. The kinetics of elimination following percutaneous absorption were assumed to be the same as after intravenous dosing. The [14C] carbaryl was applied to rat skin in a volatile vehicle (acetone) and absorption was assessed by collecting urine and assaying for [14C] which was regarded as equivalent to carbaryl. The amount of [14C] in the urine after dermal contact was then adjusted by the calculated 'correction factor' from the intravenous study (i.e. proportion in the urine) to determine percutaneous absorption. This technique has been employed successfully in monkey and human studies (5). In vitro absorption was measured into two receptor fluids (see Figure 3). The use of 50% aqueous ethanol provided the better agreement than the 6% VOLPO in saline receptor fluid and predicted accurately the in vivo data.

The percutaneous absorption of carbaryl has also been studied previously through human forearm skin (6). We have duplicated the absorption conditions and repeated the study in vitro with human abdominal skin. A comparison of our in vitro data with the published in vivo data is presented in Figure 4. Again, there is agreement between the in vivo and in vitro data, especially when the small amount of carbaryl applied and absorbed is considered together with the different application site. It is possible that a repeat in vivo study using the abdomen as the application site would give an even better correlation.

These experimental data support the view that the in vitro technique could be a genuine alternative to the in vivo determination of percutaneous absorption. In vitro data which predicted in vivo data have been obtained with different types of chemicals (physicochemical properties) and with different species (rat and man).

Extrapolation of dermal toxicity data from animal studies to man is difficult. The ability of the in vitro technique to quantify differences in absorption between animal models and man is illustrated in Figure 5. This shows the absorption profiles of [14C] carbaryl from a 40ug cm^{-2} dose, applied in acetone, to rat and human skin. The profile and rates of absorption are very different. If the rat data were used to predict human absorption

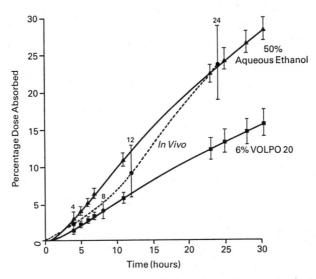

Figure 2   Cumulative <u>in vivo</u> and <u>in vitro</u> absorption of the insecticide cypermethrin from an oil-based spray dilution through rat skin

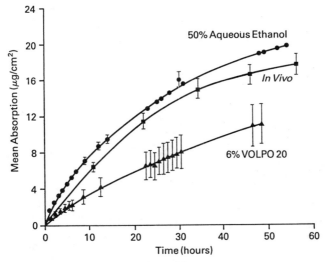

Figure 3   Absorption of carbaryl following deposition on skin in a volatile (acetone) vehicle through rat skin

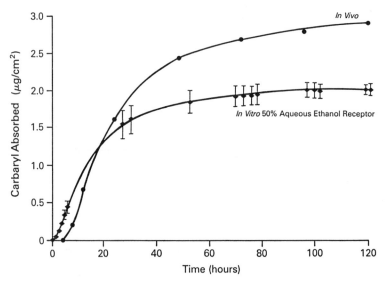

Figure 4   In vivo and in vitro absorption of carbaryl through
            human skin

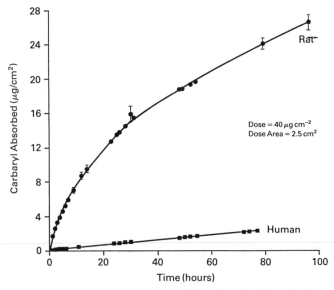

Figure 5   In vitro absorption of carbaryl through human and
            rat skin

there would be a large overestimation. These data show clearly that when absorption studies are done to predict human absorption then the best skin to use is human; there is, as yet, no animal skin which has proved to be a good model for human skin (7,8).

The difficulties of human in vivo studies have been discussed. The most rational way forward, therefore, to study and understand percutaneous absorption as it relates to man would appear to be the use of an in vitro system using human skin. This approach allows the effect of formulation changes, dose, time of contact and other variables on percutaneous absorption, as they relate to man, to be assessed readily.

Most determinations of absorption, particularly for the assessment of systemic hazard by Regulatory Authorities, lead to presentation of the data in terms of '% applied dose absorbed' at a specified time. The precise times of interest are ill-defined but often relate to the working day period (8-10 hours) and up to a 24 hour period. At present, there is no working or accepted 'classification scheme' for the extent and rate of absorption adopted amongst interested scientists in this area of investigation. The data presented in Figures 2 and 3 are further analysed in Table II. With both compounds, the extent of in vivo absorption, together with the appropriate '% applied dose absorbed' would have been predicted from the in vitro data (6% VOLPO data was less accurate than 50% aqueous ethanol) at any of the related time points. If data are required in this form then the in vitro system classified accurately the in vivo absorption.

Precisely how this type of data can be used for assessment of hazard is, however, not entirely clear. Toxicity is not related simply to 'the percentage of applied dose absorbed' but absorption rate and total amount absorbed or a combination of these. Data presented in Table III are from in vitro experiments to determine the absorption of [^{14}C] carbaryl through rat skin after application (in an acetone vehicle) at doses of 4, 40, 400 and 4000 $\mu g/cm^2$. The absorption rates and '% applied dose absorbed' have been determined and calculated over two time periods. If the data are considered in terms of '% dose absorbed' then, the higher values are obtained with the lower doses. However, the highest absorption rates, which would determine any toxicity, are from the higher doses. What is also obvious with this particular compound from this vehicle, is the non-linearity of the absorption rates with dose. The in vitro system facilitates the acquisition of such data. The '% applied dose absorbed' can only be relevant to any particular dose applied and specific time period. Absorption rates are more meaningful for toxicological/hazard assessments and enable absorption from different formulations and dose levels (as can happen in the field from spray equipment) to be compared. These rates can be obtained using the in vitro technique.

In our laboratory we have developed, an experimental in vitro percutaneous absorption scheme which we use to predict the potential hazard from pesticide formulations as a result of dermal contact (Table IV). Absorption measured from bulk 'infinite' doses to the skin provides data relevant to the worst exposure situation.

Table II.   Comparison of the '% Applied Dose Absorbed'
in In Vivo and In Vitro Experiments at Various Times After
Application to the Skin

Compound	Expt	% Applied Dose Absorbed		
		5hr	10hr	20hr
Cypermethrin	In vivo	3	6	19
	50% aq. eth	4	9	20
	6% VOLPO	2.5	5	11
Carbaryl	In vivo	10	20	33
	50% aq. eth	10	20	25
	6% VOLPO	5	7.5	12

Table III.   In Vitro Absorption of Carbaryl at a Range of
Doses Expressed as the Rate and '% Applied Dose Absorbed'
Over Specific Time Periods

Dose (μg/cm^2)	Time Period (hr)			
	2 - 6		20 - 40	
	J_s	%	J_s	%
4	1.77	100	-	-
40	1.16	15	0.28	35
400	1.75	25	0.84	10
4000	5.56	0.8	1.17	2

J_s, approximate absorption rate (μg/cm^2/hr)
%, total '% applied dose absorbed' at end of time point

Table IV. In Vitro Dermal Application Regime for Predicting Potential Percutaneous
Absorption From Different Formulations

Formulation	Apppplication Volume (μl/cm^2)
Concentrate	100
Spray dilution	100
Spray dilution (x10)	100
Spray dilution (÷10)	100
Spray dilution	10
Spray dilution (unoccluded)	10
Conc: Spray dilution (1:3)	100

To study the effects of other than the specified spray dilution contacting skin, as can happen if label instructions are not followed, absorption is measured from a range of spray dilutions which includes the recommended dilution. Additionally, to assess absorption under exposure situations likely in the field, the spray dilution is applied to the skin at a more realistic exposure rate ($10\mu l/cm^2$) with both the formulations covered (occluded) to prevent vehicle components evaporating and also open to the atmosphere (unoccluded) to mimic actual field exposure. A further application regime which we have recently introduced is to measure absorption from a mixture of the concentrate formulation and spray dilution (1:3) to study potential absorption for the 'mixer-loader' operator. Obviously, this approach is geared to the spray operator situation which we believe to be the most relevant for consideration of risk with pesticide formulations. In all our applications we apply specified volumes of formulations, rather than amounts of active ingedient (although this is known) and the data can be re-interpreted in terms of '% applied dose' if desired.

It is firmly our belief that the hazard of dermal exposure and subsequent absorption to pesticides needs to be assessed. Currently, we believe that the ideal way to do this is with full human pharmacokinetic volunteer trials, however, the accumulation of sufficient data by this method presents many problems which makes this approach impractical. In order to further aid our understanding of the factors governing the absorption of pesticides, from different formulations and the subsequent hazard to spray operators, we believe that the in vitro technique offers a genuine alternative to in vivo studies.

Literature cited

1. Scott, R. C. and Ramsey, J. D. (1987). Comparison of the in vivo and in vitro absorption of a lipophilic molecule (cypermethrin, a pyrethroid insecticide). J. Invest. Dermatol. 89: 142-146
2. Scott, R. C., Walker, M. and Dugard, P. H. (1986). In vitro percutaneous absorption experiments: A technique for production of intact epidermal membranes from rat skin. J. Soc. Cosmet. Chem. 37: 35-41.
3. Scheuplein, R. J. (1965). Mechanism of percutaneous absorption, iv. Penetration of non-electrolytes (alcohols) from aqueous solutions and from pure liquids. J. Invest. Dermatol. 60: 286-296.
4. Bronaugh, R. L. and Stewart, R. F. (1984). Methods for in vitro percutaneous absorption studies. 111. Hydrophobic compounds. J. Pharm. Sci. 73: 1255-1258
5. Bronaugh, R. L. and Maibach, H. I. (1985). Percutaneous absorption of nitroaromatic compounds: in vivo and in vitro studies in human and monkey. J. Invest. Dermatol. 84: 180-183.

6. Feldman, R. J. and Maibach, H. I. (1970). Absorption of some organic compounds through skin in man. J. Invest. Dermatol. 54: 399-404.
7. Scott, R. C., Walker, M. and Dugard, P. K. (1986). A comparison of the in vitro permeability properties of human and from laboratory animal skins. Int. J. Cos. Sci. 8 189-194 (1986).
8. Bartek, M. J., La Budde, J. A. and Maibach, H. I. (1972). Skin permeability in vivo: comparison in rat, rabbit, pig and man. J. Invest. Dermatol. 58 114-123.

RECEIVED March 8, 1988

Chapter 14

Dermal Absorption and Pharmacokinetics of Pesticides in Rats

P. V. Shah[1], H. L. Fisher[2], M. R. Sumler[3], and L. L. Hall[2]

[1]Toxic Effects Branch, Health and Environmental Review Division (TS-796), Office of Toxic Substances, U.S. Environmental Protection Agency, Washington, DC 20460
[2]Cellular Biology Branch, Health Effects Research Laboratory, U.S. Environmental Protection Agency, Research Triangle Park, NC 27711
[3]Northrop Environmental Sciences, Northrop Corporation, Research Triangle Park, NC 27709

Dermal absorption and disposition of carbaryl, carbofuran, chlordecone, hexachlorobiphenyl and dinoseb were studied in female Fischer 344 rats. Acetone solution of the [^{14}C] labeled pesticide was applied to a previously clipped mid-dorsal region of the back. At various time intervals, animals were killed and selected organs were analyzed for radioactive [^{14}C] content. A physiological compartmental model was fitted to the skin penetration, tissue distribution, and excretion data. The equilibrium tissue to blood ratios and excretion rate constants and skin absorption rate were determined from the model. In many cases, differences in kinetics and retention were found between young and adult rats. The dermal penetration function was single or biexponential, requiring a one or two compartmental model for simulating the skin penetration process.

More than one billion pounds of pesticides are being used each year in the United States alone to increase the productivity of agricultural land (1). Greater reliance on use of pesticides appears inevitable as the demand for food production increases with increasing population. Occupational exposure to pesticides occurs via oral, dermal, and inhalation routes. Although the rate of absorption may be higher by pulmonary and oral routes, the total amount absorbed after skin contact may be much greater during occupational exposure to pesticides (2,3).

Knowledge of dermal absorption (rates and extent) of pesticides is very important in risk assessment and establishment

0097-6156/89/0382-0169$06.00/0
© 1989 American Chemical Society

of reentry standards for field workers. With regard to
occupational exposure to toxicants in general, risk assessment has
usually been based on studies in adults. Skin absorption depends
on a number of factors, including the chemical and physical nature
of the penetrant and type of skin. The limited literature on the
effects of age on skin penetration has been recently summarized
(4). It appears that the effect of age on percutaneous absorption
varies with species, compound, and method of assessment.
Increased skin permeability of neosynephrine (as measured by the
blanching response) in premature infants compared to full term
infants has been documented (5).

No differences in percutaneous absorption of testosterone
between the newborn and adult rhesus monkey was noted (6), while
more rapid loss of topically applied triadimefon from the skin of
young Sprague-Dawley rats has been reported (7). A recent
comparative study on percutaneous absorption of pesticides in
young and adult Fischer 344 rats reported age-dependent
percutaneous absorption for 11 out of 14 pesticides studied (8).

We present here the comparative percutaneous absorption and
disposition of carbaryl, carbofuran, chlordecone, hexachlorobiphenyl, and dinoseb in young and adult Fischer 344 rats
utilizing identical methodology. Also, comparison of the results
of in vivo and two in vitro methods for percutaneous absorption
measurements are presented. The utility of the physiological
compartmental model in simulating dermal absorption and
disposition is discussed.

EXPERIMENTAL APPROACH:

CHEMICALS

The chemicals studied, their respective specific activities,
radiolabeling position, and sources are listed in Table I.

The radiochemical purity was greater than 98% for all
pesticides studied. Unlabeled chemicals were supplied by the
Pesticide and Industrial Chemical Repository (U.S. Environmental
Protection Agency, Research Triangle Park, NC). Minimum Essential
Medium (MEM) Eagle Formula with Earl's salts and L- glutamine and
without phenol red and sodium carbonate was purchased from Gibco
Laboratories, Chagrin Falls, OH. HEPES (N- 2-
hydroxyethylpiperazine- N '-2-ethanesulfonic acid), sodium
pyruvate, L- serine, L- aspartic acid, and gentamicin were purchased
from Gibco, Grand Island, NY. Anhydrous sodium carbonate, sodium
hydroxide, ethyl ether (anhydrous), and acetone (reagent grade)
were purchased from Fisher Scientific Co., Fairlawn, NJ.

IN VIVO APPLICATION

Female Fischer 344 rats of 33 (young) and 82 (adult) days of age
were utilized for dermal absorption experiments. Three rats were
used for each time point. Randomized offspring from timed-
pregnant rats were used in order to have better control over the
age and weight of the animals used in these experiments. The in
vivo experimental techniques employed in this study have been
described in detail by Shah et al. (8).

TABLE I. Pesticides Tested in Present Study, with Specific Activity, Radiolabeling Position, and Source

Common name	Specific activity (mCi/mM)	Radiolabeling position	Source
Carbaryl	5.8	Naphthyl[1-^{14}C]	Amersham, Arlington Heights, IL
Carbofuran	39.4	^{14}C(U) Benzofuranyl ring	FMC Corp., Princeton, NJ
Chlordecone	3.2	^{14}C Ring(U)	Midwest Research Institute, Kansas City, MO
Dinoseb	4.29	^{14}C Ring(U)	Pathfinder Lab., Inc., St. Louis, MO
PCB[1]	9.2	2,4,5,2',4',5'-[^{14}C(U)]	New England Nuclear, Boston, MA

[1] 2,4,5,2',4',5'-Hexachlorobiphenyl.

Briefly, the animal's hair was clipped 24 h prior to dermal application with Oster animal hair clippers (Oster, Milwaukee, WI). Dosing solutions (0.1 mL young and 0.2 mL adult) containing radioactivity and appropriate dose (285 nmol/cm^2) in acetone were applied to the previously clipped mid-back region of the rat. The treated area, which represents approximately 2.3% of the total body surface area (2.8 cm^2 young , 5.6 cm^2 adult), was protected from grooming by placing a nonocclusive device over it. At the end of the designated time interval, the animal was anesthetized with ether and a blood specimen was obtained from the heart. Various tissues were removed to determine the distribution of dermally absorbed radio- labeled pesticides.

All the tissues, excretory products, and carcasses were analyzed for radioactivity by liquid scintillation counting as described by Shah et al. (8).

IN VITRO PROCEDURE

In vitro absorption of pesticides through young and adult skin was determined by using both Franz cells and continuous flow-through cells. The detailed experimental and skin preparation techniques have been described in detail by Shah et al. (9). Briefly, back hair was clipped 24 h prior to experiment. Animals were killed with carbon dioxide, and back skin was carefully excised. Skin was floated on tissue culture medium (minimum essential media, Eagle formula with Earl's Salts). Split thickness (350 µm thickness) skins obtained with a dermatome (Padgett Dermatome, Kansas City, MO) were mounted in the in vitro cells with epidermis exposed to the environment. Only one skin disc was used from each animal. The amount of pesticide (in acetone) per cm^2 area was kept the same for both in vivo and in vitro experiments. Receptor fluid was manually removed periodically from the Franz cells to determine the rate and extent of penetration, while continous flow through cells with a media flow rate of 3 mL/h were automatically sampled every 3 h. Sample preparation for radioactivity determination and oxidation of treated skin were done according to procedure described by Shah et al. (8). Briefly, the treated skin was combusted in the sample oxidizer to measure the remaining radioactivity in or on the skin. All other samples were mixed with 10 mL Insta-Gel (Packard Instrument Co., Downers Grove, IL) for scintillation counting.

Data Analysis

Statistical comparisons to determine the effect of age on skin penetration of pesticides were made using the Statistical Analysis System package (10) with age and age X time as class variables in the general linear model (GLM). Reciprocal variance was used for weighting. The significance of the laboratory method used (flow, static, in vivo) was determined with the SAS using age, method, and age X method, and age X method X time as class variables in the GLM and reciprocal variance for weighting.

A mathematical model was constructed along the lines of the physiological model developed by Bungay et al. (11,12). Least-squares fitting of the model to the data was done using SAAM 27, a computer package developed at the National Institutes of Health (NIH) by Berman and Weiss (13).

RESULTS

Skin absorption of carbofuran as determined by the three methods is shown in Table II. The in vivo skin absorption of carbofuran was 4.7% at 6 h and 33.5% at 72 h in young animals. In adults, it increased from 2.0% at 6 h to 11.8% at the 72 h time point. The static system gave 3.1% skin absorption at 6 h and 12.0% at 72 h in young animals, while in adults, absorption ranged from 1.7% at 6 h to 8.8% at the 72 h time point. The skin absorption of carbofuran as determined by the flow system in young animals ranged from 27.3% at the 6 h to 41.1% at 72 h time point. In adults, it ranged from 5.0% at 6 h to 11.2% at the 72 h time point. The young/adult ratio of skin penetration at 72 h was 2.9 (in vivo), 3.7 (flow), and 1.4 (static). Thus, all three methods gave higher skin penetration values in young rats compared to adults. However, the static cell gave consistently lower skin penetration values in young rats compared to in vivo observations.

Skin absorption of carbaryl as determined by the three methods is shown in Table III. The skin absorption of carbaryl (in vivo) ranged from 2.4% at 6 h to 38.5% at 72 h in young animals, and in adults it ranged from 3.6% at 6 h to 38.4% at 72 h. The skin absorption of carbaryl (static) ranged from 5.3% at 6 h to 20.9% at 72 h in the young, and in adults, it ranged from 4.7% at 6 h to 20.3% at 72 h. The skin absorption of carbaryl (flow) ranged from 18.8% at 6 h to 29.2% at 72 h in young animals, and in adults, it ranged from 8.1% at 6 h to 18.2% at 72 h. Both in vivo and static systems showed no significant young/adult differences in skin penetration of carbaryl at the 72 h time point, while the flow system gave significant differences in skin penetration between young and adult animals, with young absorbing more carbaryl compared to adults.

Skin absorption of dinoseb as determined by the three methods is shown in Table IV. Dinoseb showed rapid penetration in both young and adult rats compared to other pesticides. The results from the in vivo method showed a statistically significant lower skin absorption of dinoseb in young animals. In the young, skin absorption ranged from 11.1% at 1 h to 55.7% at 72 h, while in adults, it ranged from 22.3% at 1 h to 84.3% at 72 h. The static method indicates significant differences in skin penetration of dinoseb in young and adult, except at 1 h sampling period. In the young, the skin absorption value (static), for dinoseb ranged from 3.0% at 1 h to 74.9% at 72 h, and in the adult, it ranged from 1.5% at 1 h to 70.8% at 72 h. The flow system indicated significant young/adult differences in skin absorption of dinoseb at all time points, and young absorbed more than twice the amount of dinoseb as adults. The skin absorption value (flow) in young ranged from 6.4% at 1 h to 47.3% at 72 h, and 2.4% at 1 h to 20.6% at 72 h in the adult.

TABLE II. Methods Comparison of Skin Penetration of Carbofuran*

% Skin Penetration

Time (h)	Flow System			Static System			In vivo		
	Young	Adult	Young/adult	Young	Adult	Young/adult	Young	Adult	Young/adult
6	27.3±4.5	5.0±0.6	5.5**	3.1±0.5	1.7±0.2	1.8	4.7±0.7	2.0±0.2	2.4
24	36.0±5.7	7.8±0.9	4.6**	7.0±0.8	4.6±0.5	1.5**	23.9±1.8	5.7±1.2	4.2**
48	39.4±6.0	9.7±0.9	4.1**	9.8±1.0	7.1±0.7	1.4**	26.1±2.6	6.8±0.1	3.8**
72	41.1±5.9	11.2±0.9	3.7**	12.0±1.1	8.8±0.8	1.4**	33.5±2.7	11.8±0.9	2.9**
All			4.3**			1.4**			3.4**
Age			**			**			**
Age X time			NS			**			**

* Reprinted from J. Toxicol. Environ. Health. 22:207-223, 1987 with permission of publisher.

** Significant at $p < 0.05$ for the hypothesis of no young-adult difference.

NS Not significant, $p > 0.05$.

TABLE III. Methods Comparison of Skin Penetration of Carbaryl

% Skin Penetration

Time (h)	Flow System			Static System			In Vivo		
	Young	Adult	Young Adult	Young	Adult	Young Adult	Young	Adult	Young Adult
6	18.8±2.1	8.1±1.2	2.33*	5.3±0.5	4.7±0.6	1.15	2.4±0.3	3.6±0.5	0.66*
24	24.6±2.6	13.3±1.9	1.86*	11.4±0.8	11.1±1.1	1.02	14.9±2.5	15.2±1.2	0.98
48	27.2±2.8	16.0±2.3	1.70*	16.5±1.2	16.1±1.6	1.02	23.6±1.0	32.4±0.7	0.73*
72	29.2±2.9	18.2±2.6	1.60*	20.9±1.5	20.3±1.9	1.03	38.5±2.4	38.4±1.3	1.00
All			1.80*			1.04			0.89*
Age			*			NS			*
Age X Time			*			*			*

* Significant at $p < 0.05$ for the hypothesis of no young-adult difference.
NS Not significant, $p > 0.05$.

TABLE IV. Methods Comparison of Skin Penetration of Dinoseb

% Skin Penetration

Time (h)	Flow System			Static System			In Vivo		
	Young	Adult	Ratio	Young	Adult	Ratio	Young	Adult	Ratio
1	6.4±1.0	2.4±0.6	2.64*	3.0±0.2	1.5±0.1	2.00*	11.1±2.1	22.3±8.8	0.50
6	29.0±3.5	11.19±2.2	2.61*	20.7±2.0	17.0±1.1	1.22	38.8±5.7	43.1±9.4	0.90
24	41.0±3.7	15.7±2.5	2.62*	59.1±7.4	52.3±3.1	1.13	63.0±2.9	85.5±1.8	0.74*
48	45.0±3.8	18.6±3.0	2.42*	70.9±8.4	66.2±3.8	1.07	55.3±9.7	85.1±1.9	0.65*
72	47.3±3.9	20.6±3.5	2.29*	74.9±8.0	70.8±3.8	1.06	55.7±2.4	84.3±2.7	0.66*
All			2.47*			1.10			0.70*
Age			*			*			*
Age X Time			*			*			*

* Significant at $p < 0.05$ for the hypothesis of no young-adult difference.

Methods comparison of hexachlorobiphenyl skin penetration in young and adult rats is shown in Table V. In vitro skin absorption values of hexachlorobiphenyl in young and adult rats were significantly lower than in vivo results. Skin absorption values in young at 6 h were 0.012%, 0.071%, and 2.5% as determined by flow, static, and in vivo methods, respectively. In adults, skin absorption values at 6 h were 0.015, 0.019, and 0.63% as determined by flow, static, and in vivo methods, respectively. Skin absorption values in young at 72 h were 1.25, 2.50, and 33.2% as determined by flow, static and in vivo methods, respectively. In adults, 72 h skin absorption values were 1.36, 1.15, and 19.6% as determined by flow, static and in vivo methods, respectively. Both in vitro methods showed nonsignificant differences in skin penetration of hexachlorobiphenyl between young and adult rats, while in vivo results showed significant differences in skin penetration between young and adult rats at all time points.

Methods comparison of skin penetration of chlordecone (Kepone) is shown in Table VI. In vitro skin absorption values of chlordecone in young and adult rats were significantly lower than in vivo values. Skin absorption values in young at 6 h were 0.45, 0.022, and 0.51% as determined by flow, static, and in vivo methods, respectively. In adults, skin absorption values at 6 h were 0.052, 0.026, and 0.398% as determined by flow, static, and in vivo methods, respectively. Skin absorption values in young at 72 h were 1.4, 2.2, and 9.1% as determined by flow, static and in vivo methods, respectively. In adults, 72 h skin absorption values were 1.2, 2.2, and 7.9% as determined by flow, static, and in vivo methods, respectively. All three methods showed higher skin penetration of chlordecone in young compared to adult animals.

PHYSIOLOGICAL MODELING

A physiological compartmental model for carbofuran dermal absorption and disposition is shown in Figure 1. The compartmental volumes (V_T) were the average weight of kidney, liver, and body found in the present study. The other compartmental volumes were derived from the body proportions given by Lutz et al. (14). Cardiac output and blood flow rates were scaled directly with compartmental size from the values given by Bungay et al. (11). A blood flow rate for a 1.9 g kidney was calculated to be 8.33 mL/min from a plasma flow rate of 5 mL/min and hematocrit of 40% (15).

The system of differential equations describing the transfer of material between organ compartments is given below. For blood

$$\frac{d}{dt}y_B = \sum_{\substack{i=K,L \\ M,S}} \frac{Q_i}{V_i R_i} y_i - \frac{Q_i}{V_B} y_B + k_a y_t$$

For muscle and nontreated skin

$$\frac{d}{dt}y_i = \frac{Q_i}{V_B} y_B - \frac{Q_i}{V_i R_i} y_i \qquad \text{where } i = M,S.$$

Table V. Methods Comparison of Skin Penetration of 2,2',4,4',5,5'-Hexachlorobiphenyl

% Skin Penetration

Time (h)	Flow System			Static System			In vivo		
	Young	Adult	Young/adult	Young	Adult	Young/adult	Young	Adult	Young/adult
6	0.012±0.003	0.015±0.002	0.83	0.071±0.022	0.019±0.005	3.63	2.50±0.20	0.63±0.06	3.94*
24	0.17±0.04	0.17±0.03	1.00	0.46±0.12	0.188±0.054	2.43	13.62±0.53	8.35±0.53	1.63*
48	0.60±0.13	0.58±0.08	1.05	1.25±0.24	0.592±0.138	2.11	28.1±3.5	18.4±0.6	1.53*
72	1.25±0.23	1.36±0.16	0.92	2.50±0.32	1.15±0.21	2.18	33.2±2.2	19.6±1.5	1.69*
All			0.96			2.20			1.65*
Age			NS			*			*
Age X time			*			*			*

* Significant at p < 0.05 for the hypothesis of no young-adult difference.
NS Not significant, p > 0.05.

Table VI. Methods Comparison of Skin Penetration of Chlordecone

% Skin Penetration

Time (h)	Flow System Young	Adult	Young/Adult	Static System Young	Adult	Young/Adult	In Vivo Method Young	Adult	Young/Adult
6	0.450±0.043	0.052±0.020	8.69*	0.022±0.007	0.026±0.007	0.86	0.513±0.063	3.98±0.108	1.29
24	0.921±0.052	0.205±0.090	4.49*	2.47±0.072	0.199±0.039	1.24	3.570±0.453	2.508±0.606	1.42
48	1.201±0.057	0.699±0.243	1.80*	1.100±0.238	0.912±0.161	1.21	6.825±0.219	5.626±0.686	1.21
72	1.398±0.057	1.234±0.310	1.13*	2.213±0.435	2.153±0.320	1.03	9.066±0.664	7.922±1.061	1.14
All			1.84*			1.09			1.21

* Significant at $p < 0.05$ for the hypothesis of no young-adult difference.

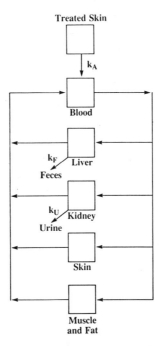

Figure 1. Physiological model for carbofuran dermal absorption and disposition in the rat. (Reproduced with permission from ref. 9. Copyright 1987 Hemisphere Publishing Corporation.)

For kidney

$$\frac{d}{dt}Y_K = \frac{Q_K}{V_B}Y_B - \frac{Q_K}{V_K R_K}Y_K - k_U Y_K$$

and for liver

$$\frac{d}{dt}Y_L = \frac{Q_L}{V_B}Y_B - \frac{Q_L}{V_L R_L}Y_L - k_F Y_L$$

For treated skin

$$\frac{d}{dt}Y_T = - k_a Y_T, \quad Y_T(0) = D_0$$

Nomenclature

		Subscripts	
D_0	Dermal dose (n moles)	B	Blood
Y_i	Radioactivity in compartment i (n moles)	K	Kidneys
Q_i	Blood flow rate to tissue i: (mL/h)	L	Liver
V_i	Volume for tissue compartment i: (mL)	M	Muscle
R_i	Equilibrum tissue/blood ratio for compartment i	S	Nontreated skin
k_A	Dermal absorption rate constant (h^{-1})	T	Treated skin
k_U	Urinary excretion rate constant (h^{-1})	F	Feces
k_F	Fecal excretion rate constant (h^{-1})	U	Urine

Carbofuran levels from blood, kidney, liver, skin, carcass, urine, and feces were fitted to the model using SAAM27 to optimize the parameters for equilibrum tissue/blood ratio (R_T), the urine (K_U), and feces (K_F), excretion-rate constant, and the dermal absorption-rate constant (K_A). The parameter values are shown in Table VII.

The dermal absorption-rate constant (K_A) for young, 0.00548 h^{-1}, is about 3 times that for adults, 0.00173 h^{-1}. The model results for dermal absorption were in agreement with the observed values after 24 h for both young and adult rats. Before 24 h, the model results were approximately half of the observed values, perhaps indicating an additional rapid component of absorption which was not incorporated in the model. The urinary excretion rate constants (K_U) were found to be 36.1 h^{-1} for young and 26.1 h^{-1} for the adult. The fecal excretion rate constants (K_F) were found to be 0.67 h^{-1} for young and 0.24 h^{-1} for the adult. The increased dermal absorption-rate constant in young compared to adult animals appears to be balanced by the increased excretion-rate in the young, such that the body burdens in young and adults are about the same at 120 h.

The equilibrium tissue-to-blood ratios (Table VII) for adult animals were higher than those of the respective organs in the young. Most notable is the difference in the kidney-to-blood ratio of 10.3 for adults as compared to 5.4 for young, indicating the greater sequestering of carbofuran-derived radioactivity in adults than in young.

TABLE VII. Parameters[a] Employed in the Physiologic Model for Carbofuran Absorption and Disposition in the Young and Adult Rat*

Rat	Organ	V_i (mL)	Q_i (mL/min)	R_T
Adult	Blood	14.18 (9)[b]	39.40	10.29
	Kidneys	1.31[b]	5.78	2.47
	Liver	5.93[b]	9.49	1.94
	Skin	25.21 (16)	3.15	3.65
	Muscle and fat	89.82 (57)		4.98
	Body	154.58[c]		
		$K_F = 0.239$ h^{-1}		$K_A = 0.00173$ h^{-1}
		$k_U = 26.09$ h^{-1}		
Young	Blood	6.38 (9)[b]	17.74	
	Kidneys	0.72[b]	3.19	5.41
	Liver	3.03[b]	4.86	1.91
	Skin	11.35 (16)	1.42	1.28
	Muscle and fat	40.44 (57)	2.24	2.38
	Body	70.94[c]		
		$K_F = 36.06$ h^{-1}		$K_A = 0.00548$ h^{-1}
		$k_U = 36.06$ h^{-1}		

[a] V_i, compartmental volume; Q_i, blood flow rate to the organs; R_T, equilibrium tissue to blood ratio; K_F, rate constant for fecal excretion; K_U, rate constant for urinary excretion; K_A, rate constant for dermal absorption.

[b] Percent of body weight given in parentheses.

[c] Observed.

* Reprinted from J. Toxicol. Environ. Health. 22:207-223, 1987 with permission of publisher.

A steady state was reached rapidly. The model predicted organ content to be maximum at 6 h, followed by a decrease in content as a result of the decline in the amount that was available for penetration. Continuous exposure was simulated with the model by maintaining a unit constant amount on the skin. Equilibrium levels calculated in the organs as fractions of the amount on the skin for young and adult, respectively, were 1.5×10^{-4}, and 0.65×10^{-4} for kidney, 3.7×10^{-4} and 1.4×10^{-4} for liver, 9.4×10^{-4} and 4.7×10^{-4} for skin, and 81×10^{-4} and 40×10^{-4} for the total body. Corresponding excretion rates (fraction/h) for young and adults were 52×10^{-4} and $17 \times 10^{-4} \, h^{-1}$ for urine and $2.5 \times 10^{-4} \, h^{-1}$ and $0.34 \times 10^{-4} \, h^{-1}$ for feces. From this temporal experiment with a single applied dose of carbofuran, the linear compartmental flow model provides a good fit to the data. A more complete validation of the model would require data at a sequence of doses as well as data from multiple dose experiments.

For chlordecone, a model developed from intravenous (iv) dosing was used but modified to accommodate the dermal absorption pathway. A time-varying dermal absorption rate constant was found to enhance the model fit. The urinary excretion rate constant was also time-dependent. Excretion began at about $0.75 \, h^{-1}$ and finished at about $0.01 \, h^{-1}$ at 120 h. Equilibrium tissue/blood ratios agreed with those found by iv dosing except for skin. Skin was found to have an equilibrium tissue/blood ratio of about 3.5 instead of 6 as determined by iv dosing. This was the lowest ratio for any tissue. The highest ratio was 10 which occurred for liver.

Dermal absorption for dinoseb was biphasic requiring two first order compartments to adequately simulate the observed data. Tissue/blood ratios were lowest in muscle, about 0.15, and highest in kidney, about 0.55. Since all ratios were less than 1.0, no sequestering of dinoseb radioactivity is indicated. The urinary pathway was the preferred route of excretion by about a 4:1 ratio as compared to the fecal route.

Hexachlorobiphenyl was modeled with separate compartments for parent and metabolite as determined from published iv experiments (14). Dermal absorption was described by a single first order compartment but delayed by about 1 h in young rats and 4 h in adult rats. The tissue/blood ratio for adipose for the parent compound was found to be in the 100's or 1000's indicating a very small release of parent from the adipose compartment. Muscle had the lowest tissue/blood ratio for parent of about 4. The metabolism constant for liver was about 0.02 mL/min which is quite slow. The metabolites are readily excreted and produced tissue blood ratios of only 1 to 4.

DISCUSSION:

A number of studies have suggested higher skin permeability in premature and full-term infants compared to adults. Behl et al. (4) and Maibach and Boisits (16) have reviewed the literature on

age-related percutaneous absorption. Behl et al. (4,17) reported
in vitro skin penetration of water, methanol, ethanol, butanol,
hexanol, and octanol in male hairless mice of different ages.
They observed increased skin permeabilities reaching maximum
values around 25 days of age, then declining sharply up to about
60 days of age, and remaining more or less invariant thereafter.
        In the present study, age-related differences in percutaneous
absorption of some of the pesticides tested were observed. In
many cases significant influence of methods employed to determine
the skin absorption of these pesticides was also observed.
Results at 72 h from the in vivo method showed age-related
differences in skin penetration for carbofuran, dinoseb, and
hexachlorobiphenyl. The flow method showed statistically
significant skin penetration differences for dinoseb, carbaryl,
carbofuran and hexachlorobiphenyl. The static method showed
significant young/adult penetration differences only for
carbofuran and hexachlorobiphenyl. This study clearly
demonstrates that significant differences in absolute penetration
values arise from the different methods used.
        A number of studies have shown good correlation between in
vivo and in vitro skin permeability values for a number of
chemicals and animal species because skin absorption has been
considered as the passive diffusion process through a rate-
limiting, nonliving barrier, stratum corneum. Franz (18) compared
the percutaneous absorption (in vitro) of 12 organic compounds
with in vivo results reported by Feldmann and Maibach (19). He
reported excellent qualitative agreement between in vitro and in
vivo methods. He further reported the discrepancies in the
quantitative agreement between the two sets of data. Later on
Franz (20) reported that discrepancies in quantitative agreement
was due simply to experimental variation based on additional in
vitro experiments to simulate in vivo conditions by washing skin
after 24 h. Bronaugh (21) reported identical in vivo and in vitro
rat skin absorption values for benzoic acid, acetylsalicylic acid
and urea.
        The two in vitro methods utilized here, namely, the static
and flow-through diffusion cells, have been recently compared by
Bronaugh and Stewart (22). The authors (22) reported the
comparative skin absorption values for water, cortisone, and
benzoic acid through rat skin as determined by static and flow-
through diffusion cells. They reported similar absorption
profiles and quantitative values between the two diffusion systems
for water, cortisone, and benzoic acid under the experimental
conditions described. However, discrepancies in absorption values
were observed for a hydrophobic compound, [3-phenyl-2-propenyl-2-
aminobenzoate (cinnamyl anthranilate)] between the two diffusion
cell systems; the flow-through diffusion cell system gave enhanced
absorption value for cinnamyl anthranilate compared to the static
cell system. They have further reported good agreement between in
vivo and in vitro (static as well as flow-through diffusion cells)
skin permeation for cortisone and benzoic acid when each was
applied in petrolatum vehicle.
        We have reported discrepancies in the skin absorption values
as determined by the two in vitro methods. We also observed poor

correlation between in vivo and in vitro results for these highly complex pesticidal chemicals. There are a number of factors that can influence the skin absorption measurements. The influence of receptor fluid for in vitro skin absorption measurements has been widely documented. For example, the in vitro absorption of chlordecone and hexachlorobiphenyl in the present study never exceeded more than than 2.5% in both diffusion cell systems. These two chemicals have poor water solubility (0.9 ppb for hexachlorobiphenyl) and the receptor fluid utilized in this investigation may not be sufficiently lipohilic to remove the chemical from the dermis (split-thickness skin). Bronaugh and Stewart (23) suggested that the lack of solubility of the hydrophobic penetrant into the receptor fluid for in vitro methods could be a contributing factor accounting for in vivo and in vitro discrepancies in skin absorption values. Bronaugh and Stewart (23) reported maximum absorption of cinnamyl anthranilate by using 6% PEG-20 oleyl ether receptor fluid with either type of diffusion cell system.

Recently, Scott and Ramsey (24) reported that the highest absorption of cypermethrin was achieved when 50% aqueous ethanol was used as the receptor fluid which was in agreement with in vivo absorption through the rat skin. They further reported that the absorption of cypermethrin measured with two other receptor fluids (6% Volpo 20 and 20% fetal calf serum) was very similar to 50% aqueous ethanol as the receptor fluid. Thus the above mentioned study suggests that, the solubility of the penetrant into receptor fluid, rather than the diffusion of penetrant through the epidermal membrane, is the rate limiting step.

It appears that the results obtained by different methods have to be carefully evaluated with the experimental conditions prescribed. It is also clear from the literature that the in vitro results can be influenced by a number of factors. Perhaps more comparative studies may improve the understanding of the in vitro and in vivo correlation. Validation of recently recommended guidelines for in vitro percutaneous penetration studies (25) with a number of chemicals may help in understanding the in vitro skin absorption process.

Utility of pharmacokinetic models has been explored for extrapolation to man, animal species scaling, extrapolation of results beyond the observed time point, simulation of continuous or multiple exposure situation, tissue dose extrapolation, improving experimental design, and overall reduction of animal usage. Physiological models have been shown to be adequate for other chemicals (26,27). The applications of physiologically based modeling and its technique has been reviewed by a number of investigators (26,28,29). In the present study, physiologically-based pharmacokinetic models were used to decribe dermal absorption and disposition processes for the chemicals studied. Rate constants for dermal absorption, and urinary and fecal excretion, as well as tissue to blood steady state ratios were determined.

A physiological model describing carbaryl radioactivity was fitted to the tissue distribution data. The dermal absorption was found to be described by a single first order compartment for both

young and adult rats over the experimental period. The order of
the equilibrium tissue/blood ratios was the same in young and
adult rats. The tissue with the largest tissue/blood ratio of
about 6 or 7 was kidney. The untreated skin has the lowest
equilibrium tissue/blood ratio of about 0.8 to 1.0. The rate
constant for kidney to urine excretion was large at 15 to 20 h^{-1}.

A more complex model to include metabolism, blood clearance,
release of chemical from solvent to skin, incorporation of viable
layer, and metabolism during absorption, etc., may aid in
improving the model's utility.

CONCLUSIONS:

Percutaneous absorption was compared in young and adult Fisher 344
rats for five pesticides utilizing both in vivo and in vitro
methods. In vivo penetration of the pesticides during a 72 h
period, ranged from approximately 8.0% (chlordecone, adult) to 84%
(dinoseb, adult), depending on compound and age of the animal.
Three pesticides, (carbofuran, hexachlorobiphenyl, and
chlordecone) showed higher skin penetration values in young
compared to adult. Differences in skin penetration values were
observed among pesticides due to methods of measurement. Two in
vitro methods, namely, static cell and flow-through diffusion cell
systems gave different penetration values. A physiological
compartmental model appears to be good for simulating dermal
absorption and disposition of the pesticides studied.

ACKNOWLEDGMENTS:

This work was conducted at Northrop Environmental Sciences,
Research Triangle Park, NC. The research described in this
article has been reviewed by the Office of Toxic Substances, U.S.
Environmental Protection Agency, and approved for publication.
Approval does not signify that the contents necessarily reflect
the views and policies of the Agency, nor does mention of trade
names or commercial products constitute endorsement or
recommendation for use.

Literature Cited

1.   *Synthetic Organic Chemicals* , United States International
     Trade Commission, 1985, pp 226-241.
2.   Durham, W.F.; Wolfe, H.R. *Bull. WHO* **1962,** *26* , 75-91.
3.   Wolfe, H.R.; Durham, W.F.; Armstrong, J.F. *Arch. Environ.
     Health* **1976,** *14* , 622-633.
4.   Behl, C.R.; Bellantone, N.H.; Flynn, G.L. In *Percutaneous
     Absorption Mechanisms - Methodology - Drug Delivery* .
     Bronaugh, R.L., Maibach, H.I.; Eds.;   Dekker: New York,
     1985; pp 183-212.
5.   Nachman, R.L.; Esterly, N.B. *J. Pediatr* . **1971,** *79* , 628-632.
6.   Wester, R.C.; Noonan, P.K.; Cole, M.P.; Maibach, H.I.
     Pediatr. Res . **1977,** *11* , 737-739.
7.   Knaak, J.B.; Yee, K., Ackerman, C.R., Zweig, G., Wilson,
     B.W. *Toxicol. Appl. Pharmacol* . **1984,** *72* , 406-416.

8. Shah, P.V.; Fisher, H.L.; Sumler, M.R; Chernoff, N.; Hall, L.L. *J. Toxicol. Environ. Health* **1987**, *21*, 353-366.
9. Shah, P.V.; Fisher, H.L.; Month, N.J.; Sumler, M.R.; Hall, L.L. *J. Toxicol. Environ. Health* **1987**, *22*; 207-223.
10. SAS Institute Inc. SAS User's Guide: Statistics Version-5 Edition, SAS Institute, Inc., Cary, NC 1985.
11. Bungay, P.M.; Dedrick, R.L.; Matthews, H.B. *Ann. N.Y. Acad. Sci*. **1979**, *320*, 257-270.
12. Bungay, P.M., Dedrick, R.L., Matthews, H.B. *J. Pharmacokinet. Biopharm*. **1981**, 309-341.
13. Berman, M., Weiss, M.F. *SAAM Manual. (Simulation, Analysis and Modeling)*, Version: SAAM 27. Department of Health, Education, and Welfare, Publication (NIH) 78-180, 1978.
14. Lutz, R.J.; Dedrick, R.L.; Matthews, H.B.; Eling, T.E; Anderson, M.W. *Drug. Metab. Dispos*. **1977**, *54*, 386-397.
15. Bischoff, K.B.; Dedrick, R.L.; Zaharko, D.S.; Longstreth, J.A. *J. Pharm. Sci*. **1971**, *60*, 1129-1133.
16. Maibach, H.I.; Boisits, E.K. *Neonatal Skin Structure and Function*; Dekker: New York, 1982.
17. Behl, C.R.; Flynn, G.L.; Kurihara, T.; Smith, W.M.; Bellantone, N.H., Gatmaitan, O.; Pierson, C.L.; Higuchi, W.I.; HO, N.F.H. *J. Soc. Cosmet. Chem*. **1984**, *35*, 237-252.
18. Franz, T.J. *J. Invest. Dermatol*. **1975**, *64*, 190-195.
19. Feldmann, R.J.; Maibach, H.I. *J. Invest. Dermatol*. **1970**, *54*, 399-404.
20. Franz, T.J. *Curr. Probl. Dermatol*. **1978**, *7*, 58-68.
21. Bronaugh, R.L.; Stewart, R.F.; Congdon, E.R. *Toxicol. Appl. Pharmacol*. **1982**, *62*, 481-488.
22. Bronaugh, R.L.; Stewart, R.F. *J. Pharm. Sci*. **1985**, *74*, 64-67.
23. Bronaugh, R.L.; Stewart, R.F. *J. Pharm. Sci*. **1984**, *73*, 1255-1257.
24. Scott, R.C.; Ramsey, J.D. *J. Invest. Dermatol*. **1987**, *89*, 142-146.
25. Skelly, J.P.; Shah, V.P.; Maibach, H.I.; Guy R.H.; Wester, R.C.; Flynn, G.; Yacobi, A. *Pharm. Res*. **1987**, *4*, 265-267.
26. Anderson, M.E.; Keller, W.C. In *Cutaneous Toxicity. Target Organ Toxicology Series*; Drill, V.A.,; Lazar, P., Eds., Raven Press, New York, 1982. p 9-27.
27. McDougal, J.N.; Jepson, G.W.; Clewell III, H.J.; MacNaughton, M.G.; Anderson, M.E. *Toxicol. Appl Pharmacol*. **1986**, *85*, 286-294.
28. Lutz, R.J.; Dedrick, R.L.; Zaharko, D.S. *Pharmacol. Ther*. **1980**, 11, 559-592.
29. Gerlowski, L.E.; Jain, R.K. *J. Pharm. Sci*. **1983**, *72*, 1103-1127.

RECEIVED July 5, 1988

CHEMICAL ANALYSIS

Advances in Analytical Methodology
for Determining Pesticides in Biological Fluids

The focus of this Section of Biological Monitoring for Pesticide
Exposure is on analytical methodology to detect pesticides and/or
pesticide metabolites in human biological fluids. Analytical techniques employed for biological monitoring have been evolving for many
years from spectrophotometric assays with percent or PPM sensitivity
to sophisticated GLC and HPLC methods as well as immunoassay techniques with PPT or greater sensitivities. Needless to say that
future methods will be even more sensitive.

One may ask then what makes a good analytical method for biological monitoring? Analytical methods used for biological monitoring must be sensitive enough to detect trace amounts of a substance in biological fluids and must be specific enough to eliminate
the possibility of false positive and false negative results. In
addition, such methods must be sensitive in the presence of the
various matrices encountered in biological fluids such as tissue,
urine, blood, saliva, sweat or feces. More than one analytical
method must be employed to positively prove the presence of an
analyte.

The first chapter in this section by T. L. Lavy and co-workers
deals with an overview of the basic criteria in analytical methodology for good biological monitoring. The following chapter by
Weisskopf and co-workers present advances in the technology of measuring organophosphates in urine by GLC. Disposable extraction
cartridges, large bore capillary chromatography columns, and use of
the injection block methylating reagent trimethylanilinium hydroxide
are used to improve upon the already highly sophisticated and precise
GLC technology. Osterloh and co-workers present an example of how
exposure assessments can be accomplished for field workers while measuring metabolites in urine. The remaining papers of this Section of
Biological Monitoring for Pesticide Exposure contain state of the art
techniques for handling large numbers of samples which one may
encounter in typical field biological monitoring programs. The paper
by Cheung et. al. explores advanced automated methods to determine
chlordimeform exposure to pilots, mixer-loaders, and flaggers
applying Galecron®. Dubleman and Campbell's chapters give the reader
excellent detail on how to set up a Biological Monitoring program
based on the latest technologies involved in organization sampling,

190

instrumentation, computation of results, and reporting of data.   In
the concluding chapter, Brady and co-workers present research which
indicates that immunoassay technology is rapidly finding its way into
the world of pesticides and may well become the analytical technique
of the future.

Finally, it is easy to see after examining the following
chapters that the analytical methodology of Biological Monitoring is
rapidly advancing and is well ahead of the regulatory process which
must develop prior to its utilization.

Richard C. Honeycutt
Agricultural Division
Ciba—Geigy Corporation
Greensboro, NC 27419

RECEIVED June 21, 1988

Chapter 15

Biological Monitoring Techniques for Humans Exposed to Pesticides

Use, Development, and Recommended Refinements

T. L. Lavy and J. D. Mattice

Altheimer Laboratory, University of Arkansas, Fayetteville, AR 72703

Observations and major conclusions on the design of human
applicator exposure studies based on 10 exposure studies
are presented. An approach for determining if urinalysis
is suitable for measuring an absorbed dose of a compound is
given along with a general approach for developing an analytical technique. Whether one uses excretion of the
intact pesticide or a known urinary metabolite as the test
criteria, it is important to have quantitative human
absorption and excretion data for each pesticide to be able
to provide accurate meaningful quantitative risk assessment
information.

Pesticides benefit us in helping to produce food and fiber, but they
also have the potential to harm us. The need for protection for
those applying pesticides or those associated with their production
is a concept that has been readily accepted for over 20 years.
Although some specific information exists for a pesticide regarding
its toxicity to rats or other test animals, there is no uniform
agreement among researchers regarding the extent of protection
needed by humans in contact with the pesticide, how to achieve the
desired level of protection, how to quantify the exposures occurring
nor how to evaluate the postulated health effects from pesticides
entering the body from contaminated clothing or dermal surfaces.
    In casual conversation the words "exposure" and "dose" are often
used for the same concept. In our context they have specific
meanings. Exposure is being accessible to something, such as a
pesticide. If it is on our skin or in the air we breathe, we are
exposed. Dose is defined as the amount that gets inside our bodies.
In this paper we plan to address some of the problems associated
with applicator exposure data obtained by analyzing patches attached
to clothing of workers exposed to pesticides, and absorbed dose data
obtained by measuring urinary excretion of the pesticide. Important
facts to be considered in designing studies which will provide quantitative absorbed dose data while at the same time allowing collection of patch data will also be discussed. The latter portions of

0097–6156/89/0382–0192$06.00/0
© 1989 American Chemical Society

the paper will outline the steps involved with developing the criteria and techniques for using human urine as a biological monitoring tool.

For the past nine years we have been conducting studies
measuring dose and exposure for people working with 11 different
compounds (Table I). During our studies in the late 1970's on
workers applying 2,4,5-T and 2,4-D in the forest (1,2), considerable
effort was devoted to collecting both patch data and data from urine
analyses of exposed workers. One of the goals of those studies was
to find if a high correlation existed between the herbicide deposited on patches and the absorbed herbicide dose as determined from
urine analysis. Earlier, Sauerhoff (3) had shown rapid and nearly
quantitative excretion of phenoxy herbicides whether they entered
the body orally or dermally. By photographing each of our workers
in his field attire, observing the photograph, and employing average
human area measurements for different body portions (4), it was
possible to calculate the total exposed dermal area for each worker.
After extrapolating the average exposure per 100 cm^2 of patch
attached to several portions of the worker's clothing near bare skin
areas, it should have been possible to predict the amount of herbicide deposited on bare dermal surfaces. We had hoped that results
from this calculation would correlate strongly with the amount of
phenoxy herbicide excreted in urine of the exposed individual.
Unfortunately, from the standpoint of simplicity of measurement, a
low correlation, 0.377 (1), was found. Aware of this low correlation, it thus became important to measure the parameter most likely
to correlate with potential health effects. Since any adverse human
health effects that may arise due to pesticide exposure will be more
a function of the levels present inside the body rather than the
amounts deposited on clothing, gloves or skin, the majority of our
efforts after the initial two forestry studies have been directed
toward obtaining quantifiable absorbed dose information. We have
chosen total urine collection and consequent urine analysis as the
tool to measure the absorbed dose.

Although blood, urine and perhaps other body fluids or excre-
tions could conceivably be used as biological monitoring mediums, we
have used urine analyses exclusively as our biological monitoring
tool. Although workers are not eager to collect their total urine
output, they much prefer to collect their urine than to have their
blood sampled daily.

Since accurate findings of a worker exposure study are so
vitally dependent upon the full cooperation of the workers involved,
all possible communications and preparations should be made several
weeks prior to the initiation of the study. It is important that
the investigator go to the field, meet the workers, and discuss the
protocol with them at least once prior to the study.

Results of our earlier studies have shown that reproducible
quantifiable pesticide excretion data can only be obtained by making
total urine collections over the measurement period. In our initial
2,4,5-T study (1), when urine was collected over consecutive 24-hour
periods there was much less variability in the concentrations of
2,4,5-T excreted in urine when compared to consecutive 12-hour
samples. Although 1500-1700 mls of urine is an average daily urinary excretion volume used by some researchers, our studies indicate

Table I. Human Exposure Studies Utilizing Biological Monitoring
Techniques Completed or Underway at the Altheimer Laboratory

Compound	Urinary metabolite	Sensitivity (ppm)	Dose excreted Urine (%)	Animal	Ref
bayleton	4-chlorophenol	0.05	90	cow, pig	a
			30-40	rat	a
benomyl	MBC, 4-MBC, 5-MBC	0.10	16	dog	19
			86	rat	19
bifenox	5-(2,4-dichlorophenoxy) -2-nitrobenzoic acid	0.02	29-53	rat	b
captan	tetrahydrophthalimide	0.03	13	rat	16,17
carbaryl	naphthyl sulfate 1-naphthol	0.20	40-70	rat	c
chlorpyrifos	3,5,6-trichloro-2- pyridinol	0.01	70	man	14
2,4-D	2,4-D	0.04	95-100	man	3
2,4-DP	2,4-DP	0.04	95-100	man	5
picloram	picloram	0.01	90-97	dog, cow	22
			90	man	6
pydrin	4-chloro-(1-methyl- ethyl)benzene acetic acid	e	62	mice	d
2,4,5-T	2,4,5-T	0.04	95-100	man	23

[a]Thornton, J. S., Mobay Chemical Corp., P. O. Box 4913, Hawthorn
Road, Kansas City, MO 64120, Personal Communication, 1985.
[b]Norris, F. A., Rhone-Poulenc Inc., P. O. Box 125, Black Horse Lane,
Monmouth Junction, N.J. 08852, Personal Communication, 1984.
[c]Harrison, S., Union Carbide Agricultural Products Co. Inc., P. O.
Box 12014, T. W. Alexander Drive, Research Triangle Park, NC 27709,
Personal Communication, 1985.
[d]Bishop, J. L., Shell Agricultural Chemical Co., P. O. Box 4248,
Modesto, CA 95352, Personal Communication, 1986.
[e]To be determined.

the use of an average daily urinary excretion volume is not sufficient to obtain good quantitative pesticide excretion data. Some
field workers regularly excreted between 500 and 600 mls per 24
hours while others excreted over 6000 mls in a similar 24-hour
period (5). Since it is not simple or convenient to collect ones
total urine output over an extended period it is imperative that the
worker be totally aware of the importance of providing all their
urine. The workers must be informed that their individual performance will dictate whether the study is a success or failure. An
important portion of the expenses associated with conducting an
exposure study involving humans should include payments for the
workers supplying their total urine output. Although the researcher
can not be absolutely certain that all workers are complying with
his instructions, some guidelines we have followed in an attempt to
collect or account for the total urine output are: (a) If a worker
is aware that a portion of the urine sample was inadvertently lost,
an estimate of the volume lost is added to the 24 hour volume
collected. (Compliance payments are to be withheld from workers
with unusually high loss records). (b) Creatinine concentrations
are run on each urine sample. By multiplying the creatinine concentration (mg/l) by the amount of urine excreted (1) it is possible
to calculate the amount of creatinine excreted on a daily basis.
Since the amount of creatinine excreted daily is relatively
constant, we can determine if substantial amounts of urine have been
lost. Knowledge on the part of the worker that we will be analyzing
each sample for creatinine, coupled with the fact that the dollars
paid to the participants are not made until a period of time later
(sufficient to allow analysis of the samples for creatinine content)
helps provide us with a fair degree of assurance of worker cooperation. Another factor of significance with respect to worker
cooperation is the fact that most workers are truly interested in
knowing whether they are being exposed to the pesticides and if the
amount of pesticide entering their body is likely to cause present
or future health problems. The negative publicity which is often
associated with the use of pesticides has increased the level of
concern for some of the workers.

The optimum urine collection period for achieving accurate
reproducible results is dependent on several factors, such as: rate
of entry into body, metabolic changes occurring and excretion rate
from the body. In the case of the phenoxy herbicides, Sauerhoff (3)
has indicated that well over 90% of the absorbed dose is excreted
within the first 5 days following exposure. Laboratory studies by
Nolan et al. (6) have shown that picloram is excreted in urine even
more rapidly than the phenoxy compounds.

In our study evaluating forest workers exposed to herbicide
spray mixtures containing 4 parts 2,4-D to 1 part picloram, the elution patterns for the two compounds were markedly different (Figure
1). This figure shows that picloram is eluted much more rapidly
than 2,4-D. Comparing Figure 1 with Figure 2 it is evident that the
rate of excretion has little, if any, relationship to the amount of
herbicide excreted. Feldman and Maibach (7) have shown that 6% of
dermally applied 2,4-D can be absorbed through the skin. In laboratory studies Nolan et al. (6) showed that only 0.18% of dermally
applied picloram would be absorbed. The composition of the spray

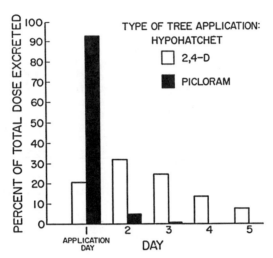

Figure 1. Rate of picloram and 2,4-D in urine of exposed workers.

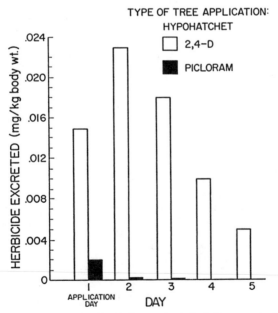

Figure 2. Amount of picloram and 2,4-D excreted (mg) (expressed as mg herbicide/kg body weight).

mix in our study was 4 parts 2,4-D to 1 part picloram. The amount
of picloram excreted in urine was much less than that of 2,4-D, and
was considerably less than the 4:1 ratio that was present in the
spray mix. Twenty years ago if one had been attempting to explain
these low picloram excretion levels it might have been suggested
that major portions were being retained in the body. However, our
findings of relatively low levels of picloram in human urine were
predictable from Nolan's (6) laboratory studies in which he found
that only 0.18% of dermally deposited picloram would be absorbed.

A popular misconception perhaps initially hampered biological
monitoring of body fluids as a quantifiable means of measuring the
absorbed dose of pesticides in humans. With the discovery that DDT
and other highly fat soluble chlorinated hydrocarbon insecticides
are stored in fatty tissues of mammals, it was perhaps inferred that
only a small fraction of any pesticide entering the body was
excreted. Thus, the chemistry of these insecticides may have inadvertently provided a major stumbling block to the use of biological
monitoring techniques for more recently developed pesticides. The
banning of some of these more persistent chlorinated insecticides
and the advent of new chemistry has in many instances resulted in
the development of compounds which are more polar and hence, less
fat soluble than the earlier pesticides. Today, feeding studies
involving small animals and ^{14}C-labeled pesticides are used to
determine if the pesticide or its metabolite(s) is excreted in
urine, feces, or both. Some information is available to the
researcher attempting to extrapolate between animal tests and actual
human excretion data. However, for most newer compounds most information regarding pesticide excretion from humans must be extrapolated from small animal studies.

Following are steps we feel should be taken when developing a
procedure for using urine analysis as a tool for biological monitoring:

Determine if the Parent Compound and/or Metabolites are Excreted in Urine

Studies with test animals using radiolabeled compounds can help
answer this question. If most of the activity is recovered in the
urine, then urine is potentially a good choice for analysis.
However, the absence of activity in urine does not necessarily mean
that urine would not be a good choice for analysis, as will be
discussed later. At the same time, the kinetics of excretion as a
function of dermal or oral dosing can be determined to establish the
length of time during which urine will have to be collected.

Identify the Excreted Compounds that Contain the Activity

Are the compounds excreted as parent compound, metabolites, or both?
Are they free or bound to some other moiety? Chromatography and
mass spectrometry or infrared spectroscopy can be used to answer
these questions. An example of this would be the work of Gardiner,
Brantley, and Sherman (8) and Gardiner, Kirkland, Klopping, and
Sherman (9) in identifying methyl 5-hydroxy-2-benzimidazolecarba-
mate (5-MBC) as a metabolite of methyl 1-(butylcarbamoyl)-2-

benzimidazole carbamate (benomyl) in rat urine. Rats given an oral
dose of ^{14}C-labeled benomyl excreted most of the activity in the
urine in 24 hr. A radioautogram of a fresh urine sample developed
on a silica tlc plate showed one major and two minor ^{14}C-containing
compounds. A radioautogram of a tlc plate developed in the same
manner of a urine sample that had been enzymatically hydrolyzed with
a β-glucuronidase aryl sulfatase solution showed one ^{14}C-containing
compound which had an R_f different from that of the other three compounds indicating that fresh urine contained glucuronide and/or
sulfate conjugates of one metabolite. The metabolite had an R_f
value the same as a known 5-MBC sample. After further clean-up with
tlc the identity of the compound was confirmed by obtaining both
infrared spectra (8) and mass spectra (9).

Decide for What Compounds the Analysis Will be Done

If several metabolites are present, it may be possible to group two
or more together and analyze for them simultaneously. For benomyl
again as an example, methyl 2-benzimidazolecarbamate (MBC), methyl
4-hydroxy-2-benzimidozolecarbamate (4-MBC), and 5-MBC can all be
analyzed for simultaneously (10).

Determine if the Amount of Metabolite Excreted Correlates with the Administered Dose

It may be that the level of metabolite is well correlated with the
amount administered orally but may not be well correlated with what
is applied dermally. The researcher would then need to know the
main route of entry into the body for the situation being studied to
decide if the metabolite in urine would provide a good measure of
dose.

Develop an Analytical Technique

A successful technique will include establishing limits of detection
which are low enough to determine if a harmful dose has been
received. Compounds which have a higher potential for harm would
require lower limits of detection. A lower limit of detection for
3,5,6-trichloro-2-pyridinol (3,5,6-TCP), the principal urinary metabolite of chlorpyrifos (11) which has an acute oral LD_{50} in rats of
97 to 276 mg/kg (12), would be needed than for bifenox acid, the
urinary metabolite of 5-(2,4-dichlorophenoxy)-2-nitrobenzoic acid
(Norris, F. A., Rhone-Poulenc Inc., P. O. Box 125, Black Horse Lane,
Monmouth Junction, NJ 08852, Personal Communication, 1984) which
has an acute oral LD_{50} in rats of over 6400 mg/kg (12). Recovery
and variation in recovery need to be established as a function of
concentration with one concentration being near the limit of detection. A means of confirming the identity of the analyte in a sample
should be established. This could be done by comparing the retention time on two columns having different selectivities on GC or
HPLC or by fingerprinting the suspect sample by obtaining a mass
spectra, IR spectra, or UV spectra and comparing it to a spectra of
a standard. Two different analytical instruments could be used such

as GC and HPLC or two different means of detection such as GC with electron capture detection and nitrogen-phosphorus detection.

An example of a typical analytical procedure follows: The first step would be hydrolysis of conjugates. This is typically, although not necessarily, accomplished with acid. The conjugates of benomyl metabolites have been hydrolyzed by mixing 25 g of urine with 25 ml of 15N H_3PO_4 and 1 g of sodium bisulfite and heating on a steam bath for 1 hr (10). The conjugates of 4-chlorophenol, the metabolite of bayleton, have been hydrolyzed by refluxing overnight with concentrated HCl (Thornton, J. S., Mobay Chemical Corp., P. O. Box 4913, Hawthorn Road, Kansas City, MO 64120, Personal Communication, 1985). Conjugates of 3,5,6-TCP the metabolite of chlorpyrifos were hydrolyzed with 2 ml of H_2SO_4 in 10 ml of urine at 90°C for 1 hr (13). The preceding conditions are at or near reflux, but this may not always be desirable. In the case of bifenox, mild acid hydrolysis (equal volumes of urine and 0.4 M HCl, 37°, overnight) is the preferred method of hydrolysis (Savage, E. A., May and Baker Agrochemicals, Lyfield Road, Ongar, Essex CM5 OHW, England, Personal Communication, 1986). Once hydrolyzed, any analyte should remain stable under the hydrolysis conditions.

The second step would typically be a partitioning step. This may involve shaking with an appropriate organic solvent in a separatory funnel. If the analyte has acidic or basic functional groups, pH can be adjusted to keep the analyte in either the aqueous or organic phase. An alternative to partitioning with an organic solvent is to pass the aqueous sample through a solid phase extraction column. Columns are available from several chemical supply companies and vary from nonpolar (analogous to partitioning with a nonpolar solvent) to polar.

After partitioning, the samples may be further cleaned up with liquid-solid chromatography. This may involve the use of commercial columns mentioned above or columns prepared in the lab using silica or florisil. Silica or florisil fully activated may retain the compounds too strongly. To partially deactivate them they can be first activated to a reproducible starting point by heating for 1 hr at 105° for silica and at least 5 hr at 130° for florisil (14). A measured amount of water is then added, the containers securely sealed, and the contents allowed to equilibrate overnight. The elution of the analyte is characterized using a standard and various solvents or solvent mixtures. Two solvents often used for elution from silica or florisil are diethyl ether and chloroform. The diethyl ether should be anhydrous. Analytical grade ether contains approximately 0.5% water which can affect the chromatography and will not be consistent from one batch of ether to the next. Chloroform is stabilized with either a nonpolar hydrocarbon (an alkene) or approximately 0.5 to 1% ethanol. Chloroform stabilized with the nonpolar hydrocarbon should be used for the cleanup chromatography. Ethanol, being much more polar than chloroform, will cause the same problems as water does in ether. An example of this is the elution of 4-nitrophenol and phenol using nonstabilized chloroform and chloroform stabilized with 3/4% ethanol. The retention time of 4-nitrophenol relative to phenol was 1.6 with stabilized chloroform but 3.8 with nonstabilized chloroform (15).

In some cases derivatization may be necessary. Derivatization may be used to increase the volatility of a compound for GC analysis

or to improve peak shape. Esterification of acids would be an
example of this use. Derivatization may also be used to separate
the analyte from interferences. The methyl ester of 2,4-D elutes
with interfering compounds in urine, but the butyl ester elutes
later and can be quantified (2). Derivatization can also create or
enhance sensitivity for a specific type of detection.

In a large study it will not be possible to analyze all samples
immediately. Fortified samples need to be interspersed with the
unknown samples to monitor storage stability. Ideally, the samples
would be fortified with the same chemical compound that is in the
unknown samples. However, the conjugates are usually not available
and fortification will need to be done with the nonconjugated analyte.

Potential Problems in Relating Animal Urinary Excretion to Human Studies

One of the difficulties in using urine as a biological monitor
is that in order to relate what is found in urine to what has
entered the body, we usually need to rely on excretion data from
test animals. Below are concerns to be aware of when interpreting
urine analysis results.

The Excretion Route Can Depend on the Type of Test Animal. As shown
below, 90% of orally administered bayleton was excreted as urinary
metabolites from cows and pigs as compared to 30 to 40% for rats
(Thornton, J. S., Mobay Chemical Corp., P. O. Box 4913, Hawthorn
Road, Kansas City, MO 64120, Personal Communication, 1985). The
distribution of benomyl metabolites in urine and feces was almost
reversed for dogs as opposed to rats (9).

Compound	Animal	Distribution (%) Urine	Feces
Bayleton	cow & pig	90	
	rat	30-40	
Benomyl	dog	16	83
	rat	86	13

The Excretion Route May Depend on Sex. For a group of five male
rats orally dosed with labeled bifenox, 29.1% of the dose was in
urine and 63.4% in feces. For a group of five female rats, 52.6%
was in urine and 46.1% was in feces (Norris, F. A., Rhone-Poulenc,
Inc., P. O. Box 125, Black Horse Lane, Monmouth Junction, NJ 08852,
Personal Communication, 1984). This may or may not be significant
since gene pools from a highly inbred species of rat may be so
narrow that a sex difference would show whereas human gene pools are
so varied that no difference in metabolism and excretion would exist
as a function of sex.

Results Using a Tracer May Depend on the Location of the Label.
Studies have been done using Captan labeled in the carbonyl carbon
and the trichloromethyl carbon (16-18). The distribution of

$$\text{structure: bicyclic ring with } N-S-^*CCl_3,\ C=O \text{ groups, } ^* \text{ labels}$$

activity as a function of the location of the label is shown below for oral doses given to rats.

Label	Distribution (%)		
	Urine	Expired air	Feces
$^*CCl_3$	52	23	16
$^*C{=}O$	85	0	12

The following hypothetical examples are extreme, but possible, illustrations of how results from a study using a radiolabel could be misleading. Given: Compound AB is metabolized with metabolite A being excreted in urine and metabolite B being excreted in feces.

$$AB \longrightarrow A(urine) + B(feces)$$

If the label were in A, the researcher would recover 100% of the activity in the urine and would discover that A is a good metabolite to analyze for to measure AB. If the label were in B, no activity would be recovered in the urine, and the researcher may conclude that there is no metabolite in urine.

A second example would be if AB were metabolized to A and B, both of which are in urine. However, B is further metabolized to C, D, E, F, G, and H.

$$AB \longrightarrow A + B \longrightarrow \begin{cases} C \\ D \\ E \\ F \\ G \\ H \end{cases} \quad \text{all in urine}$$

If the label were in A, the researcher would recover all of the activity in one urinary metabolite and conclude that metabolite is a good measure for AB. If the label had been in B it would be fractionated into the components C, D, E, F, G, and H. The researcher may conclude that there is no metabolite that represents more than 10 to 20% of the dose when, in fact, metabolite A, undetected by tracer techniques, represents 100% of the dose. Thus, although the use of radiolabels is highly beneficial for identifying some pesticide metabolites under certain conditions, their use may at times be misleading.

The Results May Depend on the Avenue of Entry Into the Body. DeBaun investigated the distribution of metabolites of Captan (16). Three of the metabolites are listed below along with their distribution in rat urine as a function of oral or interperitoneal entry into the body. The results from the oral study indicate that A would be a good analyte to use as a measure of Captan.

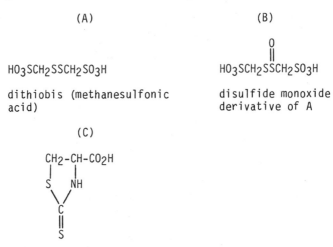

(A)

HO₃SCH₂SSCH₂SO₃H

dithiobis (methanesulfonic acid)

(B)

$$HO_3SCH_2SSCH_2SO_3H$$

disulfide monoxide derivative of A

(C)

CH₂-CH-CO₂H

thiazolidine-2-thione-4-carboxylic acid

| | % Recovered | |
Compound	Oral	Interperitoneal
(A)	54	0
(B)	14	0
(C)	19	major

However, if exposure were not oral, (A) might not be a good measure. Some studies have shown that, for applicators at least, dermal exposure is the main source of dose (19-21). For consumers eating produce, results from feeding studies would be appropriate.

In most cases, there are no data on excretion of compounds from humans as a function of dermal or oral entry, and thus we must extrapolate from animal studies as best we can.

After the analysis has been performed, the dose needs to be determined. Below are sample calculations showing how this would be done with bayleton and its metabolite 4-chlorophenol as an example.

Data

        Total urine excreted for 4 days - 4738 ml
        Humans body wt. - 75 kg
        4-chlorophenol concentration in urine - 0.27 ug/ml
        Recovery of 4-chlorophenol from urine - 80%

Amount of oral dose of bayleton excreted as 4-chlorophenol in
   urine - 35% (rat)
        - 90% (pig)
Molecular weight - 4-chlorophenol 128.5 g/mole
               - bayleton 294.5 g/mole

Calculations

   mg of 4-chlorophenol excreted

$$(4738 \text{ ml}) \ (0.27 \text{ ug/ml}) \ (10^{-3} \text{ mg/ug})/0.80 = 1.60 \text{ mg}$$

1.60 mg of 4-chlorophenol represents $1.60 \text{ mg} \dfrac{(294.5)}{(128.5)} = 3.67 \text{ mg}$ bayleton

   absorbed amount = 3.67 mg/0.35 = 10.49 mg (rat)

                  = 3.92 mg/0.9 = 4.36 mg (pig)

          dose = 10.49 mg/75 kg = 0.140 mg/kg (rat)

               = 4.36 mg/75 kg = 0.058 mg/kg (pig)

Analysis of urine can provide meaningful information regarding
the dose received by individuals for certain compounds. The goal is
to identify a detectable metabolite that can be related back to dose
of the parent compound. If no previous work has been done with the
compound in question, initial work will probably require use of a
radiolabeled compound. Care needs to be used in evaluating the
results of tracer studies since the observed results may depend on
the location of the label, on the species of test animal, or on the
method of dosing (oral vs. dermal).

Minimizing Absorbed Dose
Some specific guidelines for limiting the absorbed dose of humans
who handle or come into contact with pesticides being applied
follow:
   1. Read and obey the label.
   2. Be aware that a user can decrease his exposure.
   3. Change clothing (shirt, trousers, boots, and gloves) after
       application and launder contaminated clothing.
   4. Avoid eating, or use of tobacco when hands are contaminated.
   5. Wash hands immediately after exposure.
   6. Shower as soon as possible after potential exposure.

Future Needs

Some of the major obstacles remaining before we have a full
understanding of pesticides and their fate in humans are: a) What
factors regulate the amount and rate of pesticide that penetrates
the skin? b) What are the excretion routes and rates for pesticides
or their metabolites? c) What are the "safe" levels that a human
can absorb without the occurrence of a health effect - now or at
some time in the future?

Before researchers can be expected to make new, significant, and intelligent scientific decisions regarding the pharmacokinetics of pesticides in humans, more studies involving human subjects are necessary. Our current knowledge of the toxicological properties of pesticides, coupled with small animal feeding or dosing studies covering a wide concentration range, should allow us to choose a safe human range thousands of fold below any anticipated No Observed Effect Level (NOEL). Informed human volunteers could then be dosed with a pesticide concentration far lower than the levels commonly received by field workers mixing or applying the commercial product. Information gained from these controlled absorbed dose studies could be used in efforts to improve protective clothing, gloves, masks, hand washing, and other procedures, for field workers who are exposed to much higher levels. Legal concerns will probably prevent initiation of this proposed plan, but it is the logical plan to adopt. If it is wrong to give a volunteer a dose 100-1000 times less than the amount we know people are already receiving in their jobs, then it is wrong to allow the working conditions to exist which causes the worker to be receiving the higher dose. It is hypocritical to say that it is dangerous and wrong to give the volunteer the low dose, but it is not dangerous or wrong to allow the worker to receive a dose 100-1000 times higher.

The development of proper experiments using laboratory animals for establishing an appropriate NOEL is essential. Both short- and long-term animal trial studies are necessary before we will be in a position to make valid scientific decisions with respect to the safe use of pesticides. Since analytical methodologies now allow us to analyze down to the ppb and ppt level, we must base our toxicological decisions regarding risk assessments on appropriate NOEL concentrations rather than the mere presence or absence of the pesticide in question. It appears that not all facets of science develop at the same rate. Until society is prepared to accept using humans as test subjects, we will be forced to accept the less accurate answers found from animal studies.

Literature Cited

1. Lavy, T. L. Project Completion Report to National Forest Products Association, August 30 to October, 1978.
2. Lavy, T. L. Project Completion Report to National Forest Products Association, 1980.
3. Sauerhoff, M. W.; Braun, W.; Glau, G.; Gehring, P. Toxicology 1977, 8:3-11.
4. Durham, W. F.; Wolfe, H. Bulletin of the World Health
5. Lavy, T. L.; Norris, L.; Mattice, J. Project Completion Report to National Forest Products Association, 1984.
6. Nolan, R. J.; Freshour, N.; Kastl; P.; Saunders, J. Toxicol. Appl. Pharmacol. 1984, 76:264-69.
7. Feldman, R. J.; Maibach, H. J. Toxicol. Appl. Pharmacol. 1974, 28:126-32.
8. Gardiner, J. A.; Brantley, R.; Sherman, H. J. Agric. Food Chem. 1968, 16(6):1050-52.
9. Gardiner, J. A.; Kirkland, K.; Klopping, H.; Sherman, H. J. Agric. Food Chem. 1974, 22(3):419-27.

10. Kirkland, J. J. J. Agric. Food Chem. 1973, 21(2):171-77.
11. Smith, G. N.; Watson, B.; Fischer, F. J. Agric. Food Chem. 1967, 15:132-38.
12. Farm Chemicals Handbook, Meister Publishing Co., Willoughby, OH, 1981.
13. Nolan, R. J.; Rick, D.; Fresham, N.; Saunders, J. Toxicol. Appl. Pharmacol. 1984, 73:8-15.
14. Official Methods of Analysis of the Association of Official Analytical Chemists; William Horowitz, Ed.; 1980, 26.027, 29.002, 34.011, 13th ed.
15. Waters Associates Liquid Chromatography School.
16. Captan Position Document 2/3, Office of Pesticide Programs, Office of Pesticides and Toxic Substances, U.S. Environmental Protection Agency, Washington, D.C., June 1985.
17. Hoffman, L. J.; DeBaun, J.; Kuan, J.; Mann, J. Western Research Center, Stauffer Chemical Co., 1973.
18. DeBaun, J. R.; Miaullis, J.; Knarr, J.; Mihailovski, A.; Mann, J. Xenobiotica 19 , 4:101-19.
19. Libich, S.; To, J.; Frank, R.; Sirons, G. Am. Ind. Hyg. Assoc. J. 1984, 45:56-62.
20. Lavy, T. L.; Shepard, J.; Mattice, J. J. Agric. Food Chem. 1980, 28:626-30.
21. Lavy, T. L.; Walstad, J.; Flynn, R.; Mattice, J. J. Agric. Food Chem. 1982, 30:375-81.
22. Picloram: The effects of its use as a herbicide on environmental quality. National Research Council of Canada, Ottawa,
23. Gehring, P. J.; Kramer, C.; Schwetz, B.; Rose, J.; Rowe, V. Toxicol. Appl. Pharmacol. 1973, 26:352-61.

RECEIVED December 16, 1987

Chapter 16

New Approaches to Analysis of Organophosphate Metabolites in the Urine of Field Workers

C. P. Weisskopf and J. N. Seiber

Department of Environmental Toxicology, University of California, Davis, CA 95616

A procedure is described for the analysis of urinary dialkyl phosphate and thiophosphate metabolites using disposable extraction cartridges, large bore capillary gas chromatography (GC) columns, and the methylating reagent trimethylanilinium hydroxide. Although field worker monitoring for organophosphate pesticide exposure by measurement of urinary metabolites can have several advantages, alternate methods are frequently favored, in part due to difficulties in the analysis of these compounds. The described method overcomes many of the obstacles of conventional approaches to urinary metabolite analysis. Metabolite extraction is rapid, requiring at most 15 minutes per sample. Derivatization takes place in the GC injector block, and capillary columns lead to improved separations for all compounds. Five urinary metabolites are detectable at concentrations of 2 to 10 ng/ml (ppb) urine.

There has been a long-standing interest in the estimation of human exposure to organophosphates, particularly since these compounds are widely used and are the most frequent cause of pesticide related occupational illnesses. Upon entering the body, most organophosphorus pesticides may be metabolized to yield one or more of the six common dialkyl phosphates shown in Table I. Quantities of metabolites excreted in the urine have been found to correspond to the pesticide dose (1-3). Measurement of these urinary metabolites can thus provide a basis for comparison of exposure in a study population.

Measurement of intact pesticides or metabolites in biological samples may give a better estimation of the amount of material actually entering the body than external measurement methods. Analysis for principle organophosphate pesticide alkyl or aryl leaving groups can yield information on the identity of the pesticide to which the subject was exposed, since few pesticides share the same leaving group. However, this requires the development of an analytical method specific for each compound, and is thus not amenable to a multi-residue approach. The dialkyl phosphates in Table I represent possible metabolites of approximately 75% of the organophosphate pesticides in the EPA's Pesticides and Industrial Chemicals Repository.

0097–6156/89/0382–0206$06.00/0
© 1989 American Chemical Society

Table I. Common dialkyl phosphates

DMP	O,O-Dimethyl phosphate
DEP	O,O-Diethyl phosphate
DMTP	O,O-Dimethyl phosphorothionate
DETP	O,O-Diethyl phosphorothionate
DMDTP	O,O-Dimethyl phosphorodithioate
DEDTP	O,O-Diethyl phosphorodithioate

The primary disadvantage to the measurement of urinary dialkyl phosphates lies in the difficulty of the analysis. These compounds are highly water soluble, ionized in urine, and must be derivatized to be sufficiently volatile for gas chromatographic (GC) analysis. Although there are many published procedures for extraction and analysis of urinary dialkyl phosphates (3-8), the methods remain tedious and cumbersome. The majority rely on liquid/liquid extraction of the metabolites, derivatization with diazoalkane reagents, and analysis by packed column GC. Metabolite extraction is often incomplete or inconsistent (4), and it has been difficult to get adequate chromatographic resolution of all metabolites both from each other and from other constituents of urine (5-7).

Diazoalkanes have frequently been used for alkylation of dialkyl phosphates and thiophosphates prior to GC analysis. Diazoalkane reagents such as diazoethane and diazopentane give an isomer mixture of thionate and thiolate esters, formed in irregular proportions, when the metabolites DMTP or DETP are derivatized (8). Analysis of both isomers may be required, resulting in increased analysis time and poorer detection limits. When coupled with the hazards of the preparation and use of diazoalkanes, this makes the use of an alternative derivatizing reagent desirable (4).

Trimethylanilinium hydroxide (TMAH) is a methylating reagent frequently used in clinical tests for barbiturates. At elevated temperatures, provided in this case by the GC injector block, TMAH is able to methylate dialkyl phosphates. Dale et al. (9) first reported the use of TMAH for the hydrolysis of intact organophosphates and methylation of hydrolysis products. Miles and Dale (10) followed with a study that included the use of TMAH for the injector block methylation of DMDTP. Use of TMAH for the methylation of DMTP in the extracts of urine of exposed workers was reported by Moody et al. (11).

The present study was designed to overcome some of the complexities of previous methods by developing a simpler and faster analytical procedure through the use of disposable extraction cartridges, injector block derivatization, and quantification using large bore capillary GC columns.

Experimental Section

Solvents and Reagents. Trimethylanilinium hydroxide (TMAH) was obtained from Pierce Chemical Co, Rockford, IL, under the trade name MethElute, a 0.2 M solution of TMAH in methanol. Handeling precautions for this mixture are the same as those for methanol. Solvents were pesticide residue grade from J. T. Baker, Phillipsburg, NJ. Salts and acids were analytical reagent grade from Mallinckrodt, Inc., Paris, KY.

Extraction Apparatus. Disposable cyclohexyl extraction cartridges with a 6 ml reservoir containing 1 g sorbent were used (Analytichem International, Harbor City, CA). A ten-place vacuum manifold was used for cartridge elution (J. T. Baker Co, Phillipsburg, NJ). Sufficient vacuum (approximately 100 mm Hg) was applied to provide for a flow rate of 5 ml/min of eluting solution through the cartridges.

Preparation of Standard Solutions.   Analytical grade standards of the six metabolites in Table I were obtained from the EPA's Pesticides and Industrial Chemicals Repository.   Stock 1 mg/ml solutions of the individual dialkyl phosphates in methanol were prepared and stored at 4°C in the dark. Analytical mixed standards of all six metabolites in acetone (0.015 to 1.5 ng/μl) were prepared daily in volumetric flasks, and brought to final volume after the addition of TMAH immediately prior to GC injection. TMAH was added to the standard solutions in the proportion of 50 μl TMAH/ml solution.

Chromatographic Conditions. Apparatus: The instrument used was a Tracor model MT 220 equipped with a flame photometric detector (FPD) operated in the phosphorus mode.   The column was a 30 m x 0.5 mm ID large bore DB-1701 capillary column, with an 86% dimethyl- and 14% cyanopropylphenyl- polysiloxane bonded stationary phase and a 1.0 μm film thickness (J & W Scientific, Folsom, CA). Gas flows were: helium carrier gas 7 ml/min; helium detector make-up gas 40 ml/min; air 90 ml/min; and hydrogen 60 ml/min. Operating temperatures were: injector, 300°C; column, 110°C; and FPD and FPD transfer line, 170°C. Quantification of the methylated metabolites was performed by external standard calculations based on peak areas using a Hewlett Packard 3390 A electronic integrator. 1-3 μl aliquots of the mixed standard solutions or urine extracts were injected.   Standard curves were prepared from duplicate injections of mixed standards at a minimum of three concentrations.

Determination of Dialkyl Phosphates in Urine. The preparation of samples for analysis is outlined in Figure 1. An aliquot (4 ml) of urine was pipetted into a 15 ml test tube. Granular ammonium sulfate (ca 1.8 g) and 4 drops 70% acetic acid were added, and the mixture vortexed for 30 sec. The cyclohexyl extraction cartridges were prewashed with one column volume (ca 6 ml) each of acetone, water, and ammonium sulfate-saturated water. The urine sample was then passed through the cartridge. The cartridges were washed with 2 ml of a solution of 20% acetone in hexane, and the wash discarded. The vacuum was increased to about 600 mm Hg, and the cartridges were aspirated for 5 minutes.   The cartridges were then placed into 15 ml graduated centrifuge tubes and eluted with acetone to a volume of 1.4 ml by gravity flow or the application of positive pressure to the extraction cartridge using a pipette bulb. Immediately prior to GC injection ca 0.4 g powdered anhydrous sodium sulfate and 100 μl TMAH was added to the acetone eluate followed by brief vortexing.

Results and Discussion

The procedure reported here was capable of analyzing DEP, DMTP, DETP, DMDTP, and DEDTP. It is unsuitable for DMP due to interferences caused by the presence of inorganic phosphate.   The effect of various salts on the recovery of dialkyl phosphate metabolites was tested in developing this procedure. Salts were added to urine at amounts slightly in excess of that needed to produce a saturated solution, allowing for reproducible results without expending much time in weighing. Salt addition usually improved recovery of metabolites from fortified urine samples, with sulfate salts giving better results than either acetate or chloride salts (Table II). A saturated solution of ammonium sulfate was found to be the best of those tested.

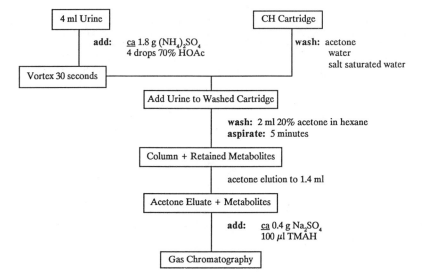

Figure 1. Flow diagram for the analysis of dialkyl phosphates in urine.

Table II. Effect of salt addition on metabolite recovery,
normalized for ammonium sulfate

salt	grams added	normalized recovery				
		DEP	DMTP	DMDTP	DETP	DEDTP
none	–	0.1	0.1	0.1	0.2	0.5
sodium sulfate	1.1	0.9	1.0	0.8	1.0	0.9
sodium chloride	1.4	0.4	0.7	0.7	0.8	1.0
ammonium sulfate	1.7	1.0	1.0	1.0	1.0	1.0
ammonium acetate	4.0	0.0	0.0	0.2	0.4	0.5

The pH of the urine was also found to have a large effect on recoveries (Table III). Recoveries dropped when the urine was made more basic than the pH of 5 of the unmodified urine. Recoveries improved when acetic acid was used to adjust the pH to approximately 4, and declined when hydrochloric acid was used to reduce the pH further. Acetic acid was used routinely as the pH modifier.

Table III. Effect of pH modification on metabolite recovery,
normalized for acetic acid

modifier	pH	normalized recovery				
		DEP	DMTP	DMDTP	DETP	DEDTP
sodium hydroxide	7	0.5	0.5	0.6	0.6	0.6
none	5	0.9	0.8	0.9	0.9	0.9
acetic acid	4	1.0	1.0	1.0	1.0	1.0
hydrochloric acid	3.5	0.4	0.8	0.7	0.8	0.8
hydrochloric acid	2.5	0.2	0.6	0.5	0.4	0.4

A hexane/acetone wash followed by aspiration was found to eliminate most of the water held by the cartridges, as well as removing some interfering compounds that reduced the efficiency of metabolite derivatization. Subsequent elution with 1.4 ml acetone removed more than 95% of the metabolites retained on the cartridges. Samples could then be analyzed directly, eliminating the possibility of evaporative loss of the compounds or expenditure of time in reducing solvent volumes, both drawbacks of prior methods which used solvent extraction rather than extraction with solid phase cartridges.

The efficiency of TMAH as a methylation reagent was tested using a variety of solvents, sample extracts, and injector temperatures. Derivatization yields were estimated by comparing molar phosphorus response of the methylated metabolites on the flame photometric detector with the response of a trimethyl phosphate standard. Derivatization yields were highest when the solvent was acetone and the injector block of the GC was above 250°C. The methylation yield of DMP could not be determined due to interference from inorganic phosphate. Both compounds are methylated to produce trimethyl phosphate (Figure 2), making TMAH unsuitable for analysis of DMP without prior removal of inorganic phosphate. Approximately 60% of the DEP and 95% of the four other metabolites in acetone are methylated. When the solvent was an acetone extract

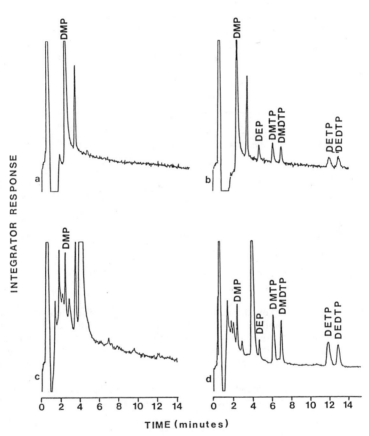

Figure 2. Gas chromatogram of dialkyl phosphates using FPD detection. a) reagent blank; b) dialkyl phosphate standards, 0.015 ng each except DEP, 0.03 ng; c) human urine with no detectable metabolites; d) human urine fortified at 10 ppb each metabolite.

of urine, DEP derivatization was reduced to 40%; the other compounds were unaffected. The FPD response for injections ranging from 0.015 to 3 ng was linear with r^2 > 0.999 for all five dialkyl phosphates tested. The minimum detectable level per injection of DEP was 30 pg, and 15 pg for DMTP, DMDTP, DETP, and DEDTP.

The recovery data in Table IV was obtained by analysis of urine samples fortified at several levels. The same blank urine sample was used for all fortifications. The low recovery of DEP was the result of both incomplete retention of the metabolite on the extraction cartridges and reduced methylation efficiency in the urine matrix. Minimum levels of detection of the metabolites in urine was 10 ppb for DEP, and 2 ppb for the remaining four metabolites.

Table IV. Recovery of dialkyl phosphates from
fortified urine samples

ppb	% recovery ± % standard deviation (n=3)				
	DEP	DMTP	DMDTP	DETP	DEDTP
2	n.d.[a]	78 ± 23	83 ± 8	98 ± 9	48 ± 7
10	8 ± 1	90 ± 5	83 ± 4	131 ± 14	79 ± 4
40	34 ± 7	106 ± 5	113 ± 6	109 ± 4	92 ± 4
100	31 ± 1	93 ± 5	104 ± 7	96 ± 9	87 ± 6
200	27 ± 4	84 ± 6	96 ± 7	103 ± 3	87 ± 5

a. n.d. = none detected

Three urine samples of different concentrations were fortified at levels of 20 ppb to test the variability of metabolite recovery from one urine sample to another in our method (Table V). Creatinine content was used as the measure of urine concentration, with 0.4 mg creatinine per ml urine indicating a sample that is quite dilute, and 3.4 mg/ml one that is quite concentrated. These values encompass the range of urine concentrations that might be encountered in a typical study. Average metabolite recovery was similar to that shown in Table IV, with little difference in standard deviation, indicating no effect of urine concentration.

Table V. Variation of recovery with urine concentration

creatinine (mg/ml urine)	% recovery (fortified at 20 ppb)				
	DEP	DMTP	DMDTP	DETP	DEDTP
0.4	23	102	95	113	91
1.1	43	113	86	97	85
3.4	25	104	75	106	86
avg (%)	30	106	85	105	87
std. dev. (%)	11	6	10	8	3

The performance of this method on authentic urine samples was examined by analyzing a group of 143 urine samples that were made available from a larger study on farm worker exposure. Concentrations of DMTP, DMDTP, DETP, and DEDTP were determined. Average metabolite concentrations for all compounds were less than 35 ppb (Table VI). Only 16% of the samples tested had no detectable metabolites. This large set of samples did not have a detrimental effect on column or instrument performance. Retention times over the course of the study varied by no more than 3%, and peak areas for standard injections by less than 15%. There was no sign of a general decrease in column, instrument, or detector performance, a problem in some previous procedures (11).

Table VI. Results of the analysis of 143 human urine samples

	DMTP	DMDTP	DETP	DEDTP
avg (ppb)	6	4	7	3
range (ppb)	2 - 27	2 - 14	2 - 31	2 - 4
% positive	55%	56%	41%	6%

Recoveries and limits of detection using the procedure presented here compares favorably with existing methods for DMTP, DETP, DMDTP, and DEDTP. One commonly used method, that of Shafik et al. (6), can detect the 6 common metabolites at levels above 5 ppb. Recoveries from urine fortified at 100 ppb were greater than 95% for all 6 metabolites with this technique. However, several researchers (1,4,5,11) reported poor recoveries and excessive variation in results, indicating that the method may be dependent on the familiarity of the operator with the procedure. Another potential drawback is that only 25-30 samples can be analyzed per week, although this was a significant improvement over existing procedures at the time when this method was developed.

The method of Lores and Bradway (8) detects DMP, DEP, DMTP, and DETP at concentrations in urine greater than 10 ppb, and 8-10 samples can be analyzed per day. Recoveries ranged from 40 to 100% when urine was fortified at 500 ppb. Variation in recovery of metabolites from one urine sample to the next averaged 15%.

All 6 common dialkyl phosphates may be detected by the method of Reed and Watts (5). The average minimum level of detection in urine is 60 ppb, with metabolite recoveries greater than 90% at fortification levels of 800 ppb.

The use of the method described here can result in more rapid analysis of samples compared to existing methods. The time necessary to prepare a single sample for GC analysis is about 15 minutes. Ten samples, the number of cartridges that can be held by our vacuum manifold, can be prepared in forty minutes. Using duplicate standard and sample injections and a three point standard curve, 12 samples can be chromatographed per day. This method is ideally suited to the use of a GC autoinjector, since the chromatographic step is the most time consuming. A single analyst using an autoinjector could easily complete 30-40 samples per day.

Existing methods for the analysis of dialkyl phosphates have generally proven inadequate due to long sample preparation and analysis time, poor or variable metabolite recoveries, or lack of sensitivity. Our method is free of these defects in the analysis of DMTP, DETP, DMDTP, and DEDTP. Although DEP recoveries were relatively low, they were consistent enough to yield valid results at urine concentrations over 10 ppb. This method is unsuitable for the analysis of DMP.

We are seeking to extend this method to the analysis of DMP, and to improve DEP analysis by increasing both the retention of DEP on the extraction cartridges and the derivatization yield. An injector block propylating reagent that produces a unique derivative for inorganic phosphate and each metabolite is being tested and appears promising. Dimethyl propyl phosphate produced upon derivatization of DMP is easily distinguished from the tripropyl derivative of inorganic phosphate. Continuing work on salt addition, pH effects, and solvents for cartridge washing and sample elution should result in better retention of metabolites on the extraction cartridges and cleaner samples. Both effects can improve the efficiency of the method.

In summary, we have developed a method for the analysis of urinary dialkyl phosphates that is both rapid and simple. It works well for the four common sulfur containing dialkyl phosphates, and adequately for DEP. DMP cannot be analyzed by this method in its present form. Preliminary work indicates that remaining problems can be overcome without a significant increase in extraction or analysis time.

References

1. Morgan, D. P.; Hetzler, H. L.; Slach, E. F.; Lin, L. I.   Arch. Environ. Contam. Toxicol. 1977, 6, 159-173.
2. Franklin, C. A.; Fenske, R. A.; Greenhalgh, R.; Mathieu, L.; Denley, H. V.; Leffingwell, J. T.; Spear, R. C. J. Toxicol. Environ. Health 1981, 7, 715-731.
3. Bradway, D. E.; Shafik, T. M.; Lores, E. M. J. Agric. Food Chem. 1977, 25, 1353-1358.
4. Bradway, D. E.; Moseman, R.; May, R. Bull. Environ. Contam. Toxicol. 1981, 26, 520-523.
5. Reid, S. J.; Watts, R. R. J. Anal. Toxicol. 1981, 5, 126-132.
6. Shafik, T.; Bradway, D. E.; Enos, H. F.; Yobs, A. R. J. Agric. Food Chem. 1973, 21, 625-629.
7. Blair, D.; Roderick, H. R. J. Agric. Food Chem. 1976, 24, 1221-1223.
8. Lores, E. M.; Bradway, D. E. J. Agric. Food Chem. 1977, 25, 75-79.
9. Dale, W. E.; Miles, J. W.; Churchill, F. C. J. AOAC 1976, 59, 1088-1093.
10. Miles, J. W.; Dale, W. E. J Agric. Food Chem. 1978, 26, 480-482.
11. Moody, R. P.; Franklin, C. A.; Riedel, D.; Muir, N. I.; Greenhalgh, R.; Hladka, A. J Agric. Food Chem. 1985, 33, 464-467.

RECEIVED April 19, 1988

Chapter 17

Pilot Study for Biological Monitoring of 1,3-Dichloropropene

John D. Osterloh[1,2], Rhoda Wang[3], Linda O'Connell[3], Peyton Jacob III[2], and Keith T. Maddy[3]

[1]Departments of Laboratory Medicine and Medicine, University of California, San Francisco, CA 94143
[2]Division of Clinical Pharmacology, University of California, San Francisco, CA 94143
[3]Worker Health and Safety Branch, State of California Department of Food and Agriculture, Sacramento, CA 94244

A pilot study was performed to estimate excretion patterns of the metabolite of dichloropropene (DCP), N-acetyl-S-cis-3-chloroprop-2-enyl)-cysteine (3CNAC). Urine from 3 applicators was collected every 2-16 hours for 3 days, while personnel air concentrations of DCP were determined by EC-GC. 3CNAC in urine was extracted, derivatized and measured on capillary gas chromatograph-mass spectrometry by monitoring the two abundant ions 117 and 176 m/e. Sensitivity was 0.1 ug/mL of urine. Air concentrations of DCP ranged from 0-10.3 ppm. Urine concentrations of 3CNAC ranged 0.9-17.1 ug/mL. Excretion of peak concentrations of metabolite followed peak exposure by variable periods of time (0-16 hours). Cumulative daily excretion of 3CNAC increased in proportion to cumulative daily air exposure.

1,3-Dichloropropene (DCP) is an agricultural fumigant applied by pressure injection into soil for pre-implantation eradication of nematodes. Commercial preparations contain 98% of approximately equal parts of cis and trans DCP. Because of its vapor pressure (28 mmHg), the primary route of exposure to human workers is suspected to be pulmonary. Low ppm air concentrations have been documented during loading, mixing and applications processes (1,2). Both isomers are metabolized to their respective mercapturic acids in rats (3-5). We have demonstrated previously that monitoring of human applicators is possible by measuring the metabolite N-acetyl-S-(cis-3-chloroprop-2-enyl)-cysteine (3CNAC) (2). Protection and biological monitoring of workers is of concern since DCP has produced forestomach squamous and urinary bladder transitional cell cancers following chronic oral gavage studies in rats and mice (6). Subchronic inhalational studies in rats and mice at

0097–6156/89/0382–0215$06.00/0
© 1989 American Chemical Society

90 or 150 ppm have demonstrated hyperplasia respiratory
epithelium, degeneration of nasal mucosa and hyperplasia of
transitional cell epithelium in the urinary bladder (W.T.
Stott, Dow Chemical Co., personal communication). Chronic
inhalation studies are not published, but increased respiratory
neoplasia are suggested (W.T. Stott, personal communication).
DCP is an indirect mutagen (7-11) which binds (8,9) and
depletes sulfhydryl groups in the liver and kidney (12).
Earlier studies indicated that the rat kidney may show toxic
effects in the renal tubular epithelium following inhaled
concentrations as low as 3 ppm after chronic inhalation (13).
This effect has not been confirmed in two subsequent subchronic
animal studies following inhalation of concentrations as high
as 150 ppm (14,15). However, a kinetic study by one of these
groups has shown that a 3 hour exposure to 90 ppm reduces
kidney sulfhydryl content 31% (12). While differences in
studies may be attributed to differences in exposure duration
or species differences, histologic and standard clinical
chemistry assays used in chronic studies may not have the
sensitivity to demonstrate such subtle renal effects.

Safe air concentrations of DCP which protect workers are not
known. Estimates of possible carcinogenic risk based on
possible air concentrations and animal studies do not yield
real or specific thresholds. Twenty-four hour cumulative
urinary excretion of 3CNAC increases in rough proportion to
increasing air concentrations · time products (2). Single
random determinations of urinary 3CNAC only indicate that some
systemic exposure has occurred, but are not indicative of known
exposure thresholds or toxic effects. It is also not known how
quickly excretion of 3CNAC follows pulmonary exposure.

Knowledge of timing and toxic effects would aid in determining
appropriate urine collection procedures. As a pilot to a
larger study, we evaluated three workers by measuring personal
air concentrations of DCP urinary excretion of 3CNAC and of N-
acetyl-glucoseamidase (NAG). The latter is an enzyme released
from injured tubular epithelium in the kidney. It has been
studied as a more sensitive indicator of renal injury following
a wide variety of nephrotoxins (16-18). Analytical concerns in
measuring 3CNAC will also be discussed.

Materials and Methods

Protocol. Three male applicators of DCP were studied for 2-3
days. Field collections were done under the auspices of the
Worker Health and Safety Branch of California Department of
Food and Agriculture. Application rates of DCP were 12 gallons
per acre. The soil was sandy and dry with air temperatures
exceeding 100°F for most of the day. The work periods of
potential exposure to DCP varied from 3.5 - 10 hours/day.
Workers wore light cotton clothes during application of DCP.
During loading, chemical resistant gloves, apron, boots, and
NIOSH-approved respirators were worn. Dermal exposure from

small spills during these closed loading operations may have occurred, but none were recorded. The extent of the contribution of dermal exposure to urinary 3CNAC excretion is unknown.

Applicators were chosen only on a first available basis in the locale where DCP was being applied. No attempt was made to exclude a subject with prior exposure to DCP in this pilot study. At the field site, prior to beginning work, the applicator was attached with a personal air sampling device and instructed as to collection of urinary specimens. Operator breathing zone air samples were drawn by personal air sampling pumps (MSA Fixt Flo) through charcoal adsorbent tubes (SKC #226-09, 400/200 mg) via tygon tubing. Tube openings were position down across the chest and did not interfere with work habits. Pumps were calibrated to 1 L/min using a Kurz 540S mass flow calibrator. Sorbent tubes were changed at up to four hours or when there was an obvious change in work practice (loading vs. repair) intervals. These tubes were capped and stored on dry ice, then refrigerated ($-20°$) until analysis. Procedures, flow rates and breakthrough volumes are given elsewhere (19,20).

Urines were collected by instructing the applicators to urinate into a separate 500 mL opaque polyethylene container for each voiding. Each container was frozen on dry ice and then $-70°C$ until analysis. Urine collection occurred only when the applicator would empty his bladder. Thus, collection intervals were variable and spanned 2-16 hours. Urine collection periods did not coincide with intervals for air collections.

Analysis of air concentrations of DCP. Amounts of DCP in sorbent tubes were determined in accord with established procedures (1,19,20) that includes elution of tubes with carbon disulfide mixed with an internal standard and direct injection onto electron capture gas chromatograph. Sensitivity and precision of these determinations is 0.1 ug collection (column).

Urinary NAG Determinations. Urinary activities of NAG were determined by the manual method of Piagen et al (1978) with modifications incorporated by Al-Bander et al (1986). This is a fluorometric method which measures the hydrolysis of 4-methylumelliferyl-Beta-D-glucosaminide. Calculated activity in nanomoles/hr/mL of urine is expressed in terms of milligrams of creatinine excreted (nanomoles/hr/mg), since this corrects for variability due to urine flow rates (23). Creatinine concentrations were determined by the Jaffe reaction (24). Intraassay coefficients of variation were <5% at 50 nmol/hour/mg of creatinine. The normal reference interval is <100 nmol/hour/mg.

Urinary 3CNAC Determinations. Synthesis of the major
metabolite, N-acetyl-S-cis-3-chloroprop-2-enyl)-cysteine
(3CNAC), and the isomeric internal standard, N-acetyl-S-2-
chloroprop-2-enyl)-cysteine (2CNAC), from N-acetyl cysteine and
the appropriate dichloropropene has been described elsewhere
(2,4). Purification procedures included multiple
recrystallizations with verification of the product and its
purity by thin layer chromatography, flame ionization gas
chromatography, electron capture gas chromatography (EC-GC),
melting points, infrared spectra, nuclear magnetic resonance
spectra and GC-MS. Analytic grade solvents were purchased from
either Mallinkrodt, Burdick and Jackson or Aldrich. Stock
standards of the 3CNAC and 2CNAC were prepared in methanol or
acetone at concentrations of 1.0 mg/ml for use in
chromatography and spiking blank urine solutions as standards.

Prior to developing a capillary GC-MS method for
quantitation, other gas chromatographic techniques were
employed, including packed column chromatography with flame
ionization, nitrogen phosphorus and mass selective detectors;
and also direct injection into various capillary columns with
electron capture detection. Most of these other
chromatographic techniques were unsuitable for analysis of
urines containing 3CNAC due to endogenous interferences or non-
symmetrical peak shapes. On-column injection into wide bore
(0.5 mm) columns of methyl silicone or methyl phenyl silicone
were generally unsuitable with EC-GC instrumentation due to
poor peak symmetry and sensitivity. However, with split
injection into narrow bore methyl silicone columns, acceptable
sensitivity (0.5 ug/mL) has been achieved, but endogenous
unknown urinary constituents limit the utility of this method.

Previously, extraction of 3CNAC from acidified urine relied
on a diethyl ether extraction (2). To improve cleanup and
yield, different extraction techniques were applied. Urine or
water (5.0 mL) containing 100 ug/mL of 3CNAC were acidified to
pH 1 with addition of 0.6 mL 6N HCl. Ten mL of each solvent
was added, gently shaken for 5 minutes and centrifuged at 2000
g for 10 minutes. Eight mL of solvent phase was evaporated at
45°C under nitrogen. Following diazomethane derivatization and
quantitation on EC-GC, peak areas were compared to 3CNAC
standards. Blank unspiked urines were carried through to
estimate interferences at the retention time of 3CNAC. Each
solvent gave the following results (% recovery, % urinary
interference): dichloromethane (16%, 15%), diethyl ether (10%,
100%), chloroform (30%, unknown), t-butyl methyl ether (80%,
<10%), ethylacetate with saturated NaCl in aqueous phase (<10%,
unknown). Ion pair extractions (tetramethylammonium salts in
various solvents) and ion exchange column separation (bonded
quarternary ammonium) gave poor recoveries of the 3CNAC
carboxylic anion. Many different derivatization techniques
following initial extraction were investigated. However, only
dimethylformamide dipropyl acetal (Propyl-8, Pierce Chemical
Co.), or diazomethane (generated from Diazald, Aldrich Chemical

Company) yielded 100% propyl and methyl ester derivatives, respectively. Following extraction and derivatization, an extraction-wash was employed to further clean up the sample. Chlorobutane partitioned with water gave better results than hexane, toluene or more polar solvents.

Procedure. Frozen urine is thawed to room temperature and 1.0 ml is mixed with 0.5 ml of 6 N HCl and 10 uL of the stock internal standard (2CNAC, 1 mg/ml) in a 13 x 100 mm screw top borosilicate tube. Standards are prepared by spiking urine with appropriate quantities of the stock 3CNAC methanolic solution. Standard concentrations were 0, 0.5, 1.0, 2.0, 5.0, 10.0, 15.0, and 20.0 ug/mL of urine. Two ml of t-butyl methyl ether (TBME) is added to each tube, capped and extracted for 10 minutes while shaking. All samples are centrifuged for 10 minutes at 2000 g. The TBME phase (1.5 mL) is transferred to a new labeled tube and evaporated under nitrogen at 40°C. In an ice bath, 200 uL of an ether solution of diazomethane is added at 5°C and capped. Following a reaction time of 30 minutes, the ether and excess diazomethane are evaporated to dryness under nitrogen flow at room temperature. Two ml of n-butyl chloride is added, mixed, followed by 1 ml of water. This extraction/wash is shaken for 5 minutes and then centrifuged for 10 minutes at 2000 g. The n-butyl chloride (1.5 mL) is evaporated under nitrogen at room temperature. Toluene (300–600 ul) is added to the residue for GC-MS analysis.

Capillary GC-MS instrumentation included a Hewlett-Packard 5970B quadrapole mass selective detector connected to a 5890 gas chromatograph. The fused silica column was 12 m x 0.2 mm and coated with cross-linked methylsilicone. Helium carrier gas flow was 1 mL/min. The injector was heated to 200°C and operated in the splitless mode. The column was heated at 70°C for 4 minutes, then increased at 20°C/min to 225°C for a total program time of 12 minutes. The quadrapole was calibrated with perfluorotributylamine at masses of 69, 219, and 502. The electron multiplier voltage was 1600 volts and ionization voltage was 70 keV. The quadrapole was run in a low resolution mode with mass peak widths at half height (resolution) were 0.5 AMU. The ions monitored were 117 and 176 with a dwell time of 50 msec. One uL of the toluene sample was injected by a Hewlett-Packard 7673 automatic sampler. After standards calibration, all samples are determined in the same run. Controls were run every 8-10 samples. Quantitation was performed by comparing peak height ratios of 3CNAC methyl ester/2CNAC methyl ester for the ion monitored (either 117 or 176) to a standard curve of peak height ratios for the standards.

Results

Urinary 3CNAC Procedure. Figure 1 shows electron capture gas chromatogram of a blank urine containing no added 3CNAC and a urine of a subject containing 10 ug/mL of 2CNAC and 20 ug/mL of

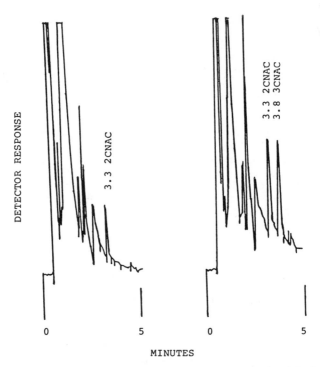

Figure 1. Electron capture gas chromatogram of a blank urine extraction (described in procedure) and a workers urine containing 10 ug/mL of 2CNAC (Rt=3.3) and 20 ug/mL of 3CNAC (Rt=3.8). Conditions were as follows. Injector: split ratio 1:50, Injector temperature: 300°C, Column: 0.25 mm x 15 m fused silica coated with methyl silicone, Column oven temperature program: 180° isothermal, Detector temperature: 300°C, Carrier gas flow: 2.3 mL/min.

3CNAC. Figure 2 shows the selected ion chromatogram of a
subject exposed to DCP. The retention time of 2CNAC methyl
ester is 10.33 minutes and 3CNAC methyl ester is 10.58 minutes.
While not quantitated in these studies, small amounts of trans
3CNAC methyl ester may appear at 10.75 min. Figure 3 shows the
mass spectrum of 3CNAC methyl ester. The 2CNAC methyl ester
has similar abundances for ions 117 and 176 used in
quantitation. Table I shows the operating characteristics of
this assay by capillary GC-MS as compared to the previously
used packed column GC-MS (2).

Table I. Operating characteristics of GC-MS Methods for
Urinary 3C-NAC Determination

		Packed	Capillary
Linearity		0-30 ug/mL	0-30 ug/mL
Regression Coefficient		0.999	0.999
Sensitivity	117 ion	0.3 ug/mL	0.1 ug/mL
	176 ion	0.3 ug/mL	0.2
Specificity	117 ion	good	good
	176 ion	excellent	excellent
Coefficient of variation at 10 ug/mL		4%	8%

Biological monitoring. Air concentrations of DCP, urinary
concentrations of 3CNAC and urinary activity of NAG are given
for each subject in Figures 4, 5 and 6. Air concentrations of
DCP varied from 0-10.3 ppm (0-47 mg/m^3). The application of DCP
accounted for >80% of the time of exposure during work hours.
Mixing/loading, repair and break periods accounting for the
remainder of the time.

Urinary concentrations of 3CNAC tended to rise and peak
during or shortly after exposure. Lags between peak exposure
and peak excretion were 0-16 hours. Urinary NAG activity did
not seem to rise and fall with exposure to DCP or urinary
excretion of 3CNAC, though it was abnormally elevated in two of
three subjects at least once during the course of this pilot
study.

Figure 7 shows that the 24 hour excretion of 3CNAC (mg)
increased with rises in the daily cumulative conc·time product
for DCP. Also, the concentration of 3CNAC in the urine on the
morning following exposure increases in rough proportion to the
cumulative conc·time product for DCP from the previous days(Fig. 8).
(The correlations for evening urine concentration or excretion
on the morning after (ug/mg C) were not as precise.)

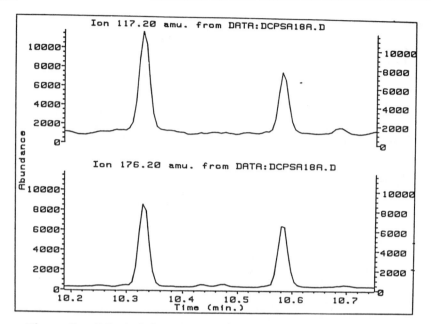

Figure 2.   Selected ion chromatogram of subject exposed to DCP.   2CNAC (Rt=10.33) is 10 ug/mL and 3CNAC (Rt=10.58) is 10 ug/mL.   Conditions in text.

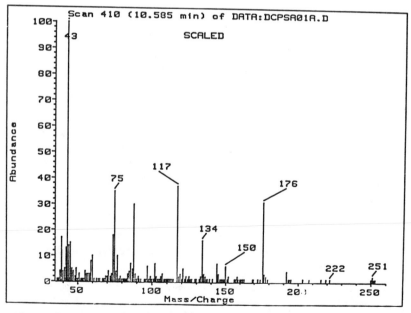

Figure 3.   Mass spectrum of the 3CNAC peak at 10.58 minutes.

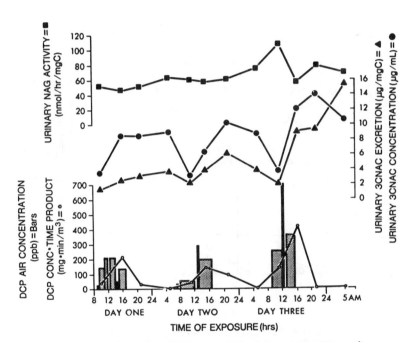

Figure 4.   Subject #1.   Air concentrations of DCP, urinary concentrations and excretion of 3CNAC, and urinary activity of NAG are given.   mgC = milligram of creatinine.   Conc·time product is computed for each preceding exposure interval.

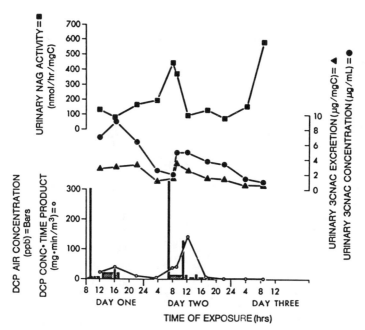

Figure 5. Subject #2. Air concentrations of DCP, urinary
concentrations and excretion of 3CNAC, and urinary activity
of NAG are given. mgC = milligrams of creatinine. Conc·time
product is computed for each preceding exposure interval.
Note change in scale for some measures as compared to Figures
4 and 6.

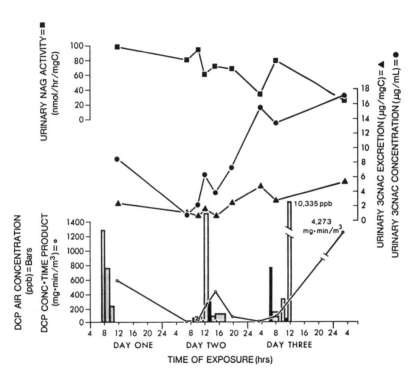

Figure 6. Subject #3. Air concentrations of DCP, urinary concentrations and excretion of 3CNAC, and urinary activity of NAG are given. mgC = milligrams of creatinine. Conc·time product is computed for each preceding exposure interval. Note change in scale for some measures as compared to previous Figures 4 and 5.

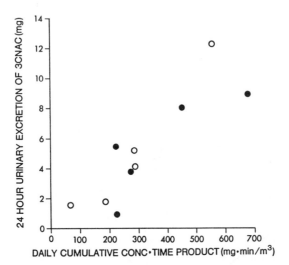

Figure 7. Plot of 24 hour excretion of 3CNAC versus
cumulative 24 hr conc·time product for DCP air exposure.
Data from subjects #1 and 2. • = 1984 study of five 24 hr
urine collections on five persons (from Ref. No. 2). ○ = Five
24 hr urine collections in this study from two persons.

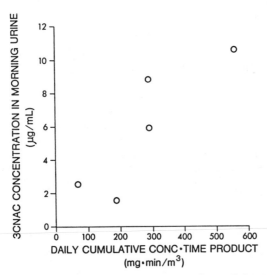

Figure 8. Plot of urinary concentration of 3CNAC from
morning urine versus cumulative 24 hr conc·time product for
DCP air exposure on preceding day.

Discussion

Urinary 3CNAC Procedures. Our prior attempts at capillary EC-GC methods have been several-fold less sensitive than GC-MS procedures in determining 3CNAC in urine samples. There are two likely reasons for this: 1) 3CNAC is polar and difficult to isolate with selectivity from other polar urinary acids (intermediary acids of metabolism and similar amino acids such as methionine); 2) the single chloro group on a polar molecule only slightly enhances the electron capture signal strength over other polar molecules. Recently, Onkenhout et al (1986) has used other detectors (nitrogen phosphorus, sulphur selective and mass selective) to detect the urinary metabolites in rats. We find that with capillary nitrogen selective gas chromatography of the 3CNAC in urine, the sensitivity is again limited due to endogenous urinary components. Onkenhout et al used different columns composed of methyl and phenyl groups to separate cis and trans 3CNAC. We have been able to separate cis and trans-3CNAC on methyl silicone columns under GC-MS conditions, but have not used trans 3CNAC as a marker for exposure since earlier animal studies indicated less was excreted in the urine (3). From qualitative observation of past chromatograms on humans, relatively little trans isomer is excreted compared to cis-3CNAC.

Our GC-MS approach has been to monitor both ions 117 and 176 m/e. An occasional human sample will have an interfering substance near the 117 ion peak, whereas the 176 ion gives routinely clean peaks. It would not seem likely that the 176 ion is more selective, since this ion is characteristic of any mercapturic conjugate if at that specific retention time. Monitoring more specific ions of lower abundance (e.g. molecular ion, 251) reduces sensitivity accordingly.

While intraassay precision was slightly worse when compared to the older packed column GC-MS (2), this is attributable to more complicated extraction in the capillary GC-MS procedure (3 steps vs. 6). This might be improved by omitting the evaporation - chlorbutane/water wash steps and choosing the above-mentioned more selective ions.

Biological monitoring. In field studies of an individual, replicate measures of personal air concentrations are difficult. Data from single personal air samplings are intrinsically "time averaged" for the period of collection. Therefore, a single high air concentration for a short period may bias the overall collection. In this pilot study of human exposure in the field, such air concentrations represent first approximations of potential exposure. The urinary concentrations of a metabolite of a pesticide are considered an estimate of actual and individual exposure. However, this is only true when relationships between absorption, distribution, metabolism and excretion are known with some certainty. Usually, inherent biovariability between individuals precludes

establishing explicit relationships or limits. General
relationships between exposure and excretion, exposure and
effect or excretion and effect can be approached. In our pilot
study, we have not established any certain relationships, but
have uncovered those to investigate. Several practical
considerations are evident as well.

In a larger study to follow, we intend to examine the
relation between various expressions of exposure (peak
concentrations, time weighted exposures and cumulative
exposure) and the measures of excretion (ug/mL, ug/hour, ug/mg
creatinine, total ug excreted). In this study, it can only be
noted that excretion of metabolite does increase in response to
DCP air exposure. This rise in metabolite excretion lags
behind DCP peak exposure for a variable period of 0-16 hours.
The few data points preclude determination of a precise
relationship or pharmacokinetic analysis. However, the
metabolite does not appear to accumulate and urinary amounts
start to decrease just before the next exposure.

If urinary excretion of 3CNAC increases in proportion to
what appears to be primarily a pulmonary exposure, then this
may affirm the pulmonary route as the major route of exposure
in workers. However, in unprotected workers dermal exposure
and biologic variability would tend to confound this
relationship. Stott and Kostl (1986) have shown that pulmonary
uptake of DCP is 82% at 80 ppm in rats. Quantitative dermal
absorption studies are not available. In actual work practice,
milligrams of DCP can easily come into direct contact with the
skin during repair and loading operations.

Since urinary excretion of a metabolite such as 3CNAC is
derived from all routes of absorption, urinary excretion may be
more closely related to effects than air concentrations of DCP.
Renal injury in animals following 3 ppm chronic inhalation
exposure (13) is controversial since others have not seen
alterations in histology or kidney weight following inhalation
studies of 1-24 months at higher concentrations   (50-90 ppm)
(14,15). In part, this may be due to purer preparations of DCP
used in recent experiments. Indeed, impurities causing direct
mutagenicity can be removed from DCP preparations (8). These
form in DCP preparations by autooxidation and may be a source
of injury to humans, in which case DCP air measurements or
urinary metabolite determinations would only serve as a marker
for the impurity. However, DCP is an indirect mutagen
following mono-oxigenase activation (8-11 and others). Thiols
are protective of DCP mutagenicity in vitro (8,9). DCP will
bind and deplete thiol stores in liver and kidney (12).
Perhaps a subtle measure of DCP kidney toxicity, the
significance of thiol depletion requires further investigation.

In this pilot, NAG enzyme activity was chosen as a possible
indicator of renal injury, should any occur at all with DCP
exposure. NAG is a lysosomal enzyme released from renal

tubular epithelial cells only during the period of acute injury. Price (1982) has reviewed its clinical relevancy. In rat models of transient renal tubular injury produced by maleic acid, NAG urinary activities begin to decrease within a few hours after injury has occurred (22). NAG excretion is considered to be increased only briefly after injury. We saw no clear correspondence between increased NAG urinary activity and excretion of metabolite in these three subjects. However, the fact that two of the three subjects had greater than normal (>100 nmol/hr/mg of creatinine) urinary activity at one point in our surveillance, requires that further investigation be made. It is reported that NAG urinary activity is constant for an individual (21). The interval to interval variability in these subjects suggests some external factor at work. It should be made clear that other unmeasured effects may contribute to elevated NAG activity such as underlying disease (other renal disease, hypertension), effects of medications (gentamicin, salicylates, phenacetin) or other chemical nephrotoxins such as heavy metals (see review by Price). Such variables were unknown in these subjects.

Of fundamental and practical concern are lessons learned from experience. Communication between worker and investigator should be clear. Missed portions of urine collections on subject 3 in this study precluded expression of urinary amounts of 3CNAC (total ug), but rather only creatinine corrected excretion. Subjects #1 and 2 excreted a total of 21.5 and 3.2 mg during the study period. But these amounts are misleading in this limited study, since pre-study exposure was not excluded. From the Figures (4-6), it is evident that subjects #2 and 3 were still excreting 3CNAC from a prior exposure at the beginning of the study. Baseline measurements are helpful when determining the magnitude of new metabolite excretion. Creatinine determinations should always be made in studies involving sequential or 24 hour urine collection. This allows not only to correct for urine flow dependency, but to assess the completeness of the collection.

Intervals of collection should coincide as much as possible with worker change in activity (end of day, end of application, lunch, repairs). Also, urine collections and air tube changes should coincide. These two recommendations enable easier data analysis.

From this pilot study, it was learned that NAG excretion during DCP exposure requires investigation and that 3CNAC excretion is not exactly concurrent with exposure. Collection of urine for sometime during and after (<24 hours) worker exposures may be representative of that earlier exposure.

Literature Cited

1. Maddy, K. T. Publication No. HS-686. <u>California Department of Food and Agriculture</u>. 1979.

2. Osterloh, J. D.; Cohen, B.; Poppendorf, W.; Pond, S. M. Arch. Environ. Health 1984, 39, 271-275.
3. Hutson, D. H.; Moss, J. A.; Pickering, B. A. Fd. Cosmet. Toxicol. 1971, 9, 677-680.
4. Climie, I. J. G.; Hutson, D. H.; Morrison, B. J.; Stoydin, G. Xenobiotica 1969, 9, 149-156.
5. Onkenhout, W.; Mulder, P. P.; Boogaard, P.J.; Buijs, W.; Vermeulen, N. P. Arch. Toxicol. 1986, 59, 235-241.
6. Yang, R. S. H.; Huff, J. E.; Boorman, G. A.; Haseman, J. K.; Kornreich, M.; Stookey, J. L. J. Toxicol. Environ. Health 1986, 18, 377-392.
7. Talcott, R. E.; King, J. JNCI 1984, 72, 113-116.
8. Watson, W. P.; Brooks, T. M.; Auckle, K. R.; Hutson, D. H.; Lang, K. L.; Smith, R. J.; Wright, A. S. Chem. Biol. Interact. 1987, 61, 17-30.
9. Creedy, C. L.; Brooks, T. M.; Dean, B. J.; Hutson, D. H.; Wright, A. S. Chem. Biol. Interact. 1984, 50, 39-48.
10. Van der Hude, W.; Scheutwinkel, M.; Gramlich, U.; Fissler, B.; Basler, A. Environ. Mutagen. 1987, 9, 401-410.
11. Valencia, R.; Mason, J. M.; Woodruff, R. C.; Zimmering, S. Environ. Mutagen. 1985, 7, 325-348.
12. Stott, W. T.; Kastl, P. E. Toxicol. App. Pharmacol. 1986, 85, 332-341.
13. Torkelson, T. R.; Oyen, F. Am. Ind. Hygiene Assoc. J. 1977, 38, 217-223.
14. Parker, C. M.; Coate, W. B.; Voelker, R. W., J. Toxicol. Environ. Health 1982, 9, 899-910.
15. Stott, W. T.; Young, J. T.; Calhoun, L. L.; Battjes, J. E. Fund. Appl. Toxicol. In submission.
16. Price, R. G. Toxicology 1982, 23, 99-134.
17. Kunin, C. M.; Chesney, R. W.; Craig, W. A.; England, A. C.; DeAngelis, C. Pediatrics 1978, 62, 751-760.
18. Lauwerys, R. R.; Bernard, A. Am. J. Ind. Med. 1987, 11, 275-285.
19. NIOSH Manual of Analytical Methods (3rd ed.) Vol. 1, 1984, U.S. Dept. Health and Human Services, Publication No. 84-100. Methods 1003 and 1013 (also 1982 ed Methods S-104).
20. Leiber, M. A.; Berk, H. C. Anal. Chem. 1984, 56, 2134-2137.
21. Piagen, K.; Peterson, J. J. Clin. Invest. 1978, 61, 751-762.
22. Al-Bander, H. A.; Mock, D. M.; Etheredge, S. B.; Paubert, T. T.; Humphreys, M. H.; Morris, R. C. Kidney International 1986, 30, 804-812.
23. Jung, K.; Schulze, G.; Reinholdt, C. Clin Chem. 1986, 32, 529-532.
24. Fundamentals of Clinical Chemistry, Tietz, N.W. (ed); W.B. Saunders Company, Philadelphia, 1976, p 995-998.

RECEIVED May 24, 1988

Chapter 18

Determination of Chlordimeform Residues as 4-Chloro-*o*-Toluidine in Human Urine Using High-Performance Liquid Chromatography

M. W. Cheung, R. A. Kahrs, W. B. Nixon, J. A. Ross, and B. G. Tweedy

Biochemistry Department, Agricultural Division, Ciba–Geigy Corporation, Greensboro, NC 27419

A rapid and specific analytical method has been developed for the monitoring of worker exposure to chlordimeform (Galecron). The method was developed prior to the second year (1979) reintroduction program of Galecron for use on cotton. Residues of chlordimeform and metabolites in urine from field workers were hydrolyzed in a test tube under basic conditions to 4-chloro-o-toluidine which was partitioned into n-hexane. Residues of 4-chloro-o-toluidine in the organic phase were then analyzed using an automated high performance liquid chromatograph equipped with a μ-Porisil column and UV detection at 254 nm. The limit of detection is 0.05 ppm and the average procedural recovery is 99 ± 10% (n=105). Chlordimeform residues in urine stored under ambient laboratory conditions are stable for at least 195 days. The method has been validated and accounts for 35–40% of the total radioactive residues in rat urine as 4-chloro-o-toluidine. The method utilized disposable culture tubes which reduced cost and eliminated glassware contamination. The method generated reliable results which were rapidly transmitted to field personnel for the purpose of monitoring and minimizing worker exposure.

Chlordimeform, N-(2-methyl-4-chlorophenyl)-N',N'-dimethylformamidine, the active ingredient in Galecron 4E, is an effective acaricide/insecticide for insect control in cotton. The analytical method published in the Pesticide Analytical Manual (1) was not suitable as a monitoring method. A gas chromatographic method was developed in 1978 prior to the first year reintroduction program of Galecron for use in cotton culture. As part of the second year (1979) reintroduction program of Galecron, a rapid and specific HPLC analytical method was developed to monitor worker exposure in

0097–6156/89/0382–0231$06.00/0

© 1989 American Chemical Society

order to ensure safe handling of the chemical in field applications. Field workers which included mixers, loaders, applicators,
pilots and other field personnel were required to submit daily
urine samples which were analyzed for residues of chlordimeform and
metabolite (total chlordimeform residues). Residues of chlordimeform and metabolites were hydrolyzed under basic conditions to
4-chloro-o-toluidine. The analyte was partitioned into hexane and
the residues were determined using normal-phase HPLC and a fixed-
wavelength UV-detector at 254 nm. The method is rapid, specific
and cost effective. Cleanup of the samples other than partitioning
is unnecessary. The details of the analytical methodology are
described in this report.

Chlordimeform (I)
N-(2-methyl-4-chlorophenyl)-N',N'-
dimethylformamidine
Code No.:   C-8514
$C_{10}H_{13}ClN_2$
M.W. = 196.6

4-Chloro-o- toluidine (II)
Code No.: CGA-41657
C_7H_8ClN
M.W. 141.6

MATERIALS AND METHODS

MATERIALS. Chlordimeform (I) and 4-chloro-o-toluidine (II) analytical standards were supplied by the Production Technical Analytical
Section, Agricultural Division, CIBA-GEIGY Corporation. The puri-
ties for (I) and (II) were >99% and >98%, respectively. HPLC grade
hexane, 2,2,4-trimethylpentane (isooctane) and 2-propanol were from
Burdick & Jackson or Baker Chemicals. Reagent grade ethyl alcohol
was from Fisher Scientific (Catalog No. A407-500). Reagent grade
sodium hydroxide, 50% (w/w) was from Baker Chemicals. Borosilicate
glass culture tubes (16 x 125 mm) were from Corning (Catalog No.
99447). Black plastic bottle caps with Poly-Seal polyethylene cap
liners, size no. 15 were from Fischer Scientific (Catalog No.
02-883-5A). Multi-Temp Block Heaters (Model No. 2093 for 36 culture tubes or No. 2097-6 for 72 culture tubes) with module block to
fit 16-mm o.d. culture tubes were from Lab-Line Instruments, Inc.
Automatic transfer pipettes for dispensing urine were Oxford Macro-
Set Transfer pipettes with disposable plastic tips (Fisher Scien-
tific Catalog No. 21-195). Reagent dispenser pipettes, Oxford
Automatic Pipettor Model S-A, were from Fisher Scientific (Catalog
No. 13-687-7A). Vortex-Genie hand mixers were from Scientific
Industries, Inc. HPLC vials were from Fischer Scientific, (Catalog
No. 06-406AA). The components of the HPLC system are described in
Table I.

PREPARATION OF STANDARDS. Standard solutions of 1 mg/mL of (I) and
(II) were prepared by dissolving 100 mg of each separately in 100
mL of ethyl alcohol in 100-mL volumetric flasks. Standard (I) was
diluted with ethyl alcohol and was used only for fortification

purposes. Standard (II) was serially diluted with isooctane to a working range of 0.02-1.25 ng/mL. A standard curve using three or more injections of different quantities of (II) could be prepared. However, the determination of (II) using HPLC and a UV fixed-wavelength detector at 254 nm has been found to be linear from 0.40 ng to 200 ng and to intersect the origin using the condition described in this method. Therefore, for routine residue determination, only one calibration point, normally 25 ng of (II), and the origin were required.

ANALYTICAL PROCEDURES. A 5.0-mL aliquot of urine was transferred to a culture tube (16 x 125 mm) using an automatic transfer pipette. Recovery samples were obtained using control urine fortified with the appropriate amount of (I). An aliquot of 1.0 mL of sodium hydroxide (50%, w/w) solution was added with an automatic dispensing pipette. The culture tube was then capped with a Poly-Seal cap and mixed well by shaking for a few seconds by hand. The culture tube was then placed in a test-tube heating block for 15-30 minutes. The heating block was maintained at 125°C. (Although the heating block temperature may drop to approximately 110°C initially if many samples were heated at once, this had no adverse effect on the analytical results.) After the 15-30 minutes of reaction time, the culture tube was removed, transferred to a test-tube rack and cooled in a water bath to 30-35°C. Alternatively, the test tube may be cooled in the air to ambient temperature. After cooling, an aliquot of 5.0 mL of hexane was dispensed into each tube using an automatic dispensing pipette. The mixture was stirred for 10 seconds using a Vortex hand mixer. The layers were then allowed to separate. If an emulsion was formed, the samples were kept at 30-35°C and immersed for several seconds in an ultrasonic bath. This procedure helped to separate the phases. An aliquot of the supernatant hexane layer was transferred to an injection vial for total chlordimeform residue analysis as 4-chloro-o-toluidine.

CHEMICAL ANALYSIS USING HPLC. The hexane extract containing (II) was analyzed by HPLC using a silica gel column (μ-Porisil) and UV detection at 254 nm. The HPLC system was standardized by injecting 25 ng of 4-chloro-o-toluidine (20 μL of the 1.25 ng/μL standard solution). The mobile phase was 10% 2-propanol:90% isooctane. Details for the HPLC analysis are given in Table I.

Although a standard curve using several injections of standard at different concentrations could be prepared, the UV-detector response for (II) has been found to be linear, intersecting the origin, using the conditions described. Typical calibration data of standard (II) are presented in Table II. Least squares linear regression analysis of these data produced correlation coefficient better than 0.999 and the calibration curve intersected the origin or very close to it. Therefore, only one calibration point was required. A 20-μL aliquot of hexane extract from the urine sample was injected into the HPLC system using the conditions described in Table I. An autoanalyzer, such as the Waters WISP 710 or 712B, could be used for sample injection.

Table I. HPLC Conditions for the Analysis of 4-Chloro-o-Toluidine
          Residues in Human Urine

Instrument: Waters Associates Model 6000A Solvent Delivery System,
             or Kratos Spectroflow Model 400 pump; Waters Model 440
             Absorbance Detector or Kratos Spectroflow Model 783
             Variable Wavelength UV detector, and Waters
             Intelligent Sample Processor WISP 710 or 712B
Detector Wavelength: 254 nm
Column: Silica Gel, 10 micron particle size 4.6-mm id x 25-cm
         length
             eg: Rheodyne, Inc., No. SI 10A [LiChrosorb SI 100 (E.
             Merck)] or Waters, No. 27477, μPorasil
Column Temperature: Ambient
Mobile Phase: 10% 2-propanol in isooctane
Flow Rate: 3.0 mL/min.
Solvent Temperature: Ambient
Retention Time: 2.7 min.
Limit of Sensitivity: 0.4 ng

Table II. Least Squares Linear Regression Analysis of Typical
           Calibration Data of 4-Chloro-o-Toluidine

Nanograms of (II)	Peak Height (cm)	Correlation Coefficient	Slope	Intercept
10.0	16.80	--	--	--
5.0	8.05	--	--	--
5.0	8.05	--	--	--
2.0	3.10	--	--	--
1.0	1.60	--	--	--
0.5	0.80	--	--	--
0.5	0.80	--	--	--
--	--	0.9997	0.5963	0.0894

DETERMINATION OF SAMPLE RESIDUES. An aliquot of 20 μL of the
hexane extract equivalent to 20 mg of urine was injected into the
HPLC using an automatic injector. The peak height of (II) was
measured and the ng of (II) calculated by Equation 1.

$$\text{ng of (II)} = \frac{\text{peak height in sample}}{\text{peak height of 25 ng (II) Standard}} \times 25 \text{ ng} \qquad (1)$$

     Alternatively, a computer data system could be used to
integrate peak area of compound (II). If a standard curve was
constructed, the data could be inputted into either a computer

data system, or an electronic calculator such as Hewlett-Packard Model 11C calculator using least squares linear regression plot to obtain the ng present in the injected aliquot.

The ppm of chlordimeform equivalents in urine was calculated using Equation 2.

$$\frac{ppm}{chlordimeform} = \frac{ng\ (II)\ found}{mg\ urine\ injected} \times 1.39 \times \frac{1}{R} \quad (2)$$

The factor 1.39 is the molecular weight ratio of (I) to (II) which converts the ppm (II) to ppm equivalents of (I), and R is the percent recovery factor expressed as a decimal (e.g., 100% = 1.0, 85% = 0.85).

The mg equivalents of urine injected were calculated by Equation 3.

$$5,000\ mg\ urine \times \frac{20\ \mu L\ injected}{5,000\ \mu L\ total\ hexane\ volume} = 20\ mg \quad (3)$$

A flow diagram of the analytical procedures is presented in Figure 1. Representative HPLC chromatograms of standards, control, spiked and field worker urine samples are shown in Figure 2.

RESULTS AND DISCUSSION

The validity of the method has been investigated by analyzing urine from rats orally dosed with ^{14}C-chlordimeform. The accountability of the method as (II) is 35-40% of the total ^{14}C residue in the urine.

The residue concentrations of (II) were determined by using automated HPLC normal-phase chromatography and fixed-wavelength UV detector at 254 nm. The absorption spectrum of 4-chloro-o-toluidine with an absorption maximum at 235 nm is shown in Figure 3. This spectral characteristic rendered minimal to no matrix interferences from urine. However, some interference from intake of drugs such as Darvon and Tolinase and some antibiotics has been observed. If a variable wavelength UV detector is available, detection at 235 nm can be an advantageous alternative.

Urine samples submitted by field personnel were contained in Nalgene bottles under ambient conditions. The storage stability of total chlordimeform residues determined as 4-chloro-o-toluidine was investigated. Three large composite urine samples, each approximately one liter, were obtained by combining several field workers' urine samples which contained total chlordimeform residues. These samples were analyzed for compound (II) at various intervals up to six and one-half months (195 days) while kept in Nalgene bottles under ambient laboratory conditions. No degradation of total chlordimeform residues was observed. An average of 102 ± 3% (n=3) of the zero-day values was recovered after six and one-half months of storage. Results are shown in Table III.

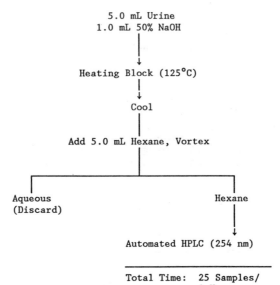

Figure 1.   Flow Diagram of the Miniaturized HPLC Analytical
Procedures

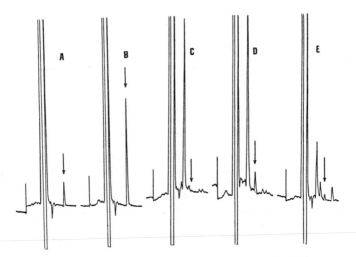

Figure 2.   Representative HPLC Chromatograms of Standard (II),
Control, Spiked and Field Worker Urine Samples
(A: 1.0 ng of (II); B: 5.0 ng of (II); C: Control
Urine, <0.05 ppm; D: Spiked Control at 0.05 ppm,
105%; E: Field Worker Urine, <0.05 ppm)

Table III. Storage Stability Results of Total Chlordimeform Residues in Urine

| Sample Code | Percent Recovered | | | | |
	Day 0	Day 1	Day 58	Day 132	Day 195
Composite Sample No. 1 (from Site 702)	100	103	N/A	97.8	103
Composite Sample No. 2 (from Site 702)	100	106	88.9	87.3	98.4
Composite Sample No. 3 (from site 901)	100	93.2	88.6	84.1	105

Samples were composited from field personnel to obtain homogeneous storage samples. Urine samples were stored in Nalgene bottle under ambient laboratory conditions. An aliquot was analyzed at various intervals.

N/A = Not Analyzed

A second storage stability study using control urine spiked with (I), stored in a Nalgene bottle and analyzed for (II) was also performed. Results showed that 103% of the residues were accounted for as compound (II) after four weeks of storage in Nalgene bottles under ambient laboratory conditions. Results are contained in Table IV.

The validity of the method was further demonstrated by procedural recovery experiments conducted during monitoring programs in 1979 and 1980. Urine samples were spiked with (I) and analyzed as (II). The overall average recovery over the fortification range of

Table IV. Storage Stability of Chlordimeform Residues in Human Urine Determined as 4-Chloro-o-Toluidine Under Ambient Laboratory Conditions

| Sample Code | Percent Recovered | | | |
	Day 0	Day 7	Day 14	Day 28
Spiked Sample	100	99.6	103.3	100.3

Aliquots were withdrawn and analyzed at various intervals. Average values of duplicate analyses of control urine samples spiked with 0.50 ppm of chlordimeform.

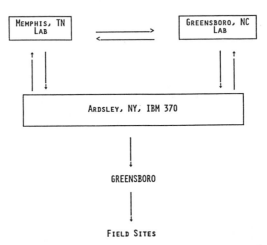

LAB INFORMATION FLOW

Figure 3.   UV-Visible Absorption Spectrum of
             4-Chloro-o-Toluidine

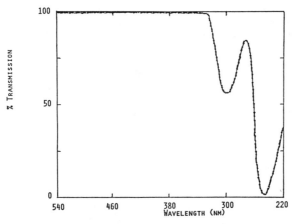

Figure 4.   Information Flow Between Analytical Laboratories and
             Field Coordinators Via IBM Computer

0.05 ppm to 10 ppm was 99 ± 10% (n=105). A summary of the
recovery data is shown in Table V.

Another feature of the method described in this report was the
incorporation of a computer system (Hewlett-Packard HP-1000 computer) in this monitoring program. The Hewlett-Packard computer
collected HPLC analytical data generated in laboratories in
Memphis, Tennessee, and Greensboro, North Carolina, performed the
quantitation of residue levels, and transferred the data to an IBM
370 mainframe computer in Ardsley, New York. Residue results were
transmitted to field personnel typically within 24 hours after
sample receipt. The computer system enabled rapid transmittal of
results to field personnel. Figure 4 shows a graphical representation of the data and information transmitted. During 1979-1980,
over 40,000 urine samples were analyzed using this HPLC method.

Table V. Procedural Recoveries of Chlordimeform Detected as
4-Chloro-o-Toluidine

Fortifi-cation Levels (ppm)	Range of Recovery (%)	Average Procedural Recovery (%)	Standard Deviation (%)	N
0.05-10.0	72-116	99	± 10	105

In summary, a rapid, simple, cost effective and specific urine
monitoring method was developed in conjunction with the reintroduction of chlordimeform (Galecron) for use on cotton using versatile
HPLC techniques. Under normal conditions, 25 samples can be
analyzed in two hours. By virtue of the spectral characteristics
of 4-chloro-o-toluidine, specific residue determination using a
fixed-wavelength UV detector at 254 nm was accomplished. Inexpensive, disposable culture tubes reduced cost and eliminated glassware contamination. Reliable monitoring results were generated and
rapidly communicated to field personnel.

LITERATURE CITED

1. FDA Pesticide Analytical Manual, Vol. II, U. S. Department of
   Commerce, National Technical Information Service, Pesticide
   Reg. Sec. 180.285 (11/1/73).

RECEIVED June 23, 1988

Chapter 19

Biological Monitoring Technology
for Measurement of Applicator Exposure

S. Dubelman and J. E. Cowell

Monsanto Agricultural Company, Monsanto Company, St. Louis, MO 63198

The measurement of a pesticide and its metabolites in urine is a direct and accurate means of determining actual applicator exposure. Biological monitoring studies with alachlor are used here to exemplify the techniques necessary for conducting a study and determining body dose. Animal metabolism and pharmacokinetic studies provided data about the nature of the metabolites, the elimination pathway (urine/feces) and the kinetics of excretion. Urine from applicators using alachlor was collected for a 5 day period following application. Twelve-hour urine composites were analyzed by GCMS or HPLC for DEA and HEEA, the chemophores derived from alachlor and its metabolites. Method sensitivity was 5.0 ppb (μg/L) for the total measured residue. Appropriate correction factors derived from animal studies were applied to the measured urinary excretion to determine the body dose.

Background

A number of techniques are currently used to monitor applicator exposure to pesticides. These include passive dosimetry, biological monitoring and fluorescence video imaging. Table I shows a comparison of the distinctive features of each technique. The main advantage of passive dosimetry is the ease with which samples can be obtained and analyzed. Analysis is usually for the parent pesticide only, and no metabolism information is necessary. This method produces data that is suitable for inclusion in generic databases containing large numbers of studies with different pesticides. This technique can be used to measure expo-

0097–6156/89/0382–0240$06.00/0
© 1989 American Chemical Society

Table I. Comparison of Exposure Measurement Techniques

Technique	Measurement	Advantage/Best Use
Passive Dosimetry	Dermal Deposition (Patches) Inhalation (Air Sampling) Parent Pesticide Analysis	Discrete Work Activities Most Vulnerable Body Areas Simple Analysis Separate Dermal & Inhalation Values
Fluorescence/ Imaging	Dermal Deposition (Video Imaging) Fluorescent Dye Quantitation	Most Vulnerable Body Areas Estimation of Dermal Deposition Education/Training
Biological Monitoring	Excreted Portion of Body Dose (Urine) Pesticide + Metabolite Analysis	Integrated Exposure: Inhalation + Dermal + Ingestion No Need for Dermal Absorption Factor No Clothing Penetration Assumption Closest Estimate of Total Body Dose

sures received during discrete work activities within a workday,
which makes it valuable in evaluating exposure reduction practices. There are several disadvantages in using passive dosimetry
for calculation of body dose. One is the need to measure the
amount of chemical absorbed through the skin and lungs, or to
assume 100% absorption of the compound. The latter assumption is
not supported by a number of recent studies. A large source of
error is also inherent in the extrapolation of residues found in
relatively small trapping devices (e.g., gauze patches) to entire
body surface areas. Since the patches generally cover 6% or less
of the body, exposure could be grossly over- or under-estimated if
pesticide droplets hit or miss the patch. An additional assumption
leading to over- or under-estimation involves the amount of pesticide intercepted by clothing during pesticide application. Scenarios using no protection (nude applicator), 50%, 80%, or 100%
clothing protection have been used by EPA in calculating body
doses from gauze patch data for a number of pesticides. Estimates
of body dose can range several orders of magnitude depending on
how much body surface is assumed to be protected by clothing.
    Video imaging with fluorescent tracers is not yet widely used.
An obstacle to widespread use is the current unavailability of
nontoxic fluorescent tracers which would be compatible with a wide

range of agricultural formulations. The technique quantifies
dermal deposition, which is often the major component of the
exposure, but does not account for the portion of the dose resulting from inhalation or ingestion. Estimates of dermal penetration
are still necessary for calculation of body dose. An important
advantage of the technique is its ability to provide a visual
qualitative assessment of the affected body areas. This knowledge
can be used to design exposure reduction measures and to educate
agricultural workers.

The primary advantage of biological monitoring is that the
actual body dose can be directly determined by measuring the
concentration of the pesticide or its metabolites in the urine.
This dose includes exposure from all sources: dermal, inhalation
and ingestion. There is no need to determine dermal absorption or
clothing penetration factors, since all these are intrinsic and
accounted for in the monitoring. The main disadvantage of the
technique is that detailed knowledge of metabolism and excretion
kinetics is needed before quantitative studies can be conducted.
In addition, this technique is applicable only to those chemicals
where urine is the major route of excretion. Neither blood nor
feces are practical matrixes for the measurement of total exposure.

Alachlor Studies: Metabolism, Excretion and Methods

Metabolism and excretion kinetics should be known before the
biological monitoring study are conducted. Results of these
studies for alachlor, 2-chloro-2',6'-diethyl-N-(methoxymethyl)
acetanilide, the active ingredient in Lasso herbicide (Monsanto
Co.), are shown in Table II. The rat metabolism study (oral
dosing), required for registration under FIFRA, provided metabolite
identification data which served as a basis for developing analytical methods for use in the applicator exposure study.

TABLE II. Results of Metabolism and Excretion
Studies on Alachlor

Study	Results
Oral Dosing ^{14}C-Rats	Identification of Many Metabolites Yielding Either DEA or HEEA Upon Hydrolysis
Oral Dosing ^{14}C-Mice	Identification of Metabolites Containing DEA and HEEA; Species Comparison
Intravenous Dosing ^{14}C-Monkeys	97% Dose Recovered in Urine + Feces 87% Dose Excreted in Urine 80% Dose Excreted in 48 Hours Quantitation of DEA/HEEA Ratio
Dermal Absorption ^{14}C-Monkeys	8.5% of Dose Absorbed Through Skin 88% of Dose in Urine

For alachlor, the mouse metabolism study did not provide much additional knowledge applicable to the exposure study, except for corroboration of metabolite profiles and additional species comparison of excretion pathways.

The intravenous injection of ^{14}C-labeled pesticide to monkeys was used to determine excretory recovery and distribution of the total amount of chemical between urine and feces. This study provided correction factors for human excretory recovery.

Dermal application of ^{14}C-labeled alachlor to monkeys provided excretion data to determine the length of time for urine collection by humans.

The intravenous and dermal monkey studies showed that 87-88% of the administered dose was excreted in the monkey urine, and excretion was essentially complete four days after dose administration. This served as a basis for determining that urine samples would be collected for 5 days in the applicator exposure studies, and analytical results would be corrected for the 88% excretory factor in order to arrive at a total body dose. This correction was in addition to analytical corrections normally applied for losses in the residue method.

A species comparison for excretory recovery and metabolite classification is given in Table III, which showed the metabolite pattern in human and monkey urine to be nearly identical.

Table III. Comparison of Excretion Profiles and Metabolite Classification in Various Species

	% ^{14}C-Excretion		% Metabolite Class	
	Urine	Feces	DEA	HEEA
Rat	50	50	35	65
Mouse	35	65	40	60
Monkey	88	12	80	20
Human	--	--	80	20

The rodent and monkey metabolism studies indicated that alachlor was rapidly transformed to a number of metabolites that contained diethyl-aniline (DEA) and 2-(1-hydroxyethyl)-ethylaniline (HEEA) moieties. An analytical method for measuring these metabolites in the urine of applicators was then developed based on hydrolytic conversion of all metabolites to DEA and HEEA, as shown in Figure 1.

The liberated anilines were then quantitated by negative chemical ionization GCMS (Indiana and Canada studies) after conversion to the corresponding heptafluorobutyric anhydride (HFBA) derivatives, or directly by HPLC with electrochemical detection (Missouri studies).

The sensitivity of the methods was 5.0 PPB, or 2.5 ppb for
each metabolite class.

Field Procedures

Based on the monkey excretion studies, a period of 5 days was
established for collection of applicator urine. Male applicators
collected each urine void in a separate glass bottle and delivered
the containers daily to the study administrator. The study administrator combined the various urine voids into 12-hour composites
for each applicator and recorded the daily volumes. All samples
were labeled with name, date and time of collection and stored
frozen until analyzed. Control or baseline urine samples were
collected from each applicator prior to the exposure study.
Control urine was fortified in the field with representative
metabolites and handled exactly as the "exposure" samples. These
samples provided recovery data and correction factors to compensate
for any losses during transport, storage or analysis.
    Field information was collected on specially designed field
survey forms. Data collected describe the conditions of each
application, and included weather, application details, personal
clothing and hygiene, wind speed and direction, humidity, type of
equipment, amount of alachlor applied, protective equipment (gloves,
goggles), body weight and a number of other items. Photographs and
continuous videotapes provided additional documentation.
    For the Missouri and Canadian studies, an attempt was made to
correlate the biological monitoring results with results from
passive dosimeters. For that purpose, 6 gauze patches, 10 X 10 cm
were attached to the clothing near the forehead (cap), back
(shirt), chest (shirt), chest (undershirt), forearm (sleeve on
dominant arm) and thigh (pant leg). Care was taken to locate these
so as not to block exposed skin surfaces. No gauze pads were used
in the Indiana study.

Results and Discussion

Results from recovery experiments of laboratory and field fortifications are shown in Tables IV (urine) and V (gauze pads). These
were used to correct the values obtained in each corresponding
study. In general, there was reasonable agreement between laboratory and field recoveries, indicating that losses were largely due
to analytical procedures, not transport or storage stability
factors.
    A summary of data obtained for all applicators is shown in
Table VI. The body dose is expressed in micrograms per kilogram
body weight per pound active ingredient applied (µg/kg/lb). This
is a convenient unit that allows extrapolation to any number of
conditions when the data is later used for risk assessment. Any
one of the biological monitoring values in Table VI can be calculated as follows: The total amount of alachlor metabolites
excreted by the applicator during the days following the application is obtained by adding the values found in each urine sample

TABLE IV. Alachlor Recovery Studies - Urine

| | DEA - Yielding Metabolites | | | | | | HEEA - Yielding Metabolites | | | | | |
| | LAB | | | FIELD | | | LAB | | | FIELD | | |
	1984C	1984I	1985	1984C	1984I	1985	1984C	1984I	1985	1984C	1984I	1985
Fortification Range (ppb)	10-200	2.5-2500	2.5-50	10-200	5-1000	2.5-25	10-200	2.5-2500	2.5-50	10-200	5-1000	2.5-250
No. of Spikes	34	72	143	24	48	18	34	72	141	24	48	18
Recov. Mean (%)	96.2	95	85.9	100	95	85.1	65.6	67	87.2	67.8	64	74.1
Std. Dev.	15.3	8	14.3	20.3	18	8.1	13.2	16	11.6	8.9	16	7.5

1984C = Canada   GC/MS

1984I = Indiana

1985 = Missouri   HPLC/EC

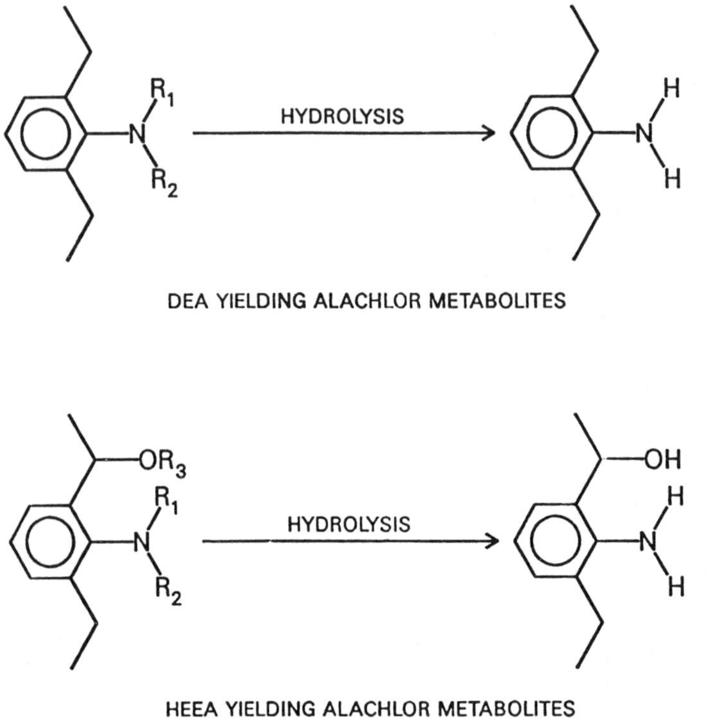

DEA YIELDING ALACHLOR METABOLITES

HEEA YIELDING ALACHLOR METABOLITES

Figure 1. Hydrolysis of Alachlor Metabolites to DEA and HEEA.

TABLE V. Alachlor Recovery Studies - Gauze Pads

	LAB		FIELD	
	1984 (c)	1985	1984 (c)	1985
Fortification Range (μg)	0.01-600	0.5-5000	0.01-40	0.5-5000
No. of Spikes	12	27	16	56
Recovery Mean (%)	104	89.7	69.6	89.2
Std. Dev.	11.5	7.3	24.5	11.2

1984 = Canadian Study
1985 = Missouri Study

TABLE VI.   Alachlor Body Dose Estimates

Study/ Applicator No.	Applicator Weight(kg)	Formul. Oper.(1)	Body Dose (µg/kg/lb)	
			Biol. Monit.(2)	Passive Dos.(3)
IND 01	85	EC/MLA	0.00526	-
IND 03	80	EC/MLA	0.00574	-
IND 05	86	EC/MLA	0	-
IND 07	84	EC/MLA	0.000676	-
CAN 01	70.5	EC/MLA	0.0270	0.0151
CAN 05	81.8	EC/MLA	0.0199	0.128
IND 02	86	MT/MLA	0.0218	-
IND 04	59	MT/MLA	0.0227	-
IND 06	89	MT/MLA	0.00425	-
IND 08	64	MT/MLA	0.00249	-
CAN 03	95.5	MT/MLA	0.112	1.38
CAN 04	79.5	MT/MLA	0.0405	0.0813
MO 05	68.1	MT/MLA	0.000722	0.000153
MO 07	77.2	MT/MLA	0.00123	0.000566
MO 09	63.6	MT/MLA	0	0.00135
MO 10	90.8	MT/MLA	0.00149	0.000201
MO 06	95.3	WDG/MLA	0.00158	0.000268
MO 08	88.5	WDG/MLA	0.00231	0.000354
MO 11	79.5	WDG/MLA	0.000559	0.000332
MO 12	86.3	WDG/MLA	0	0.000927
MO 27	70.4	EC/ML	0	0
MO 28	74.9	EC/ML	0	0.0000127
MO 29	74.9	EC/ML	0.00269	0.0000224
MO 30	70.4	EC/ML	0	0
MO 25	77.2	MT/ML	0.000559	0.0000702
MO 26	84.0	MT/ML	0.000135	0.0000112
MO 31	81.7	MT/ML	0.000372	0.000184
MO 32	77.2	MT/ML	0.00130	0.000403
MO 33	81.7	WDG/ML	0.000294	0.000118
MO 34	77.2	WDG/ML	0.000300	0.000389
MO 35	102.0	WDG/ML	0.000398	0.000102
MO 36	72.6	WDG/ML	0.000228	0.000310

MLA = Mixer/Loader & Application   IND = Indiana
ML = Mixer/Loader Only   CAN = Canada
                                      MO = Missouri

(1) All US applicators applied 80 lb alachlor to 20 acres; Canad-
     ians applied 160 lb to 40 acres (EC) or 150 to 37 acres (MT).
(2) Corrected for 88% urinary excretion (14C/monkey excretion)
(3) Adjusted for 8.5% dermal absorption (14C/monkey dermal study)

collected from the applicator. For example, Table VII shows that
Missouri Applicator #10 excreted a total of 9.48 μg alachlor after
application of 80 lb alachlor to a 20 acre plot (4 lb/acre).

This value is then corrected for the 88% excretory recovery
obtained in the ^{14}C-monkey studies, and normalized for body weight
and pounds of active ingredient applied:

$$\frac{9.48\ \mu g}{0.88} \times \frac{1}{90\ \text{kg body weight}} \times \frac{1}{80\ \text{lb applied}} = 0.00149\ \mu g/kg/lb$$

The value 0.00149 μg/kg/lb is shown in the body dose column
(biol. monitoring) of Table VI under applicator "MO 10". The
values in the next column of Table VI, i.e., body dose from the
passive dosimetry studies, are calculated from gauze pads by
multiplying the pad value by the exposed body area which it
represents:

$$\text{Body dose }(\mu g/kg/lb) = \frac{\text{measured }(\mu g/cm^2)\ \times\ \text{exposed skin }(cm^2)}{\text{body weight }(kg)\ \times\ \text{lb applied}}$$

Areas of exposed skin were 650 cm^2 for the face, 150 cm^2 for
the front of the neck and 110 cm^2 for the back of the neck (Davies
1980). All other areas were assumed to be protected by the clothing. The hands were protected by rubber gloves, as per label
directions. The measured values were corrected for the 8.5% dermal
absorption obtained in the ^{14}C-dermal monkey studies, producing the
body dose values shown in Table VI. Inhalation was not measured,
but was previously shown to be negligible in comparison to dermal

TABLE VII.   Excretion Profile for Missouri Applicator #10

[1]Hours After Application	[2]Combined* Pesticide/ Metabolite Residue (μg/mL)	[3]Volume of Urine (mL)	[4]Total≠ μg
0-12	0.01414	434	6.14
12-24	0.00499	451	2.25
24-36	0.00280	388	1.09
36-48	N.D.	691	0
48-60	N.D.	1214	0
60-72	N.D.	270	0
72-84	N.D.	809	0
84-96	N.D.	875	0
96-108	N.D.	1042	0
108-120	N.D.	531	0

Total excreted   9.48 μg

* Results corrected for analytical/field fortification recovery
N.D. = not detected (LOD = 0.0025 μg/mL)
≠ Total μg is obtained by multiplying the value in column 2 with
the corresponding value in column 3.

deposition.   (Lauer and Arras, 1982; Libich, et al., 1984; Lavy, 1978).

There appears to be no difference in exposure for the three formulations tested, judging by the values obtained for mixer-loaders (applicators MO25-MO36) applying the emulsifiable concentrate (Lasso), microencapsulated (Lasso MT), or water dispersible granule (Lasso WDG) formulations. Variability within formulations overshadows any potential differences between formulations, as shown in Figure 2.

Since each of the studies was performed under a different set of conditions (open versus closed-cab tractor, etc.), average body doses were calculated for each separate study. Values are shown in Table VIII.

These values can be used for risk assessment calculations under any number of assumed farm sizes or conditions. It should be noted, however, that these values are applicable only to applicators using small containers, 2.5 - 5.0 gallons, which are predominant in small farms (<300 acres). Large farmers and commercial applicators use mainly bulk or mini-bulk containers, such as the Monsanto Shuttle, which delivers the formulation into the sprayer in a "closed-system" fashion. Body doses for such systems have been reported elsewhere (Cowell, 1987) and average 1.8 X 10^{-4} µg/kg/lb, several fold lower than the small container studies described in Table VIII.

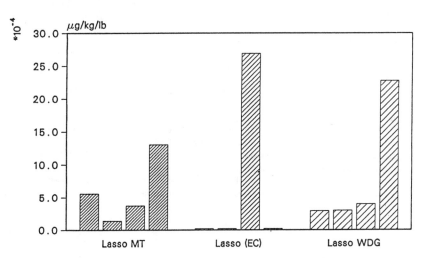

Figure 2.   Exposure Levels of Mixer/Loaders.

Table VIII. Average Body Dose in Biological Monitoring Studies

Study	Conditions	Avg. Body Dose (μg/kg/lb)
Indiana (8 Applicators)	Closed-Cab Tractor Soil Incorporated	7.8×10^{-3}
Canada (4 Applicators)	Open Tractor Small Sprayer Surface Applied	5.0×10^{-2}
Missouri (20 Applicators)	Large Closed Tractor Farmer Education	8.1×10^{-4}

Conclusion

Biological monitoring of urinary metabolites is a direct and
effective way of determining actual applicator exposure. Knowledge
of animal metabolism and excretion kinetics is necessary for
calculation of body dose. Studies with alachlor showed that body
dose averages can range from 5×10^{-2} μg/kg/lb for farmers using
small open tractors and small containers, to 1.8×10^{-4} μg/kg/lb
for large farmers or commercial applicators using large equipment
and bulk containers.

Literature Cited

1. Cowell, J. E., et al; Arch. Environ. Contam. Toxicol 1987,
    16, 327-332.
2. Davis, J.E.; Minimizing Occupation Exposure to Pesticides
    Residue Reviews 1980, 75, 34-50.
3. Lauer, R. and Arras, D.D.; Aerial and Ground Applicator
    Exposure Studies with Lasso Herbicide 1982, Monsanto Final
    Report MSL-1889; EPA Accession No. 70591.
4. Libich, S.; To, J.; Frank, R.; Sirons, G. Am. Ind. Hyg.
    Assoc. J. 1984, 45:56-62.
5. Lavy, T. L. Project Completion Report to National Forest
    Products Association, August 30 to October 1978.

RECEIVED November 24, 1987

Chapter 20

Quantitative Determination of Haloxyfop in Human Urine by Gas Chromatography—Mass Spectrometry

R. A. Campbell, P. E. Kastl, B. E. Kropscott, and M. J. Bartels

Analytical and Environmental Chemistry, Health and Environmental Sciences, Dow Chemical Company, Midland, MI 48674

An analytical method has been developed for the quantitative determination, at low to sub ppb levels, of haloxyfop in human urine. This method could be used to determine potential worker exposure to VERDICT herbicide during typical product use. Urine samples containing haloxyfop were fortified with isotopically labeled haloxyfop, extracted using benzene, derivatized, cleaned-up via HPLC and analyzed by gas chromatography-mass spectrometry. The mean relative recovery (±S.D.) of haloxyfop from urine (test material vs. internal standard) for the 7 concentrations ranging from 100 ng/mL to 0.2 ng/mL, was 107±7%. The coefficient of variation for relative recovery from urine was 3% at the highest (100 ng/mL) concentration and 58% at the lowest (0.2 ng/mL) concentration.

A stability evaluation showed haloxyfop to be stable in urine samples stored at room temperature for at least two weeks.

Haloxyfop methyl ester (I), [methyl 2-(4-((3-chloro-5-(trifluoromethyl)-2-pyridinyl)oxy)phenoxy)propionate], the active ingredient in VERDICT herbicide formulations, is being evaluated for registration as a herbicide for eradication of annual and perennial grasses. The method described in this report was developed using a racemic mixture of haloxyfop and does not differentiate between the S and R forms.

0097–6156/89/0382–0251$06.00/0
○ 1989 American Chemical Society

Unpublished data show haloxyfop methyl ester is
rapidly hydrolyzed to the acid in man. An analytical
method was required to determine low level
concentrations of haloxyfop in human urine. A method
using an isotopically labeled (D_4-haloxyfop) internal
standard and gas chromatography-mass spectrometry with
multiple ion detection (GC/MS MID) was developed to
quantitatively determine haloxyfop in urine as low as
0.2 ng/mL. This procedure includes an automated high
resolution sample cleanup using reversed-phase HPLC.

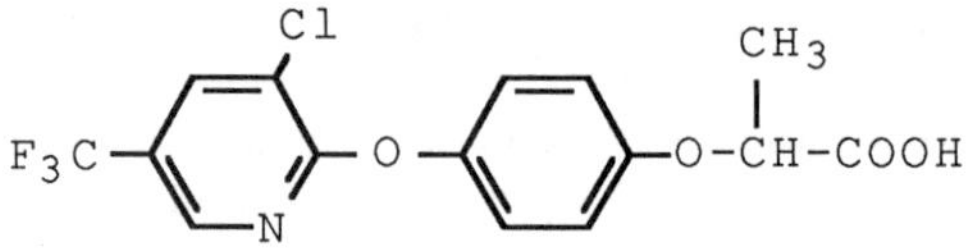

(I) HALOXYFOP

MATERIALS AND METHODS

MATERIALS. Haloxyfop was supplied by Agricultural
Products Department, The Dow Chemical Company. The
chemical purity of the test material, a racemic
mixture, was determined to be ±99% by liquid
chromatography. Isotopically labeled haloxyfop,
(99.5% pure) for use as an internal standard was
synthesized using a deuterated intermediate [prepared
by refluxing with D_2SO_4 at 95°C] (Bartels, M. J.;
Gatling, S. C. J. Labelled Compounds Radiopharm., in
press.) This procedure resulted in a nearly complete
exchange of deuterium for the four hydrogens on the
phenyl (center) ring. Distilled-in-glass benzene,
methanol, UV spectrophotometric grade hexane,
acetonitrile and concentrated hydrochloric acid were
obtained from Fisher Scientific (Fair Lawn, NJ). WISP
Limited Volume Inserts for HPLC analysis were obtained
from Waters Div. (Millipore, Milford, MA). Conical
GC/MS autosampler vials were obtain from Wheaton
Scientific (Millville, NJ). Human urine for method
validation was obtained from volunteers within the
Toxicology Lab, The Dow Chemical Company.

STANDARDS. Stock solutions A and B were prepared by
dissolving accurately weighed amounts of haloxyfop and
D_4-haloxyfop, respectively, in methanol. Aliquots of
each of these stock solutions were combined and
diluted in methanol to prepare a third stock solution
(C). External standard solutions for the GC/MS were
prepared by methylating an aliquot of stock solution C
using diazomethane, evaporating to dryness under
nitrogen and then diluting with hexane to achieve the

desired concentration [i.e. (249 ng/mL haloxyfop / 503 ng/mL int. std.) to (4.98 ng/mL haloxyfop / 10.1 ng/mL int. std.)]. Solutions for spiking urine were prepared by diluting an aliquot of stock solution C with methanol to yield solutions of [2.49 μg/mL haloxyfop / 5.03 μg/mL int. std.) to (0.249 μg/mL haloxyfop / 0.503 μg/mL int. std.). For recovery determinations urine samples were spiked with 10-125 mL of the appropriate spiking solution prior to extraction.

EXTRACTION METHOD AND HPLC CLEAN-UP. The appropriate amount of haloxyfop and internal standard were spiked into 30 mL of urine. Concentrated HCl (1 mL) was added to the urine and the sample was heated at 80°C for 1 hour. After allowing to cool, 5 mL of benzene was added to the sample which was agitated for 30 seconds on a vortex mixer followed by centrifugation at 1500 rpm for 5 minutes. The benzene extract was removed by pipet and an additional 5 mL of benzene was added to the sample which was agitated and centrifuged again. The second benzene extract was combined with the first extract. An ethereal solution of diazomethane was generated using Diazald (Aldrich Chemical Company, Inc., Milwaukee), and approximately 1 mL added to each sample. After complete methylation (~10 min.) the solutions were evaporated under a gentle stream of nitrogen. The residue was then reconstituted in diethyl ether and quantitatively transferred to a WISP Limited Volume Insert. The ether was evaporated under nitrogen and the sample was reconstituted in 125 μL of methanol.

For automated clean-up of the derivatized urine extracts, a 100 μL aliquot was injected on a reversed-phase HPLC system collecting the fraction (typically 3.75 to 5.2 minutes) containing the haloxyfop methyl ester and the co-eluting internal standard peak. The clean-up was performed using a Waters Radial Compression Module (RCM-100) and a NOVA-PAK column. A guard column (2.54 cm x 3.9 mm) containing μBondapak C_{18} (37-50 μm) was used for the protection of the analytical column. The HPLC conditions were as follows: autosampler: Waters WISP (Model 510B) with Limited Volume inserts; Detector: Waters 481 (λ = 227 nm) with sensitivity at 0.01 AUFS; pump: Waters 590; column: NOVA-PAK C_{18} (10 cm x 5 mm id); flow rate: 1.0 mL/min; pressure: 1700 psi; injection volume: 100 μL; mobile phase: 70/30 acetonitrile/distilled water. A fraction collector fitted with an air-actuated valve that alternated the column effluent between waste and a new collection vial was used. The timing of the valve switching was controlled by the Waters 590 pump.

The UV detector was used only for checking the
retention window of standards. Samples contained high
levels of UV absorbing components, thus fractions were
collected based on retention times.

The 3.75 to 5.2 minute fraction of the effluent
from the UV detector was collected in a 1 dram vial.
500 µL of hexane was added to the vial which was
agitated for 15 seconds on a vortex mixer and
centrifuged at 3000 rpm for 1 minute. The hexane
(top) layer was removed and placed in a 500 µL
conical vial. The sample was blown to dryness under
nitrogen and reconstituted in 100 µL of hexane prior
to injection on the GC/MS. The 10 and 100 ng/µL
spiked urine extracts were reconstituted in 1.0 and
10.0 ml hexane, respectively.

GAS CHROMATOGRAPHY-MASS SPECTROMETRY. A Finnigan 4600
GC/MS equipped with a SuperIncos data system (Finnigan
MAT, San Jose, CA), a Hewlett Packard 7673 autosampler
and operated in the MID mode, was used for
quantitative analysis of final extracts.

Separation of the haloxyfop as its methyl ester
from interfering species in the urine was achieved
with a 15 m x 0.32 mm i.d. DX-3 capillary column, 0.25
µm film thickness (J&W Scientific, Inc. Folsom, CA).
Helium at 11 psig was used as the carrier gas. During
the analysis, the column was maintained at a
temperature of 220°C, the injection port and interface
oven temperatures were 275 and 270°C, respectively.
The injection volume was 3.0 µL. A modified fixed-
ratio splitting system (1) was used. A 10 cm x 0.1 mm
fused silica restrictor tube was sealed in the
injector split vent on the front instrument panel. The
split valve was fully opened, allowing flow control by
the restrictor tube. The effluent was vented to a
fume hood through 1/8 inch teflon tubing. The GC/MS
was also equipped with a reduced-pressure interface
(2). Other MS operating parameters are as follows:
preamp: 10^{-8} amps/volt; electron energy: 70 eV;
emission current: 0.4 mA; multiplier voltage: 1.4
kV; source temperature: 150°C; indicated pressure: 5
x 10^{-6} torr. Haloxyfop was quantified using internal
standard techniques by monitoring the molecular ions,
m/z 375 for the methyl ester of haloxyfop and m/z 379
for the deuterated haloxyfop internal standard methyl
ester.

CALCULATIONS

Internal standard calculations were used in this
analysis. The response factor (Rf) for a standard was
calculated from the following equation:

$$Rf = \frac{C_{HAL} \times A_{IS}}{A_{HAL} \times C_{IS}} \tag{1}$$

where C_{HAL} and C_{IS} are the concentrations of the compounds in ng/mL of haloxyfop and D_4-internal standard respectively. A_{HAL} and A_{IS} are the respective GC/MS peak areas obtained for these two compounds in the analysis of the standard solutions.

The relative recovery of haloxyfop vs. D_4-haloxyfop from the spiked urine samples was calculated from the following equation:

$$\% \text{ Recovery} = \frac{\overline{Rf} \times (A_{HAL}-BKG) \times Ng_{IS}}{A_{IS} \times Ng_{HAL}} \times 100 \tag{2}$$

where Ng_{IS} is the amount (in ng) of the internal standard added to the sample. Ng_{HAL} is the amount (in ng) of haloxyfop spiked into the urine sample. $\overline{Rf}$ is is the mean of the response factors obtained from the external standards. A_{HAL} and A_{IS} are the peak areas obtained for haloxyfop and D_4-internal standard in the analysis of the sample. BKG is the average of the background (at m/z 375) observed in the analysis of blank urine samples, adjusted for any difference in dilution factor between the control and spiked urine samples.

The concentration of haloxyfop in unknown urine samples was calculated from the following equation:

$$C_{HAL} = \frac{\overline{Rf} \times (A_{HAL} - BKG) \times Ng_{IS} \times 100}{A_{IS} \times \text{volume of urine (mL)} \times \% \text{ recovery}} \tag{3}$$

RESULTS AND DISCUSSION

To determine the relative recovery from urine, standards were prepared by adding a known amount of haloxyfop and internal standard to 30 mL of urine. Full-scan mass spectra for those two compounds are shown in Figure 1. Urine samples were acidified and heated for 1 hour at 80°C to hydrolyze any conjugates. The urine samples were then extracted with benzene, methylated and reconstituted in methanol prior to clean-up by HPLC. The samples were then analyzed by GC/MS using multiple ion detection. Relative recovery of haloxyfop from urine ranged from 120% to 99% (mean = 107±7%) for the concentration range of 100 ng/mL to 0.2 ng/mL (see Table I). The coefficients of

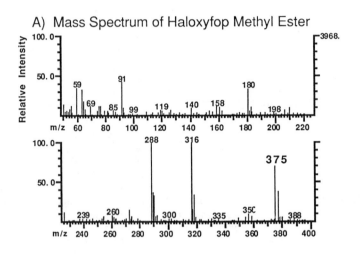

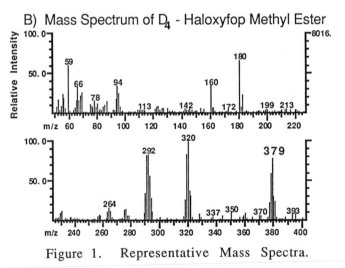

Figure 1.   Representative Mass Spectra.

variation for the highest and lowest urine concentrations were 3% at the 100 ng/mL concentration and 58% at the 0.2 ng/mL concentration.

HPLC purification of the urine extracts was performed for two reasons. Without this clean-up step there were large interferences present in the GC/MS peak for the unlabelled haloxyfop methyl ester (m/z 375). Purification of the samples by this method was also found to significantly extend the life of the fused silica capillary GC column.

Another feature of the method described in this report is the use of a reduced-pressure GC/MS interface. This interface, developed by Langvardt, et. al (2), utilizes a computer-controlled solenoid valve to divert the majority of the GC effluent away from the mass spectrometer source (Figure 2). This modification minimizes the amount of unwanted sample components entering the MS source and thereby extends the source life.

The incorporation of the stable-isotope-labelled internal standard into this assay was highly useful. Its use automatically corrected for loss of the test material during sample extraction, derivatization and HPLC purification. It also corrected for possible errors in dilution during sample preparation, due to the small sample volumes used in this assay. Finally, the deuterated haloxyfop compensated for the variability in the absolute response of the mass spectrometer over the course of the analysis.

The relative recoveries of 99-120% for the D_0- vs.D_4-haloxyfop (above) indicate that there is no appreciable difference in the absolute recoveries for these two compounds from urine. The absolute recoveries were not routinely calculated but were estimated to be less than 50%.

GC/MS chromatograms of a blank urine extract and a urine extract spiked at the lowest concentration studied are presented in Figure 3. The retention time for haloxyfop and the internal standard was 3.5 minutes. No peaks that would interfere with the analysis were noted in either the blank hexane, or standard solutions. However, there was an interference seen at m/z 375 in control urine samples. To compensate for this interference, 9 control samples were analyzed and the area response for m/z 375 was averaged. This area average of the background (equivalent to 0.02 ng/mL haloxyfop) was then subtracted from the haloxyfop area response (m/z 375) in the spiked urine samples. However, if the sample dilution factor was greater than the control dilution factor then the background area was divided by the ratio of the dilution factors prior to subtracting it from the sample's area response. The detection limit was defined as the mean background response plus three

Table I.   Recovery Data for Haloxyfop from Human Urine

Level (ng/mL)	% Recovery[a] Individual Samples			Mean %[b] Recovery	Std. Dev.	Coef. of Var.
100	104	98.3	104	102	3	3
10	116	121	94.1	110	14	13
1	97.9	96.0	123	106	15	14
0.8	116	101	110	109	8	7
0.6	124	91.4	99.7	105	17	16
0.4	40.9	164	154	120	68	57
0.2	161	47.0	89.9	99	58	58
				107±7[c]	35[d]	32[e]

[a]Individual data points not rounded to significant figures; mean of two injections.
[b]Each data point is the mean of 3 determinations.
[c]Mean ± standard deviation.
[d]Average standard deviation
[e]Average coefficient of variation.

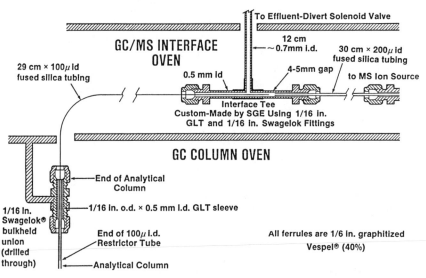

Figure 2.   Reduced-Pressure GC/MS Interface.

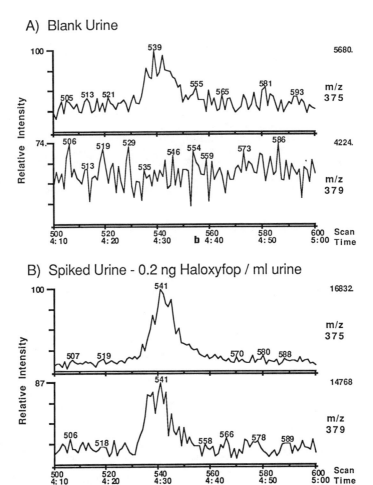

Figure 3. Representative Selected Ion Chromatograms.

times the standard deviation of the background
response.

The external standard solutions and fortified
urine samples contained fixed ratios of test
material/internal standard. The GC/MS response ratio
(m/z 375/379) for these compounds was constant,
ranging from 0.56 to 0.60 (mean = 0.58±0.02) for
external standard solutions in the concentration range
of 249/503 ng/ml to 4.98/10.1 ng/ml (D_0/D_4-haloxyfop),
respectively. One assumption made when quantitating
haloxyfop by this method is that the relative response
of the mass spectrometer (D_0/D_4-haloxyfop) is linear
over the concentrations of the external standard
solutions. This is supported by the consistent
response ratios obtained in this study. However,
future work with this method would be further
supported by the addition of a linear standard curve,
containing fixed amounts of the internal standard and
varying levels of the test material, in either
external standard solutions or fortified control urine
samples.

During the course of a field study, it is likely
that all samples could not be analyzed immediately.
Therefore, stability of haloxyfop in urine samples was
investigated to determine if the samples could be
stored until analysis could be performed. A stability
evaluation showed haloxyfop to be stable in urine
samples stored at room temperature for at least two
weeks (data not shown).

In summary, a method was developed for the
quantitative determination of haloxyfop in human urine
over the concentration range of 200 pg/ml to 100
ng/ml. The method involved fortification of urine
samples with a deuterium-labelled haloxyfop internal
standard, hydrolysis of acid-labile conjugates, HPLC
purification of derivatized urine extracts, followed
by GC/MS analysis of the methyl ester of the test
material. The HPLC purification was required to
obtain samples without significant levels of
interferences. The internal standard was employed to
correct for 1) loss of test material during sample
preparation and 2) variability of the mass
spectrometer during sample analysis. Finally, the MID
GC/MS method, employing a reduced-pressure interface,
was found to be sufficiently selective and sensitive
for the determination of haloxyfop at these levels.

ACKNOWLEDGMENTS

The authors would like to acknowledge Patrick
Langvardt for his technical guidance and review of
this work, and thank Karen Foster and Fran Stafford
for their efforts in preparing this manuscript.

LITERATURE CITED

1.   Nestrick, T. J., Lamparski, L. L. and Peters, T.
      L. (1983). Low-Splitting-Ratio Injector for
      Capillary Gas Chromatography. Anal. Chem. 55,
      2009-2011.

2.   Langvardt, P. W., Shadoff, L. A. and Kastl, P. E.
      (1985). Proc. 33rd Conf.Amer. Soc. Mass
      Spectrom. 1985, pp 837-838.

RECEIVED February 25, 1988

Chapter 21

Enzyme Immunoassay for Aldicarb

James F. Brady[1], James R. Fleeker[2], Richard A. Wilson[3], and Ralph O. Mumma[1]

[1]Pesticide Research Laboratory, Department of Entomology, Pennsylvania State University, University Park, PA 16802
[2]Biochemistry Department, North Dakota State University, Fargo, ND 58105
[3]Department of Veterinary Science, Pennsylvania State University, University Park, PA 16802

An enzyme immunoassay (EIA) for aldicarb has been developed. The assay is simple to perform, requires minimal sample preparation and time of analysis is less than 2.5 hr. The assay has been applied to a variety of sample types including citrus juice products, body fluids and water. The analyses demonstrated a linear response from 15.6 to 2000 ng of aldicarb with coefficients of determination typically exceeding 0.98. The least detectable dose was 0.3 parts per million (ppm). The enzyme immunoassay was characterized by high precision of measurement as coefficients of variation were less than 5%. The assay is highly specific to aldicarb and has no cross-reactivity with the sulfoxide or sulfone.

The application of immunochemical techniques to the analysis of agrichemicals has expanded dramatically in recent years (1). Immunochemical methods offer many advantages including ease of analysis, speed, sensitivity, specificity and cost effectiveness (2). More importantly, they offer an alternative means of quantitating chemicals whose water solubility, instability at high temperature, or lack of strong ultraviolet absorbance may render classical analytical approaches insensitive or unsuitable.

Aldicarb (2-methyl-2-(methylthio)propionaldehyde 0-(methyl-carbamoyl)-oxime) is such a compound. It is moderately soluble in water (0.6% by weight), forms a nitrile degradation product at high temperatures and exhibits a weak ultraviolet absorbance maxima at 247 nm. Classical

0097–6156/89/0382–0262$06.75/0
© 1989 American Chemical Society

analytical techniques developed for aldicarb are consequently cumbersome or require specialized instrumentation.
A sample is usually extracted with an acetone-water solution, oxidized with peracetic acid to the sulfone, cleaned
up by passage through a Florisil column, and analyzed by
pyrolytic gas-liquid chromatography (GLC) (3-5). Aldicarb
is thus quantified indirectly via measurement of an oxidation product which, coincidentally, is also a metabolic
degradation product. Direct high-pressure liquid chromatographic (HPLC) techniques for aldicarb monitor the weak
absorption at 247 or 254 nm (6-8). Post-column derivatization HPLC procedures involve hydrolysis of aldicarb with
base, derivatization of the liberated methylamine with
ortho-phthalaldehyde and 2-mercaptoethanol, and subsequent
analysis of the fluorescent product (9,10). This report
describes the development of an enzyme immunoassay for
aldicarb. The assay is rapid, sensitive, simple to perform, and requires minimal sample preparation.

Materials and Methods

Apparatus. Kinetic studies were performed on a Perkin-
Elmer Lambda 3B UV/VIS spectrophotometer. The cuvette was
thermostated by a Haake A80 temperature controller. Assay
plates were scanned on an Artek Vertical Beam spectrophotometer. NMR spectra were obtained on a Varian 360
spectrophotometer.

Reagents. All chemicals used were of reagent grade
quality. 4-Aminobutyric acid, iso-butylchloroformate,
trans-4-(aminomethyl)cyclohexanecarboxylic acid, poly-
oxyethylene sorbitan monolaurate (Tween 20), and alkaline
phosphatase, type VII-T, from bovine intestinal mucosa,
were obtained from Sigma Chemical Co. Rabbit gama globu-
lins, fraction two, were purchased from Miles Laboratories,
Inc. HPLC grade acetonitrile was purchased from J.T. Baker
Chemical Co. 4-Nitrophenyl phosphate and 1-(3-dimethyl-
aminopropyl)-3-ethylcarbodiimide hydrochloride were
obtained from Aldrich Chemical Co., Inc. Carnitine was
purchased from Calbiochem and choline chloride was obtained
from Merck & Co. Aldicarb, aldicarb oxime, aldicarb oxime
sulfoxide, aldicarb sulfoxide, aldicarb sulfone, methomyl,
mesurol and cyanazine reference standards were obtained
from the Environmental Protection Agency, Reno, NV. Water
for HPLC analysis was distilled and further purified on a
Milli-Q reagent grade water system, Millipore, Inc.

Synthesis of Ligands. The preparation of aldicarb oxime
and the chloroformate derivative have been described by
Payne et al. (11). A cold solution of aldicarb oxide
chloroformate (40 mmole) in 40 mL of diethyl ether was
added alternately with 40 mmole NaOH in 15 mL water to a
stirred and cooled solution of 42 mmole of *trans*-4-(aminomethyl)cyclohexanecarboxylic acid and 43 mmole NaOH in 20

mL water. The addition was carried out over a 20 min
period. After the addition, stirring was continued another
45 min. The mixture was diluted with 20 mL of 2 M HCl and
25 mL diethylether and the layers separated. The aqueous
solution was extracted twice again with 25 mL portions of
ether and the combined ether extracts washed twice with
water. The ether solution was dried over anhydrous Na_2SO_4
and the solvent removed with a rotary evaporator. The
residue was recrystallized from benzene-hexane, m.p. 102-
105°C with decomposition. ^1H NMR: (90 MHz, CDCl$_3$) δ 0.6-2.8
[10H, m, C$_6$H$_{10}$]; 1.5 [6H, s, C(CH$_3$)$_2$]; 2.0 [3H, s, CH$_3$-S];
3.1-3.4 [2H, s (broad), CH$_2$-N]; 6.2 [1 H, s (broad), NH];
7.6 [1H, s, CH=N]; 12.4 [1H, s, COOH]. This compound was
labeled aldicarb Ligand 1 (Figure 1).

Ligand 2 (Figure 2) was prepared from 4-aminobutyric
acid (GABA) and aldicarb oxime chloroformate in the same
manner as Ligand 1 and recrystallized from benzene-hexane,
m.p. 116-117°C. ^{1}NMR: (90 MHz, acetone-d$_6$) δ 1.5 [6H, s,
C(CH$_3$)$_2$]; 2.0 [3H, s, CH$_3$-S]; 1.8-2.1 [2H, m, CH$_2$CH$_2$,CH$_2$];
2.3-2.5 [2H, t, CH$_2$COH]; 3.2-3.4 [2H, q, NH-CH$_2$]; 6.8 [1H,
s (broad), NH]; 7.6 [1H, s, CH=N]; 12.0 [1H, s, COOH].

Preparation of Immunogen. Aldicarb Ligand 1 was conjugated
to bovine serum albumin (BSA) by adapting the procedure
described by Erlanger et al. (12) (Figure 1). The ligand
(2.25 mmole) was dissolved in 15 mL dioxane and 0.31 mL
triethylamine. The solution was cooled, diluted with 0.3
mL of isobutylchloroformate and stirred 20 min. This
suspension was added in one portion to a solution of 2.5 g
BSA in 65 mL water, 2.5 mL 1M NaOH and 65 mL dioxane which
was cooled and stirred in an ice water bath. After 2 min,
1.25 mL of 1 M NaOH was added and stirring continued 4 hr.
The solution was dialyzed overnight in running water and
the pH adjusted to 4.5. After cooling 2 hr in ice water,
the precipitate was collected by centrifugation and the
pellet dissolved in 150 mL 1% NaHCO$_3$. The solution was
diluted with 1 L cold acetone and the precipitate collected
by centrifugation. The pellet was suspended in cold
acetone, filtered and washed with acetone. The pellet was
then dried, ground in a mortar and stored desiccated at
-20°C.

Antibody Formation. The powdered immunogen (50 mg) was
suspended in 1.5 mL of 0.9% (w/v) sterile NaCl and homoge-
nized in 1.5 mL of Freund's complete adjuvant. This preparation was injected (0.5 mL) into the thigh muscle of
female New Zealand white rabbits. The injection was
repeated every 25-30 days, subcutaneously, at several sites
on the back. Serum was treated with an equal volume of 70%
saturated ammonium sulfate and the γ-globulin collected by
centrifugation. The γ-globulin pellet was dissolved in one
volume of water, dialyzed against phosphate-buffered saline
and freeze-dried.

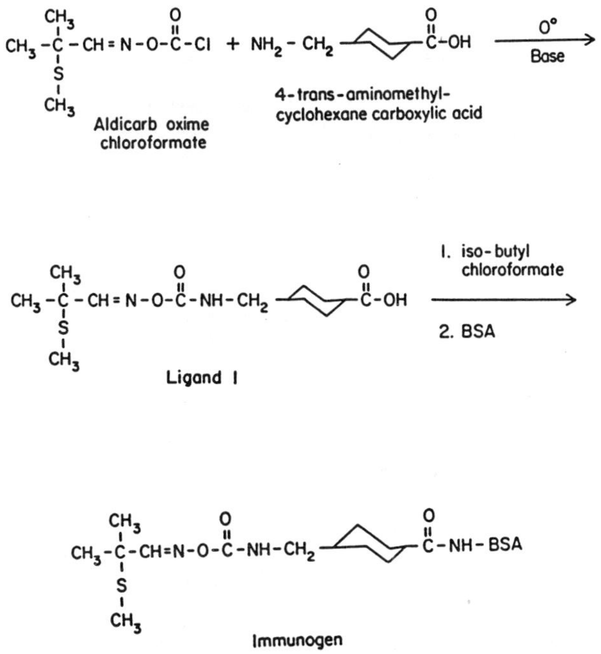

Figure 1. Synthesis of Ligand 1 and aldicarb immunogen.

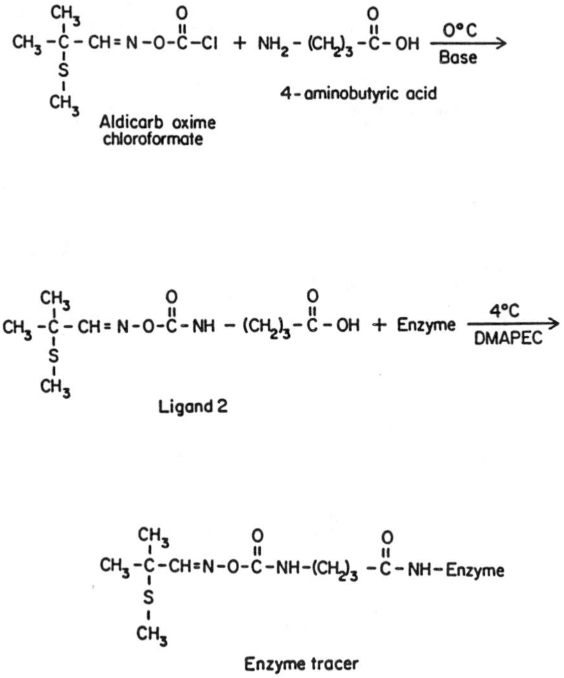

Figure 2.   Synthesis of Ligand 2 and aldicarb enzyme tracer.

Synthesis of Enzyme Tracer. Aldicarb Ligand 2 was conjugated to alkaline phosphatase by a method similar to that
of Weiler (13) (Figure 2). A solution (200 µL) of 10 µmol
ligand in 1.0 mL DMF:H_2O (1:1, v/v) was added to 200 µL
H_2O, pH 6.4, in a 5 mL vial in an ice bath with stirring.
Four 25 µL aliquots of 15 µmol 1-(dimethylaminopropyl)-3-
ethylcarbodiimide hydrochloride dissolved in 100 µL H_2O
were added drop-wise to the vial over 2 min. The solution
was allowed to stir for 15 min after which four 25 µL
aliquots of alkaline phosphatase stock solution (10 mg
protein per mL) were added drop-wise over 2 min. The
resulting cloudy solution was left to stir for 45 min. The
solution and a 500 µL H_2O rinse were dialyzed against 2 X 1
L of Tris-buffered saline (TBS) (50 mM Tris, 1 mM magnesium
chloride and 10 mM sodium chloride; pH adjusted to 7.5 with
concentrated hydrochloric acid) at 4°C. The dialysate was
centrifuged at 1100 X G for 5 min. The supernatant was
transferred to a 5 mL vial and the pellet set aside for
further evaluation.

Characterization of Enzyme Tracer. The activity of the
enzyme tracer was compared to that of the stock alkaline
phosphatase solution. Enzyme activity was measured by
monitoring hydrolysis of 4-nitrophenol phosphate at 405 nm
(A_{405}), an absorbance maxima of 4-nitrophenoxide anion.
Enzyme was diluted in buffer (0.05 M carbonate, 22 mM
disodium carbonate, 28 mM sodium hydrogen carbonate and 1
mM magnesium chloride, pH 9.8) to yield a change in
absorbance (ΔA_{405}) of approximately 1.0 per minute when
incubated with 5 mM substrate at 30°C.
     To incubations containing 250 µL of the enzyme prepara-
tion were added 250 µL of substrate in buffer. Reactions
were monitored for four minutes. Each enzyme dilution and
substrate concentration was measured twice. Reaction
velocity was determined by measuring the slope of the
initial linear portion of the absorbance-time graph.
Previous experiments showed that non-enzymatic hydrolysis
of substrate did not affect assay performance under these
conditions. Slope measurement, ΔA_{405}/min, were converted
to velocity units, mM/ng protein/min, by insertion of the
absorbance values into an equation regressing absorbances
onto known concentrations of 4-nitrophenol. The inverses
of reaction velocities and substrate concentrations were
graphed in a double reciprocal plot from which the K_m and
V_{max} of each enzyme preparation were calculated.

Enzyme Immunoassay. Determination of Reagent Concentration. Appropriate concentrations of antibody and enzyme
tracer were determined by checkerboard assay (14). All
solutions excluding enzyme substrate were cooled to 4°C
prior to use. Lyophilized antiserum was reconstituted in
H_2O and diluted in buffer (0.1 M sodium carbonate, 32 mM
disodium carbonate, 68 mM sodium hydrogen carbonate, and

3 mM sodium azide, pH 9.6). Adsorption of antiserum to
individual wells of Nunc (A/S Nunc, Roskilde, Denmark) 96-
well flatbottom polystyrene disposable assay plates was
accomplished by addition of 1.25, 2.5, 5, 10 and 20 μg
antibody in 100 μl 0.1 M carbonate buffer. The plate was
placed in a closed chamber lined with wet paper towels and
incubated overnight (12 to 15 hr) at 4°C. The following
morning the plate's contents were removed by aspiration.
All wells were washed 3 X 5 min with a Tween 20-NaCl solution (27 g sodium chloride and 1.5 mL Tween 20 dissolved in
3 L H$_2$O). 50 μL of enzyme tracer serially diluted in TBS
from 10- to 160-fold were added to the plates which were
then placed in a refrigerator and incubated at 4°C. After
30 min, the plates were removed from the cold, aspirated
and washed 2 X 5 min with Tween 20-NaCl. Substrate solution (100 μL, 1 mg 4-nitrophenyl phosphate per ml of 0.05 M
carbonate buffer) at 30°C was added to each well and the
plate set aside to incubate 1 hr at room temperature. The
reaction was terminated by addition of 50 μL 1 M NaOH to
each well. Extent of reaction was measured spectrophoto-
metrically at 405 nm. Each combination of antibody and
enzyme tracer concentration was replicated four times. The
lowest concentrations of antibody and enzyme tracer that
resulted in a mean A$_{405}$ of approximately 1.3 were selected
for use.

Principle of Immunoassay. Reagent concentrations determined by the above procedure were used in the competitive
assay. Each standard and sample were run in quadruplicate.
Antibody diluted in 0.1 M carbonate buffer was adsorbed to
the plate as described above. Outer wells were not used
due to non-specific color development (15). Standard
curves were prepared by adding to individual wells 40 μL
H$_2$O and 10 μL of a stock solution of aldicarb dissolved in
acetonitrile (ACN) (1 mg/ml) and serially diluted in H$_2$O.
This resulted in final concentrations of aldicarb ranging
from 15.6 to 2000 ng. Four wells received zero concentration of aldicarb. An antibody control, to evaluate non-
specific binding, was included on each plate. This consisted of wells coated with non-immune rabbit γ-globulin to
which no aldicarb was added during the inhibition step.
The plate was incubated 30 min at 4°C. A solution of
enzyme tracer (50 μL) was then added to each well and the
plate returned to the cold for an additional 30 min. After
that time, contents of the plate were removed by aspiration
and the plate was washed. Assay of bound enzyme tracer was
carried out as previously described. Absorption readings
were converted to 'Percent Inhibition' by the following
equation:

$$\text{Percent Inhibition} = \left[1 - \left(\frac{A_S - A_{NSB}}{A_O - A_{NSB}} \right) \right] \times 100$$

in which A_S represents the A_{405} of an individual sample or standard well, A_{NSB} represents the mean A_{405} of the non-specific binding control wells and A_0 represents the mean A_{405} of wells coated with anti-aldicarb serum inhibited by zero concentration of aldicarb. These results were used to calculate the equation of a line describing the relationship of percent inhibition (ordinate) to the logarithm of the concentration of aldicarb (abscissa). This line was plotted on semi-logarithmic paper with each concentration of aldicarb expressed as a single point representing the mean percent inhibition of each level plus or minus one standard deviation. The coefficient of variation (CV) for each level and coefficient of determination (r^2) of each line were also determined.

Assay Specificity. The ability of the anti-aldicarb antibody to discriminate between aldicarb and other compounds which share structural similarities was evaluated. Each chemical was tested as above using the concentration range of aldicarb except that for some water replaced ACN as the carrier solvent. From the percent inhibition data obtained in these experiments, the concentration of each chemical that resulted in a 50% inhibition (I_{50}) of enzyme tracer binding was determined.

Chemicals selected for screening as potentially cross-reactive included the aldicarb metabolites aldicarb sulfoxide, aldicarb sulfone, aldicarb oxime, and aldicarb oxime sulfoxide. Agrichemicals tested which may be present in samples included the N-methyl carbamates methomyl and mesurol as well as a representative triazine herbicide cyanazine. Acetylcholine and its hydrolysis product, choline, were examined since aldicarb was designed as a structural mimic of the neurotransmitter (11). A biochemical of similar structure, carnitine, was also screened.

Sample Preparation. Lemonade, limeade and orange juice frozen concentrates were purchased from a local supermarket and prepared according to label directions. A 2 mL aliquot of lemonade and limeade was adjusted to pH 6.0-6.2 with 2 M NaOH and filtered with a 0.8 μm filter (Type AA 25 mm, Millipore Filter Corp.). Two mL of orange juice was adjusted to pH 6.0-6.2 by addition of a concentrated Tris buffer (0.4 M Tris, 1 mM magnesium chloride, and 10 mM sodium chloride adjusted to pH 7.5 with concentrated HCl) and similarly filtered. Fresh watermelon tissue was crushed and the liquid processed similarly. Stream water was collected from a local source and filtered in the same fashion. Human urine was filtered (0.8 μm) and saliva was prepared by passing through a cellulose absorbent pad (Millipore Filter Corp.). Rabbit serum was collected from female white New Zealand rabbits and filtered with a 0.8 μm

filter. Plasma was collected from Suffolk-Dorset mix-breed
sheep, passed through a 0.8 μm filter and diluted with TBS
(1:1, v/v). All samples were cooled at 4°C prior to assay.

Results and Discussion

Assay Design. Design considerations incorporated into the
aldicarb enzyme immunoassay included taking advantage of
the sensitivity of enzyme-linked immunosorbent assays
(ELISA) while reducing time of analysis and sample
handling. ELISAs developed as alternative pesticide
residue methods (1) are heterogeneous assays typically
requiring 18-22 hr to complete excluding the 12-15 hr
needed for adsorption of coating antigen to the wells of a
microtitre plate. Antibody inhibition by sample or
standard solutions is carried out in separate vessels from
which aliquots are subsequently transferred to the plate.
A solid-phase enzyme immunoassay technique similar to that
of Weiler (13) was developed to overcome these problems.
This method involves coating the wells of the microtitre
plate with antibody directed against the hapten of choice.
The coated plate serves as the reaction vessel for all subsequent steps, eliminating transfer of solutions incubated
in other containers. Antibody inhibition is followed
immediately by incubation of an enzyme tracer whose binding
is measured by spectrophotometric evaluation of an appropriate substrate.
     The net effect of this methodology is to reduce
analysis time from that of a typical ELISA of 18-22 hr to
less than 2.5 hr. This method permits a technician to make
two runs in a single eight-hour workday and allows use of
automated equipment and instrumentation already available
for ELISA. In consideration of these advantages, it is
surprising this approach has not been widely adapted to
other immunological pesticide residue methods. Huber (15)
developed an EIA for atrazine utilizing antibody-coated
plates and had a total analysis time of 4.5 hr. Schwalbe
et al. (16) synthesized an enzyme tracer for the analysis
of diclofop-methyl and ran homogeneous assays that required
separation of free and bound hapten before transfer to the
microtitre plate.
     The aldicarb enzyme immunoassay requires an anti-
aldicarb antibody and the synthesis of an enzyme tracer.
Rabbit antibodies were developed in response to inoculation
of an immunogen consisting of aldicarb coupled to BSA in
the form of Ligand 1, which mimics the structure of
aldicarb attached to a cyclohexanecarboxylic acid bridge.
The enzyme tracer, in contrast, consisted of Ligand 2,
incorporating a GABA bridge, conjugated to alkaline
phosphatase. The use of ligands differing in geometry and
length prevented antibody which may be specific to the

bridging structure of the immunogen from binding to a
similar structure on the enzyme tracer. Antibody binding
of the enzyme tracer was therefore restricted to the
aldicarb component of the conjugated ligand, effectively
preventing non-specific tracer binding.

Success of the enzyme immunoassay depends on synthesis
of an appropriate enzyme tracer. Typical ELISAs utilize
commercially available second antibodies bound to an enzyme
label. These labels require a two-hour incubation, adding
to the analysis time. The enzyme tracer used in this
assay, in comparison, required only a 30-minute incubation.
Synthesis of the tracer was a straight-forward application
of Weiler's procedure (13) and, surprisingly, did not
significantly affect the enzyme's catalytic properties
(Figure 3). The K_m and V_{max} of the conjugate and AP stock
solution were calculated, respectively, to be 2.95 and 2.65
mM and 76.8 and 85.4 mM/ng protein/min. The usefulness of
alkaline phosphatase as a marker was thus not impaired by
the conjugation reaction. The reagent also proved to have
a long shelf life and showed no loss of activity over a
six-month period at 4°C. This observation supports
Weiler's contention that a large batch of tracer could be
synthesized at a single time and used with confidence for
months afterwards.

Concentrations of antibody and enzyme tracer for use
in the immunoassay were determined by checkerboard assay
(14). From this test, 2.5 µg anti-aldicarb antibody and an
80-fold dilution of enzyme tracer stock were selected.
These concentrations resulted in aldicarb-free solutions
producing a maximal A_{405} of approximately 1.3 with
aldicarb-fortified solutions producing absorbances down to
approximately 0.3 at 2000 ng.

The aldicarb standard curve (Figure 4) shows a typical
dose response relationship between 15.6-2000 ng of
aldicarb. The response is linear (r^2 = .980) across three
orders of magnitude and measurement at each level is
precise as indicated by the coefficients of variation for
all levels less than 3%. The least detectable dose was 0.3
ppm with a time of analysis less than 2.5 hr.

Assay Specificity. Inhibition studies were carried out to
determine the ability of the antibody preparation used in
this study to discriminate between aldicarb and similarly
structured compounds. Aldicarb, not surprisingly, yielded
the highest percent inhibition, 84.6%, and was calculated
to have an I_{50} of 125 ng (Table I). Aldicarb sulfoxide,
however, demonstrated no inhibition of the antibody what-
soever. Nor was any recognition of aldicarb sulfone
apparent. These findings are significant not only because
of the implications for residue analysis but are also of
interest from an immunological standpoint. Aldicarb is
known to degrade chiefly to its sulfoxide in cotton (18,19)
and soil (18,20) and further to the sulfone in potatoes
(21). For ease of analysis, several analytical methods

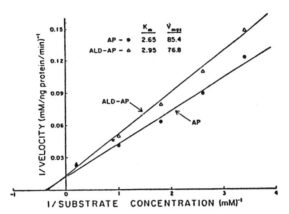

Figure 3. Double reciprocal plots for the hydrolysis of 4-nitrophenyl phosphate by alkaline phosphatase before (AP) and after (ALD-AP) conjugation to Ligand 2.

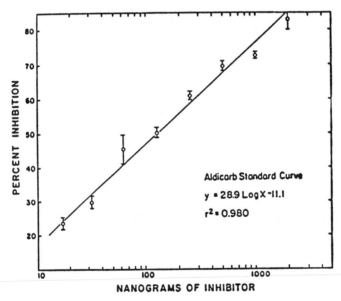

Figure 4. Enzyme immunoassay aldicarb standard curve.

Table I. Percent Inhibition of Selected Chemicals in the Aldicarb Enzyme Immunoassay

CHEMICAL NAME	STRUCTURE	PERCENT INHIBITION AT 2000 NG	I_{50}
ALDICARB	$CH_3-C(CH_3)(CH_3)S-CH=N-O-C(=O)-NH-CH_3$	84.6	125 NG
ALDICARB SULFOXIDE	$CH_3-C(CH_3)(S=O \cdot CH_3)-CH=N-O-C(=O)-NH-CH_3$	0	>2000 NG
ALDICARB SULFONE	$CH_3-C(CH_3)(O=S=O \cdot CH_3)-CH=N-O-C(=O)-NH-CH_3$	0	>2000 NG
ALDICARB OXIME	$CH_3-C(CH_3)(S \cdot CH_3)-CH=N-OH$	42	>2000 NG
ALDICARB OXIME SULFOXIDE	$CH_3-C(CH_3)(O=S=O \cdot CH_3)-CH=N-OH$	0	>2000 NG
METHOMYL	$CH_3-C(=N-O-C(=O)-NH-CH_3)(S-CH_3)$	0	>2000 NG
MESUROL	$CH_3-S-\text{(dimethylphenyl)}-O-C(=O)-NH-CH_3$	0	>2000 NG
CYANAZINE	$N\equiv C-C(CH_3)(NH)-\text{(chlorotriazinyl)}-NH-CH_2-CH_3$	0	>2000 NG
ACETYLCHOLINE	$CH_3-N^{\oplus}(CH_3)(CH_3)-CH_2-CH_2-O-C(=O)-CH_3$	13.8	>2000 NG
CHOLINE	$CH_3-N^{\oplus}(CH_3)(CH_3)-CH_2-CH_2-OH$	13.8	>2000 NG
CARNITINE	$CH_3-N^{\oplus}(CH_3)(CH_3)-CH_2-CH(OH)-CH_2-C(=O)-O^{\ominus}$	0	>2000 NG

(3,4) have clumped the three metabolic species together as
'total toxic residue' (22), a consequence of sample treatment by oxidation with a peracid. However, information
about the relative amounts of each species is lost through
such an approach. Possessing the inability to recognize
either oxidation product, the immunoassay can derive information about the amount of parent pesticide in a sample.
Work to develop an antibody to detect the sulfone is
currently underway.

From an immunological viewpoint, such specificity can
be traced to the structure of the immunogen. The
thiomethyl group was poised in an immunodominant position,
distal to the surface of the carrier protein. Thus, any
structural change in aldicarb at this point would be
expected to bring about a decrease in antibody recognition.
However, the complete elimination of binding following the
inclusion of a single oxygen atom was not anticipated.

This effect is also evident by the failure of aldicarb
oxime sulfoxide to be recognized, although aldicarb oxime
inhibited the binding of the enzyme tracer 42%. The oxime
has the identical structure of aldicarb excluding the N-
methyl group and the carbonyl functionality. Excepting an
accidental industrial release (23), it has not been found
in nature and would not be expected to interfere with assay
performance.

Other agrichemicals tested also failed to display
antibody recognition (Table I). Methomyl and mesurol are
both N-methyl carbamates and each contains a thiomethyl
group, but their inability to bind suggests that neither
the carbamate linkage nor the thiomethyl group by
themselves are sufficient to warrant cross-reactivity.
Cyanazine is a typical triazine herbicide with three side
chains. However, the N-ethyl group or the chain containing
a tetrahedral carbon bound to two methyl groups and a cyano
group did not contribute to antibody inhibition at any
level tested. It is interesting to note that failure of
the latter chain to elicit recognition in light of Payne et
al.'s observation (11) that an identical group substituted
into aldicarb in place of the thiomethyl actually enhanced
some insecticidal properties. Thus, the anticholinesterase
activity and antibody recognition of the cyano and
thiomethyl functionalities do not correlate.

Aldicarb was originally designed as a structural mimic
of acetylcholine in an attempt to increase the acetylcholinesterase inhibition of aryl carbamates (11). Therefore, the ability of acetylcholine and its hydrolysis
product, choline, to bind to anti-aldicarb antibody were
examined. Both compounds showed a small degree of inhibition (13.8%) suggesting some complementarity of fit with
the antibody combining site. However, both chemicals
inhibited 9% less at the highest level tested (2000 ng)
than did the lowest level (15.6 ng) of aldicarb used so
neither material should affect assay reliability. A biochemical of similar structure, carnitine, was also tested.

No cross-reactivity was observed at any level, perhaps due to the presence of the hydroxy group on the β-carbon. A plot to the percent inhibition of aldicarb relative to the percent inhibition of aldicarb oxime, acetylcholine, and choline over the same range of concentrations is shown in Figure 5.

Applications. The aldicarb enzyme immunoassay was applied to a variety of sample types. Samples included human and animal fluids which may be analyzed to evaluate aldicarb exposure, juice products derived from crops to which aldicarb is applied and stream water representative of water samples examined to monitor environmental dispersal of the compound. Minimal sample preparation was required, typically involving passage through a 0.8 μm filter. The necessity of maintaining sample pH at a threshold level was indicated by early experiments with citrus products that showed the antibody preparation to be inactivated by solutions having a pH lower than 6.0. Adjustment to pH 6.0-6.2 by the addition of either 2 M NaOH or a special Tris buffer containing eight times the amount of base eliminated this problem. To assess the linearity of response over a range of fortifications, samples were spiked with 15.6 to 2000 ng of aldicarb. Regression lines and coefficients of determination were calculated from these data. Each fortification level was run in quadruplicate so the coefficient of variation could be determined.

Aldicarb is applied to the soil, usually at time of planting. Uptake by a plant's root system renders the entire plant toxic to potential pests. However, irrigation and rainfall tend to enhance migration of the pesticide through sandy or acidic soils. As a result, the leaching of aldicarb into drinking water supplies has become a widespread concern, particularly in Florida ([24]), Suffolk County, New York ([25,26]), Wisconsin ([27,28]) and Eastern Canada ([29]). The principal analytical procedures for the analysis of aldicarb in water are indirect HPLC methods ([9,10]) and a GLC technique requiring sample oxidation prior to injection ([30]). These techniques are not widely applied, however, since the HPLC method requires a substantial capital investment in dedicated instrumentation and the GLC technique involves extensive manipulation of the sample. In contrast, enzyme immunoassay of fortified stream water (Figure 6) was simple to perform and, except for filtering, did not necessitate sample modification nor pretreatment. The assay could detect aldicarb at a concentration of 0.3 ppm and demonstrated high linearity of response (r^2 = .995) with CVs for all levels approximately 5%. Sample concentration by solid phase extraction could increase sensitivity even further ([8]), making enzyme immunoassay an attractive analytical alternative.

Sampling of body fluids for the estimation of pesticide exposure can be regarded as intrusive or non-intrusive, depending upon whether or not the bloodstream of

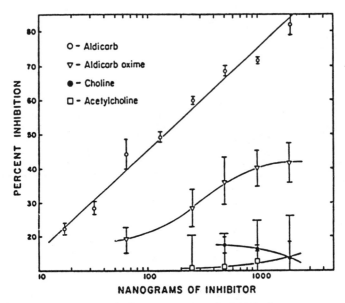

Figure 5.   Enzyme immunoassay inhibition curves of
aldicarb, aldicarb oxime, choline and acetylcholine.

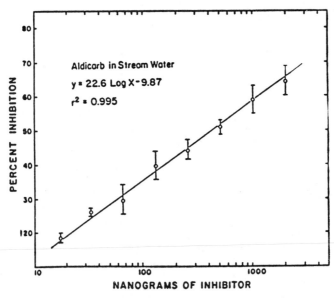

Figure 6.   Enzyme immunoassay of aldicarb fortified
stream water.

a subject must be accessed. Contamination of the blood is determined through analysis of plasma or serum. Enzyme immunoassay of sheep plasma yielded a linear response (r^2 = .982) over the range tested with CVs at each level typically 5% or less (Figure 7). Since the plasma was diluted (1:1, v/v) with Tris buffer, the least detectable level was 0.6 ppm. Assay of rabbit serum gave approximately the same response (r^2 = .969) with CVs less than 6% and a detection limit of 0.3 ppm (Figure 8).

Non-intrusive samples included human saliva and urine Immunoassay of saliva gave a linear response as indicated by a high coefficient of determination (r^2 = .990) (Figure 9). The detection limit was 0.3 ppm and CVs were 4% or less. Analysis of urine by EIA yielded a linear response (r^2 = .983), small variation of measurement per fortification level (CVs less than 4%) and a sensitivity of 0.3 ppm (Figure 10). Body fluids were the most complex sample matrices tested. This complexity was reflected two ways. First, points representing individual fortification levels are somewhat dispersed about the fitted regression lines. However, these coefficients still imply strong dose response relationships. Second, the length of substrate incubation for the analysis of plasma and serum needed to be increased by an additional 30 min to enhance color development such that absorbance values fell within the range of approximately 1.3 to 0.3. This increased overall analysis time to slightly less than 3 hr, but the additional time did not involve any extra manipulation. These results point to the potential utility of the aldicarb enzyme immunoassay as a tool to monitor exposure of pesticide applicators and provide analytical results within a meaningful time frame. Saliva or urine, for example, may be collected at the end of a work day and exposure data could be available the following morning.

EIA analysis of juice products necessitated adjustment of sample pH to 6.0-6.2 as previously described. pH adjustment consisted of the addition of 10 µL of 2 M NaOH or a concentrated Tris buffer and had a small dilution effect upon the samples, reducing sensitivity from 0.3 to 0.38 ppm. Analysis of lemonade samples was linear over the entire range of fortification (r^2 = .990) and CVs for each level were 4% or less (Figure 11). Immunoassay of limeade samples yielded similar responses with a high coefficient of determination (r^2 = .993) over the concentrations examined and low CVs with only one level (125 ng) exceeding 4% (Figure 12). Titration of orange juice samples with 2 M NaOH indicated too high a concentration of acids to be counteracted with 10 µL of base so a concentrated Tris buffer (pH 7.5) was utilized in its place. Analysis of these buffered orange juice samples was linear from 2000-31.3 ng (r^2 = .988) and exhibited high precision of measurement (all CVs less than 4%) (Figure 13). The least detectable concentration was 0.75 ppm. In a similar fashion, linearity of watermelon samples (r^2 = .993)

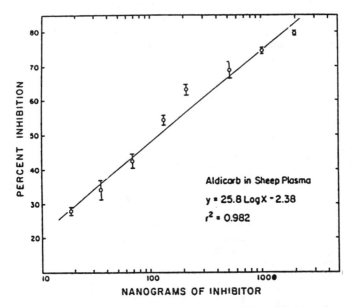

Figure 7. Enzyme immunoassay of aldicarb fortified with sheep plasma.

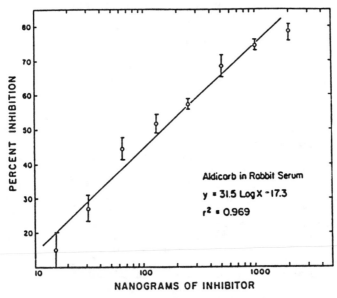

Figure 8. Enzyme immunoassay of aldicarb fortified with rabbit serum.

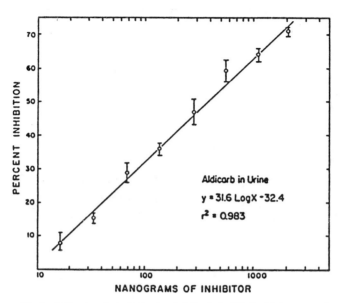

Figure 9. Enzyme immunoassay of aldicarb fortified with human urine.

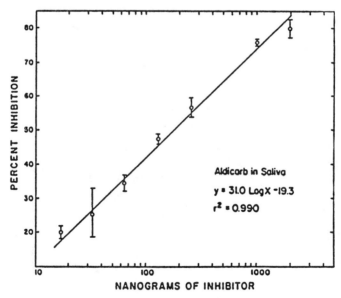

Figure 10. Enzyme immunoassay of aldicarb fortified with human saliva.

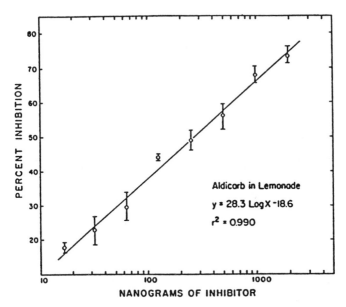

Figure 11. Enzyme immunoassay of aldicarb fortified with lemonade.

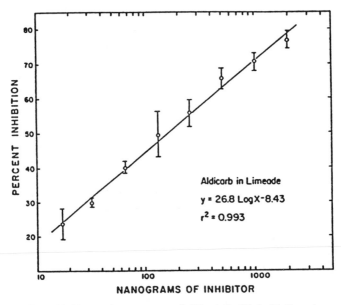

Figure 12. Enzyme immunoassay of aldicarb fortified with limeade.

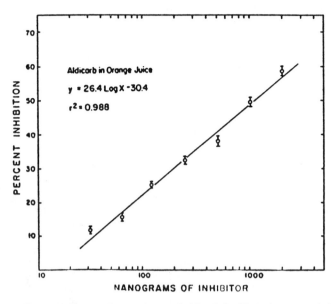

Figure 13. Enzyme immunoassay of aldicarb fortified with orange juice.

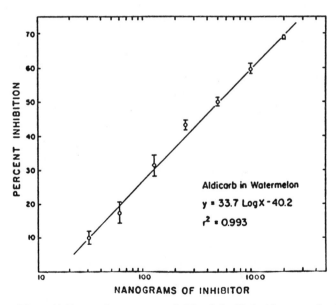

Figure 14. Enzyme immunoassay of aldicarb fortified with watermelon juice.

extended across the same range with a sensitivity of 0.75 ppm (Figure 14). The coefficient of variation for all levels did not exceed 5%. Although not registered for use on watermelons, the illegal application of aldicarb to this crop in 1985 in California (31) was widely publicized. Literally thousands of watermelons were sampled to determine the extent of contamination (32). The cost-effectiveness of enzyme immunoassay would have been dramatically demonstrated in such a situation. The expense incurred by extensive sampling could have been sharply reduced by prior screening of the samples by EIA followed by the application of classical procedures to suspect samples.

Conclusion

The enzyme immunoassay for aldicarb has been shown to be applicable to a variety of sample matrices, yet be simple to perform and exhibit rapid time of analysis. A micro-titre plate adsorbed with antibody serves as the reaction vessel for all steps in the assay reducing time of analysis while eliminating the transfer of solutions incubated in other vessels. The least detectable aldicarb concentration was 0.3 ppm. Lower sensitivities can be achieved by solid-phase extraction of aldicarb in the water. Precision of measurement was high with coefficients of variation for all fortification levels typically 5% or less.

This work suggests that EIA could prove useful for human or animal exposure studies and for screening of agricultural crops for aldicarb contamination. This enzyme immunoassay is highly selective to aldicarb and does not demonstrate any cross reactivity to the sulfoxide or sulfone. Immunoassay for detection of the sulfoxide or sulfone would require development of antibodies specific to the oxidation products.

Acknowledgments

Supported in part by Northeastern Regional Research Project NE-115 and Regional Research Funds, and the North Dakota Agricultural Experiment Station.

Literature Cited

1. Mumma, R.O.; Brady, J.F. In Pesticide Science and Biotechnology; Greenhalgh, R.; Roberts, T.R., eds.; Blackwell Scientific Publications: Oxford, Great Britain, 1987; pp. 341-348.
2. Hammock, B.D.; Mumma, R.O. ACS Symposium Series 1980, 136, 321-352.
3. Andrawes, N.R.; Romine, R.R.; Bagley, W.P. J. Agric. Food Chem. 1973, 21, 379-386.

4. Union Carbide Corporation. "A Method for the Deter-
    mination of Total Toxic Aldicarb Residues in Agricul-
    tural Crops by Gas Chromatography," (May, 1973).
5. Dorough, H.W.; Thorstenson, J.H. J. Chromatog. Sci.
    1975, 13, 212-222.
6. Cochrane, W.P.; Lanouette, M. J. Assoc. Off. Anal.
    Chem. 1981, 64, 724-728.
7. Cochrane, W.P.; Lanouette, M. J. Chromatog. 1982,
    243, 307-314.
8. Spalik, J.; Janauer, G.E.; Lau, M.; Lemley, A.T. J.
    Chromatog. 1982, 253, 289-294.
9. Hill, K.M.; Holowell, R.H.; DalCortivo, L.A. Anal.
    Chem. 1984, 56, 2465-2468.
10. Union Carbide Agricultural Products Co., Inc. "A
    Method for Determination of Aldicarb Residues in Water
    by HPLC," (February, 1984).
11. Payne, L.K.; Stansbury, H.A.; Weiden, M.H.J. J.
    Agric. Chem. 1966, 14, 356-365.
12. Erlanger, B.F.; Borek, F.; Beiser, S.M.; Lieberman, S.
    J. Biol. Chem. 1957, 228, 713-727.
13. Weiler, E.W.; Jourdan, P.S.; Conrad, W. Planta 1981,
    153, 561-571.
14. Voller, A.; Bidwell, D.E.; Bartlett, W. Bull. W.H.O.
    1976, 53, 55-56.
15. Clark, M.F.; Adams, A.N. J. Chem. Virol. 1977, 34,
    475-483.
16. Huber, S.J. Chemosphere 1985, 14, 1795-1803.
17. Schwalbe, M.; Dorn, E.; Beyermann, K. J. Agric. Food
    Chem. 1984, 32, 734-741.
18. Coppedge, J.R.; Lindquist, D.A.; Bull, D.L.; Dorough,
    H.W. J. Agric. Food Chem. 1967, 15, 902-910.
19. Bull, D.L. J. Econ. Entomol. 1968, 61, 1598-1602.
20. Andrawes, N.R.; Bagley, W.P.; Herret, R.A. J. Agric.
    Food Chem. 1971, 19, 727-730.
21. Andrawes, N.R.; Bagley, W.P.; Herret, R.A. J. Agric.
    Food Chem. 1971, 19, 731-737.
22. Richey, F.A.; Bartley, W.J.; Sheets, K.P. J. Agric.
    Food Chem. 1977, 25, 47-51.
23. The New York Times 1985, Aug. 12: 1(6) 12(1-3).
24. Foran, J.A.; Miller, W.L.; Doyan, S.; Krtausch, M.
    Environ. Pollut. (Series A: Ecol. Biol.) 1986, 40,
    369-380.
25. Zaki, M.H.; Moran, D.; Harris, D. Am. J. Public
    Health 1982, 72, 1391-1395.
26. Zaki, M.H. Northeast. Environ. Sci. 1986, 5, 15-22.
27. Rothschild, E.R.; Manser, R.J.; Anderson, M.P. Ground
    Water 1982, 20, 437-445.
28. Krill, R.M.; Sonzogni, W.C. J. Am. Water Works Assoc.
    1986, 78, 70-75.

29.   Priddle, M.W.; Jackson, R.E.; Novakowski, K.S.;
       Denhoed, S.; Graham, B.W.; Patterson, R.J.; Chaput,
       D.; Jardine, D. Water Pollut. Res. J. Can. 1987, 22,
       173-186.
30.   Lemley, A.T.; Zhong, W.Z. J. Agric. Food Chem. 1984,
       32, 714-719.
31.   Chem. Eng. News 1985, 63(28), 3-4.
32.   Agri-Chemical Issues. Union Carbide Agric. Products
       Co., Inc., Vol. 1(1) (1985).

RECEIVED June 29, 1988

RISK ASSESSMENT AND REGULATION

Exposure Data
and the Risk-Assessment Process
Regulatory Considerations

While the topics covered in this section of the book can
be separated conceptually, in practice they are closely related.
Most quantitative risk assessments are conducted by or for
regulatory agencies charged with protecting public health, and
scientists must deal directly with the uncertainties inherent in
all aspects of the continually moving field of risk assessment.
Regulators must also face the proper public scrutiny of decisions
made on based these assessments.

The exposure end of the risk assessment equation is obviously
critical and is an area where a great deal of uncertainty exists.
Occupational exposure to pesticides is typically estimated either
by passive dosimetry techniques (measuring the amount of chemical
available for absorption into the body using residue trapping
devices) or by biological monitoring (in most cases by calculating
body burden from the amount of pesticide or metabolite excreted
from the body). Each method has distinct advantages and disadvantages, and the investigator must consider carefully these
factors when preparing a protocol for an exposure monitoring study
designed to achieve specific goals.

The Environmental Protection Agency as well as other regulatory agencies must insure that individuals are not exposed to
pesticides to an extent that would cause unreasonable health risks.
Pesticides are used in a great many nonagricultural situations as
well as on the farm. Homes and offices are often treated for pest
control. Lawns and swimming pools are other potential sources of
pesticide exposure. To prevent unacceptable risk situations, the
extent of exposure must be known. The agencies responsible for
protecting the public must attempt to reconcile differences,
frequently large differences, encountered in exposure estimates
generated by different investigators or by different monitoring
methods, i.e., passive dosimetry and biological monitoring. In
the latter case a comparison of the results obtained by each
methodology is only possible if the extent of percutaneous absorption is known. Studies designed to estimate dermal penetration
are difficult to carry out, and the results difficult to interpret
and extrapolate to people in actual pesticide exposure scenarios.

Another problematic area regulators face is the extreme range of exposure values commonly encountered in field studies. A major component of this large range is the variation in individual work habits. Should regulatory decisions be geared to protecting the average person, the most careful person, or everyone? Another difficulty encountered is that most often the toxic effect of concern is identified in a laboratory animal feeding study, and the results must be extrapolated to another route of exposure. Ideally the chemical should be administered in effect studies by the appropriate route of exposure, but such information is rarely available. The route of exposure can not only affect the potency of the effect but the nature of the toxicity as well due to the possibility of route dependent metabolism.

A delicate area is estimating pesticide exposure to infants. Due to their physiology and activity patterns, they may be most vulnerable in situations such as home carpet treatment and lawn care pesticide use. Actual exposure monitoring studies are questionable because of ethical considerations, so extremely protective and theoretical assumptions may often be necessary to make a determination if a certain pesticide use is safe enough for these children. This is an area where creative thought and novel approaches are distinctly needed.

The first studies measuring pesticide exposure to workers were carried out in the 1950's to assess the safety of use of the acutely toxic synthetic insecticides then being introduced. Passive dosimetry techniques were routinely used. They served us well in defining such things as the most important routes of exposure, which areas of the body are subject to the most dermal contact, and which work activities related to pesticide application are associated with highest exposure. Over the years however the use of exposure monitoring data has expanded dramatically. Quantitative risk assessments are now required for effects that may result from subtle physiological events caused by chronic exposure to low levels of pesticide components. Quantifying such chronic effects are by far the most common assessments carried out by regulators of pesticides. Biological monitoring will be a critical tool in improving the ability of scientists and regulators to protect the public from adverse health effects.

Joseph C. Reinert
Office of Policy, Planning and Evaluation (PM–223)
U.S. Environmental Protection Agency
Washington, DC 20460

RECEIVED April 25, 1988

Chapter 22

Mixer–Loader–Applicator Exposure and Percutaneous Absorption Studies Involving EPTC Herbicide

Safety Related to Exposure

James B. Knaak[1], M. A. Al-Bayati[2], O. G. Raabe[2], J. L. Wiedmann[3], J. W. Pensyl[3], J. H. Ross[3], A. P. Leber[3], and P. Jones[4]

[1]State of California Department of Health Services, Sacramento, CA 95814
[2]Institute for Environmental Health Resources, University of California, Davis, CA 95616
[3]PPG Industries, Barberton, OH 44203
[4]Pan–Ag, Fresno, CA 93711

The skin penetration potential of EPTC was evaluated by the topical application of [propyl-1-^{14}C] -EPTC (specific activity, 1.67 mCi/mmole) in water to the clipped back skin (22.9 ug/cm^2, 25 cm^2 and 21.5 ug/cm^2, 2.54 cm^2) of adult male Sprague-Dawley rats. All glass metabolism cages were used to collect respiratory ^{14}CO$_2$ while special skin mounted XAD-2 resin traps were used to collect ^{14}C-volatiles. Approximately 14.7% of the applied dose was absorbed and/or excreted during 24 hours post administration. The remaining dose evaporated (77.8%) or remained on the surface of the skin (1.3–2.8%). Less than 1% was recovered as respired ^{14}CO$_2$. In a separate field study, a mixer/loader/applicator was monitored while applying a PPG brand of EPTC, GENEP 7EC. Air samples, cloth patches, hand rinses, and urine samples were obtained and analyzed for EPTC or metabolites. Total absorbed dose was determined to be 5.6 mg/day (0.074 mg/kg of b.w.) for a 75 kg man applying EPTC to 120 acres of soil/day. On the basis of a percutaneous absorption rate in the rat of 14.7%/24 hours, a worker exposure of 0.074 mg/kg/day of b.w., and a NOEL of 5.0 mg/kg/day from animal toxicity studies, margins of safety of 68 to 340 were determined for workers applying EPTC herbicide.

GENEP EPTC 7 EC, containing the active ingredient, S-ethyl-N,N,-dipropyl thiocarbamate, is registered by PPG Industries, Inc. for use on vegetable and field crops as a preplant herbicide requiring soil incorporation.

Toxicity studies conducted with EPTC in the rat indicated that this material can induce early appearance of degenerative heart disease and hind limb paresis frequently as late-in-life changes in this animal. The mouse and dog were refractory to these effects.

The finding of a dose related effect in the rat necessitated the development of mixer/loader/applicator exposure and rat dermal absorption data for determining the margin of safety afforded agricultural workers using this chemical. The field portion of the mixer/loader/applicator study was carried out in Chico, California by Pan-Ag, Fresno. Field samples were analyzed at PPG Industries, Inc. The rat dermal absorption studies were conducted at LEHR, University of California, Davis, CA.

0097–6156/89/0382–0288$06.00/0
© 1989 American Chemical Society

Percutaneous Absorption of EPTC Herbicide

All-Glass Metabolism Cage Study.   Young adult male Sprague-Dawley rats weighing 280 g were purchased from Bantin-Kingman, Fremont, CA. Three rats were prepared for dosing one day prior to treatment according to the procedure of Knaak et al. (1). The animals were individually weighed, and hair removed from their backs using an electric clipper. An area representing 7% of the body surface (25 cm^2) was marked off with a rubber template glued to the skin. A Queen Anne collar made of polyethylene sheeting (1.0 mm in thickness, 11.25 cm in diameter) with a neck opening of 2.5 cm in diameter, was placed around the neck of each animal and fastened with staples to prevent the animals from grooming treated areas.

An aqueous dosing suspension (500 uL, water emulsion of EPTC) containing 574 ug of [propyl-1-^{14}C]-EPTC (19,400 dpm/ug) was applied using a digital microliter pipet.

Following topical application, each animal was immediately placed in an all-glass metabolism cage (Figure 1; Metabolic Cages, Series, 600 Vangard International, Inc., Neptune, N.J.) for the separate and complete collection of urine, feces, respiratory carbon dioxide, and ^{14}C-volatiles (see Figure 1 schematic). A smaller adsorption column (drying tube) containing 1.5 g of washed Amberlite XAD-2 resin (10/50 mesh) was placed between the bottom male joint of the feeder arm (joint normally used for feed residue flask) and the CO_2 adsorption tower to collect [propyl-1-^{14}C]-EPTC lost from skin by evaporation. Approximately 150 mL of 2.0 N KOH was used in the CO_2 absorption tower (Medinsky, 2) to collect $^{14}CO_2$ resulting from the metabolism of radiolabeled EPTC. A house vacuum system supplied air at the rate of 600 mL/ minute. Cage flow was split after the XAD-2 adsorption column using two critical flow orifices. Calibrations were made using spirometer volume techniques to determine the actual flow through each orifice. Upstream pressure was monitored to assure constant flow through the system during the experiment. The split allowed a 2:1 separation of all gases leaving the XAD-2 adsorption column. Two-thirds of the total flow was removed through the by-pass orifice, while one-third of the total air volume passed directly through the KOH $^{14}CO_2$ adsorption tower. This system allowed for total organic vapor collection and 24 hr CO_2 quantification without saturating the adsorption media.

The animals were sacrificed 24 hr after the topical application of the dose. Each animal was anesthetized with sodium pentothal (70 mg/kg I.P.). Skin was removed at the application site and blood collected by cardiac puncture using a disposable 5.0 mL heparinized syringe, 20 gauge needle and a 10 mL BD Vacutainer (heparin). A midline chest incision was made to expose the heart for proper placement of the needle. Heart, liver, kidney, gastrointestinal tract (GIT), fat and the remaining carcass were taken and frozen at 0°C until they were analyzed for radioactivity. Urine, feces, ^{14}C-volatiles on XAD-2 resin and $^{14}CO_2$ in 2N KOH were also collected. Excised skin was stretched across a four-inch funnel and washed with 100 mL of soapy water. Washed skins were frozen to await further analysis.

Skin-Depot/XAD-2 Absorption Study.   Two studies were performed using young adult male Sprague-Dawley rats to assess the fate of ^{14}C-EPTC applied to the skin, volatilization, retention on or in skin, or passage through the skin to internal organs and/or excretion. The first study was a pilot study using three-431 g rats. The second study used four-280 g rats. One day prior to treatment, the hair on the back was clipped between the shoulder blades, and the circular aluminum base (Figure 2) of a skin-depot (Susten et al., 3) was glued (cyanoacrylate glue) and sutured to back skin while the animal was under anesthesia.

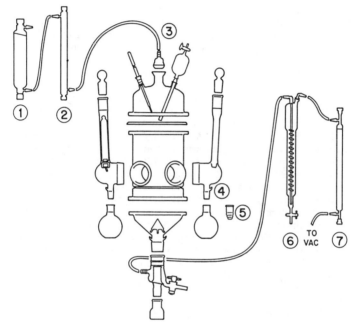

Figure 1.   All-Glass Metabolism Cage equipped with (1) silica gel absorption column, (2) ascarite/CO_2 absorption column, (3) glass cage, (6) KOH trap, and (7) silica gel absorption column. This configuration was modified by replacing the vacuum line between the KOH trap and the urine collection device with a vacuum line connected to the feeder side arm (4) via a hose bib (5). An XAD-2 resin absorption column was placed in the line after the feeder side arm. A T was placed in the line between the XAD-2 trap and the KOH trap. The open end of the T was connected to vacuum.

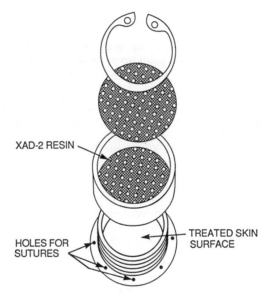

Figure 2. Aluminum Skin-Depot consisting of base (threaded, male) and XAD-2 resin absorption column (threaded, female) equipped with two fine mesh screens and a retainer ring.

Twenty-four hours after the operation, the skin area inside the aluminum base (1.8 cm in diameter, 2.54 cm^2) was treated with 50 uL of aqueous dosing suspension (emulsion of EPTC and water). In studies 1 and 2, 91.8 and 54.7 ug, respectively, of [propyl-1-^{14}C]-EPTC were applied to the skin of rats inside the aluminum base. A specially designed adsorption column containing 1.0 g of XAD-2 resin (Figure 2) was immediately screwed onto the base and the animals individually placed in stainless steel metabolism cages for the complete and separate collection of urine and feces.

The animals were sacrificed 24 hr after dosing, and tissues [skin at the application site, blood, heart, liver, kidney, fat, gastrointestinal tract (GIT), and carcass] were taken using the procedure previously described for the animals placed in the all-glass metabolism cages. The skin-depot (base and absorption column) and skin at the application site were removed prior to collecting blood and other tissues. The XAD-2 resin was removed from the absorption column and slurried in 25 mL of ethyl acetate, while the base and column were washed with an equal volume of the solvent. Excised skin was washed with 25 mL of soapy water and frozen to await further work.

^{14}C-Analysis.   All collected samples were analyzed for radioactivity according to Knaak et al. (1) in a Packard 300 C scintillation counter equipped with CPM to DPM conversion and quench correction. Sealed quench standards were used for standardization. Aliquots of liquid samples (plasma, skin surface washings, skin extracts, urine, skin-depot (base/absorption column/resin washings) washings, and KOH] were counted directly in scintillation fluid. Carcasses, GIT, feces, and skins were frozen in dry ice and individually ground in a Model ED-5 Wiley Mill. After extraction with 50 mL of methanol followed by 50 mL of acetone, the ground skins were air dried and reground in the Wiley Mill. Aliquots of carcass, GIT, heart, liver, fat, feces, and kidney (50 mg) were combusted wet, while the dried ground skins were combusted dry in a Harvey Oxidizer, Model OX-300. The resulting CO_2 was trapped in 15 mL of the Harvey CO_2 absorbent-scintillation fluid and counted.

Calculations.   The count data were analyzed on an individual animal basis utilizing a C-Calc Spread Sheet Program (Data General) to convert DPM to ug of EPTC herbicide and to calculate the percentage of the applied dose recovered.

Worker Exposure Study with EPTC Herbicide

Mixing/Loading/Application.   The worker exposure study was conducted at Chico, CA during a commercial application of GENEP EPTC to 281 acres prepared for planting red beans. One man, 27 years of age, weighing 75 kg mixed/loaded and applied EPTC herbicide.

The mixing operation consisted of hand pouring GENEP 7EC from a 5 gal container to a 2½ gal clear plastic measuring device. The measured volumes were then poured into a 150 gal spray tank and diluted with water. The mixer/loader wore rubber gloves during this operation.

The application equipment consisted of a Farmall 504 high clearance tractor, a 150 gal rear mounted fiber glass spray tank, a rolling cultivator mounted between the tractor wheels, and a power takeoff (PTO) driven sprayer (6 sets of double flat fan nozzles directed to the front and to the rear) mounted in front of the rolling cultivator.

Diluted pesticide (23 lb A.I.) was applied to 7 acres at the rate of 3.3 lbs A.I. per acre in 20 gals of water. Exposure was monitored during mixing/loading (15 replicates) and application (15 replicates) of 23 lb. A.I. Separate data were obtained for each batch of EPTC herbicide applied.

Dermal Exposure. For each monitoring replicate, gauze monitoring patches (23.75 cm^2) were applied to 11 regions of the body as per Popendorf (4). Ten of the patches were placed on the outside of the clothing and one was placed inside. The monitoring sites are given in Table I. The feet were covered by boots and were not monitored during the study. Hand washes were used to monitor residues on the hands for the mixer/loader with gloves and the applicator without gloves. The worker wore short sleeve shirts, long pants, baseball cap, and boots. Patches were applied prior to mixing/loading, removed after this operation was completed and new patches applied prior to application of EPTC. Upon completion of the application of EPTC, the patches were removed. Patches were placed individually in 2 oz wide-mouth bottles and frozen to await analysis.

Hands were individually washed in 200 mL of water containing surfactant. The wash water was then stored frozen to await analysis.

Table I. Positions of Monitoring Sites Used to Represent
Regions of the Body (4)

Represented Region of the Body	Surface Area (cm^2)	Monitoring Site[1]
Face	650	Chest at throat (outside)
Front of neck	128	Chest at throat (outside)
Back of neck	100	Back (outside)
Head	430	Back (outside)[2]
Shoulders	2210	Shoulders (outside)[2,3]
Forearms	2190	Forearm (outside)[3]
Hands	1310	Handwash
Chest	1520	Chest (inside)[3]
Back	1520	Back (outside)[2]
Hips	1730	Thighs (outside)[2,3]
Thighs	3420	Thighs (outside)[2,3]
Calves	2570	Shin (outside)[2,3]
Feet[4]	1220	None[4]

[1] Inside represents a patch on the worker's skin and outside represents a patch on the outside of clothing.
[2] 20% of outside patch values were used as estimate for inside patch value since no corresponding inside values were available.
[3] Average of 2 patches.
[4] Negligible exposure: not included in the calculation.

Inhalation Exposure. Air sampling was performed continuously in the breathing zone of the worker during mixing/loading and application using charcoal tubes and a Bendix personal monitoring pump operating at 1L/min. The respiration volume of the mixer/loader-applicator was assumed to be 25 L/min (Guyton, 5). The mixing/loading operation required 10 to 15 minutes, while application required a minimum of 200 minutes.

Urine Monitoring. Urine samples, twenty-one 68 to 319 mL volumes, were collected during the course of the study from the mixer/loader/applicator, immediately frozen, and stored in a freezer to await analysis for S-(N,N-dipropyl carbamoyl) cysteine and S-(N,N-dipropyl carbamoyl)-N-acetylcysteine (Hubbell and Casida, 6).

Analysis of Gauze Pads. Pads placed in 2 oz wide-mouth bottles in the field were transferred to the laboratory and extracted in situ by shaking for one minute with 40 mL of methanol. After shaking, 20 mL were removed, evaporated to 1.0 mL using a rotary evaporator after the addition of 2.0 mL of internal standard (3 ug/mL azobenzene in 2-propanol), and analyzed by gas chromatography equipped with a thermionic detector. Chromatography was performed on a 30m x 0.25 mm I.D. OV-1701 column with a film thickness of 0.25 um. Column temperature was programmed from 100° to 150°C at a rate of 5°C/min. Column temperature was initially held for 2 min at 100°C with a final hold time of 20 min. The injection port temperature was 200°C and the detector temperature 300°C. Helium flow rates were set at 1.29 mL/min for carrier, 5.9 mL/min for splitter, and 30 mL/min for make up. Hydrogen was supplied to the detector at 3.8 mL/min and air at 200 mL/min. The injection volume was 1 uL and the split ratio 4.6:1. EPTC and azobenzene had a retention time of 9.13 and 16.78 minutes, respectively.

Preliminary data on the recovery of EPTC from cloth patches were obtained prior to the field study by spiking four patches with 0.995 ug of EPTC. Extraction with methanol recovered 88% of the EPTC after application to the patches, while a slightly larger amount (108%) was recovered from a patch stored in a 2 oz bottle for 4 hrs, at 70° F and then extracted with methanol. Smaller amounts, however, were recovered when patches were left in the open air after spiking, 71% recovery was obtained for the patch left in the open for 2½ hrs, while 54% was recovered from a patch left in the open for 4 hrs. Losses from these patches averaged 12% per hr. Eight gauze patches were spiked with 1.09 ug EPTC during the course of the worker exposure study. The recoveries ranged from 57 to 111% with a mean of 78% and a standard deviation of 20%. The patch data (ug EPTC/23.75 cm^2) was corrected for recovery and normalized to regional body surface area on the basis of each batch of GENEP applied. A protection value of 80% for clothing was used to adjust the apparent exposure to 20% of the externally monitored value. Exposed areas such as the neck, face and forearm were not adjusted by a protection factor. The adjusted values were then multiplied by the skin adsorption factor (14.7%) determined in the rat percutaneous absorption study.

Analysis of Hand Rinses. Hand water rinses containing surfactant (200 ml) were analyzed by high performance liquid chromatography using a 25 cm x 4.6 mm I.D. Zorbax ODS column, 70% methanol and 30% water, and a flow rate of 2.0 mL/min. A 20 uL sample of the rinse water was injected. Detector wavelength was set at 225 nm. A Hewlett-Packard Laboratory Automation System was used to quantify the samples. Calibration was performed using a standard solution containing 4.372 ug/mL of EPTC in water. Samples were spiked in the field with 219 ug of EPTC. Eight recovery extractions had a mean recovery of 80% with a range of 71–101% and a standard deviation of 10%. The spikes were stored for the same time intervals as the samples. The hand rinse data was corrected for recovery and multiplied by 14.7% to determine the absorbed dose.

Analysis of Air Samples. The air samples were collected by drawing air through activated charcoal tubes. The EPTC was desorbed (7) from the charcoal with 2 mL of CS$_2$ and analyzed for EPTC using a gas chromatograph equipped with a Supelco Wax 10 capillary column and a flame ionization detector. Storage stability data were obtained from tubes stored for 25 days at 0°C, 23°C and 33°C. Mean EPTC recoveries for three tubes at each temperature were 92.1, 93.3 and 91.8% respectively. The ability of activated charcoal to retain EPTC was determined by passing 0.35 L/min of air through the tube for a period of 2 hrs after 20 mg was adsorbed on the charcoal. No EPTC was detected in the opposite end of the tube. Recoveries of 82 and 91.3% were obtained at 80 and 45% relative humidity, respectively, using 9.37 ug of EPTC. Additional validation was obtained by spiking charcoal tubes in the field during the study with 54 ug of EPTC. The mean recovery was 91% and the standard deviation 5.3%. The EPTC values obtained from the charcoal tubes were corrected for recovery. Inhalation exposure estimates were calculated using the NACA recommended method (Mull and McCarthy, 8). These estimates were reduced by 50% for inhalation exposure on the basis of lung retention data recently developed (9) for a variety of volatile organics.

Analysis of Urine Samples. The S-(N,N-dipropylcarbamoyl) cysteine metabolite and its acetylated derivative in 1.0 mL of urine were acetylated in a 15 ml centrifuge tube using 25 mL of 0.1 N NaOH and 25 uL of acetic anhydride for one hr at room temperature. The reaction mixture was adjusted to pH 10 using 250 uL of 10% NaOH and extracted with methylene chloride (2 x 2.0 mL.). The organic phase was discarded. the water phase acidified to pH 3 with 0.5 mL of 1N HC1 and reextracted with methylene chloride (2 x 2.0 mL.). The methylene chloride was evaporated off and the N-acetyl derivative was dissolved in 0.5 mL of acetonitrile and methylated with diazomethane. The unreacted methylating reagent was removed by evaporation under a gentle stream of nitrogen and the residue was dissolved in 1.0 mL of toluene and a 3 uL volume gas chromatographed on a 30 m x 0.25 mm I. D. DX-1 column (J & W Scientific, Rancho Cordova, CA) using a thermionic detector. Column temperature was programmed from 80° to 200°C at a rate of 30°C/min. Column temperature was initially held for 2 min. at 80°C with a final hold time of 20 min. The injection port temperature was 200°C and detector temperature 300°C. Flow rate was set at 0.9 mL/min for helium carrier and 25 mL/min for nitrogen makeup. Hydrogen was supplied to the detector at 3.8 mL/min and air at 200 mL/min.

The acetylation/methylation method was validated by adding known amounts of the cysteine and N-acetylcysteine metabolites to control urines. The results were compared to an analytical sample of S-(N,N-dipropylcarbamoyl)-N-acetylmethyl cysteine. Results were confirmed using GC/MS analysis.

Two urine samples were spiked with each of the two urinary metabolites (10). Recovery of the S-(N,N-dipropylcarbamoyl)-N-acetylcysteine averaged 89%. The S-(N,N-dipropylcarbamoyl) cysteine, which is acetylated prior to analysis, averaged 74% recovery. The mean for all recoveries was 81%. The quantity of EPTC equivalents (ug) found in each urine collection was determined by multiplying the ratio of the molecular weights of EPTC to S-(N,N-dipropyl carbamoy)-N-acetyl cysteine by the ug of this metabolite found in urine. According to Hubbell and Casida (6), in rats this metabolite comprises 28% of the absorbed dose (40% of the absorbed dose was eliminated in urine over a 24 hr period; 70% of the urinary metabolites were identified as the cysteine or N-acetyl derivative).

Safety Margins

Margins of safety were calculated using an estimated NOEL (no-observable-effect-level) of 5.0 mg/kg/day for myocardial degeneration in a two-year rat chronic/oncogenicity study (11), a daily absorbed dose of 0.074 mg/kg/day and a lifetime average exposure of 0.0017 mg/kg/day determined in this study from patch and inhalation data. A margin of safety was also determined using a daily absorbed dose of 0.0147 mg/kg/day estimated from urinary metabolites. This was accomplished by dividing the NOEL in mg/kg/day by the estimated absorbed dosages in mg/kg/day.

Results

Table II gives the average recovery for the CO_2/glass metabolism cage study and the two skin-depot studies. According to the recovery data from the three studies, [propyl-1-^{14}C] -EPTC rapidly evaporated from the skin and was trapped by the XAD-2 resin. In the glass metabolism cage study, the volatilized EPTC was partially recovered on the XAD-2 resin with the remaining EPTC adsorbed to the sides of the glass cage or was absorbed by urine in the collection funnel. Recovery studies were performed prior to conducting the studies, utilizing [propyl-1-^{14}C]-EPTC applied to glass wool in the center of the cage. The studies indicated that the XAD-2 resin adsorbed only 20% of the EPTC evaporating from the glass wool. The remaining radioactivity was partially recovered on the walls of the glass metabolism cage. The poor recovery necessitated the development and use of the skin-depot containing XAD-2 resin. The use of the skin-depot ultimately resulted in the total recovery of 95.3% of the applied dose with 77.8% being recovered on the XAD-2 resin and skin-depot. Approximately 85.9% of the dose was recovered in the pilot study with 69.8% recovered on the XAD-2 resin and parts of the skin-depot. Similar quantities, 2.63 and 2.77% of the dose, were found on the surface of the skin after 24 hr in the two skin-depot studies. The tissues (heart, liver, kidney, and fat), skin extracts, extracted skin (bound residues), urine, and feces contained in the three studies an equivalent percentage of the topically applied dose. In the two skin-depot studies, 13.7 and 14.7%, respectively, of the topically applied doses were absorbed by the skin.

Table II. Dermal Absorption of [Propyl-1-^{14}C]-EPTC
in Young Male Rats One Day Post-Treatment

	Percentage of Topical Dose		
Sample Type	Glass Cage (n = 3)	Skin-Depot XAD-2/Pilot (n = 3)	Skin-Depot XAD-2/Study (n = 4)
XAD-2 resin (1)	53.14	63.51	65.38
Skin-depot (2)	–	6.33	12.56
Evaporated (1 + 2)	53.14	69.84	77.84
Skin surface (H_2O)	1.34	2.36	2.77
Skin extract (internal)	0.75	1.08	1.15
Skin combustion (Bound)	2.19	1.81	2.78
Plasma	0.00	0.00	0.00
Kidneys	0.05	0.09	0.14
Liver	0.92	1.63	1.47
Heart	0.01	0.01	0.01
GIT	1.12	1.35	1.84
Fat	0.03	0.02	0.12
Carcass	0.11	1.30	1.27
Feces	0.54	0.41	0.16
Urine	12.20	5.78	5.76
CO_2	1.18	–	–
Total Recovered	76.58	85.67	95.32

Dosages: Glass metabolism cage, 574 ug/25cm^2
Skin-depot XAD-2/Pilot, 91.8 ug/2.54 cm^2 (stainless steel cages)
Skin-depot XAD-2/Study, 54.7 ug/2.54 cm^2 (stainless steel cages)
Animal weight: Glass metabolism cage, 280 g
    Skin-depot XAD-2/Pilot, 431 g
    Skin-depot XAD-2/Study, 280 g

Tables III and IV summarize the analytical results for the patches (ug of EPTC/ 23.74 cm^2) removed from the mixer/loader and applicator. In the mixing operations, the primary locations where EPTC was detected were thighs, shins, and forearms. This was expected because the pouring operation occurs below the waist. The forearm patches were located on the underside of the arms. During the transfer of the formulations to the mix tank, arms were often rested on the spray tank while transferring formulations to the tank. Upper body exposure was low and infrequent.

Table III. Summary of Patch Data, Mixer/Loader[1]

Position of Patch	Total EPTC Detected (ug)	Number of Samples with EPTC	ug EPTC/Patch Highest Values
Back	0.460	2	0.340
Chest[2]	0.840	4	0.415
Shoulder	0.125	1	0.125
Forearms	7.860	8	4.435
Thighs	20.550	8	13.150
Shins	366.440	10	361.860

[1]   Amount of EPTC found on the skin patch (ug/23.75 cm^2).
[2]   Chest values are from inside patches.

Table IV. Summary of Patch Data, Applicator[1]

Position of Patch	Total EPTC Detected (ug)	Number of Samples with EPTC	ug EPTC/Patch Highest Values
Back	23.88	9	13.81
Chest[2]	5.86	8	1.84
Shoulders	24.14	10	10.15
Forearms	9.68	12	3.41
Thighs	27.96	13	8.09
Shins	27.23	13	7.21

[1]   Amount of EPTC found on skin patch (ug/23.75 cm^2).
[2]   Chest values from inside patches.

The application process involved an even distribution of EPTC to both the upper and lower body with twice as many patches showing detectable residue. The lower portion of the body received 60% of the exposure. No exposure monitoring data was taken for feet. Exposure to the feet was assumed to be very slight since the worker wore boots throughout the study.

The two inside patches used in this study (Table V) were placed on either side of the exterior "chest at throat" patch to estimate the amount of EPTC reaching the skin. For the applicator, about 40% of the EPTC measured on the external patches were found inside the shirt. The external patches for the mixer only amounted to 2.5% of the levels found in external patches of the applicator, because the same person alternately performed both mixing and application, and did not change shirts between operations. The EPTC levels on the inside mixer patches are thought to represent amounts transferred from the shirt (which was not changed during operations) following previous spray applications.

The applicator levels were also generally low except for the hands as shown in Table VI. Maintenance exposure, involving the unclogging of nozzles plugged by fiber glass particles, doubled the hand values over normal operations. By contrast, the mixing step averages less than 1/3 the exposure experienced in applicator functions where gloves were used on both hands.

Table V. Exterior and Inside Patch Data

Mode of Exposure	ug, EPTC Exterior Chest Patch	Inside Left Chest	Inside Right Chest
Applicator (14 replicates)	0.960	0.320	0.460
Mixer (14 replicates)	0.024	0.057	0.064

Table VI. Summary of Hand Wash Data, Mixer/Loader/Applicator

Time	Amount of EPTC Found in ug[1] Mixer/Loader	Applicator	/maintenance
6/10	—	266.00	—
6/11	60.00	55.50	—
6/11	69.50	33.50	1518.00
6/12	36.50	87.00	829.00
6/12	—	9.50	472.00
6/16	18.00	7.00	236.50
6/16	38.50	0.00	581.50
6/17	69.00	0.00	527.50
6/17	22.00	8.00	—
6/17	47.00	—	—
6/18	75.30	822.50	—
6/18	429.50	310.50	—
6/18	—	40.00	—
6/19	10.50	71.00	—
6/19	48.00	74.50	—
6/19	72.50	1790.50	—
6/19	167.50	—	—
Mean	83.13	238.36	519.57
SD	106.75	479.69	535.20

[1] Values are from hand rinses.

The average daily inhalation exposure observed was 28.97 ug for the mixer and 147.42 ug for the applicator. The applicator was expected to be highest due to the longer exposure times (100–200 minutes). Mixing times ranged from 11–23 minutes.

Tables VII and VIII give the exposure values and the absorbed dosages, for the mixer/loader and applicator obtained from clothing patches, hand washings, and inhalation data. The exposure values, dermal and inhalation, were converted to absorbed dosages by multiplying the dermal exposure by the dermal absorption percentage, 14.7%, obtained from the rat study and the inhalation exposure values by 50% based on dog and human inhalation studies of Raabe ([6]). The total absorbed dosages for Tables VII and VIII are given in Table IX along with the absorbed dose expressed in terms of 1.0 and 23 lbs of applied EPTC. The mean dose absorbed per lb of pesticide applied was 14.23 ug.

Table X shows the sum of the EPTC urinary metabolites S-(N,N-dipropylcarbamoyl) cysteine and S-(N,N-dipropylcarbamoyl)-N-acetyl cysteine, found in urine samples taken over the course of the study. The detection limit was set at 0.05 ug/ml based on the 0.023 ug/ml background interference peak found in the prestudy control urine. Four samples had metabolite levels of 0.079 to 0.136 ug/ml, which converts to EPTC equivalents excreted of 9.53 to 24.38 ug. The sample with the highest residue

Table VII. Exposures and Estimated Absorbed Dosages
During Mixing/Loading (ug)

Time	Dermal		Inhalation	
	Exposure	Absorbed Dose (14.7%)	Exposure	Absorbed Dose (50%)
6/10	–	–	65.79	32.89
6/11	8387.80	1234.69	0.00	0.00
6/11	93.50	13.76	0.00	0.00
6/12	80.73	11.89	0.00	0.00
6/16	51.27	7.55	0.00	0.00
6/16	41.53	6.11	25.00	12.50
6/17	69.00	10.15	0.00	0.00
6/17	22.00	3.23	0.00	0.00
6/17	147.18	21.66	15.79	7.89
6/18	126.54	18.62	213.16	106.58
6/18	664.97	97.88	27.03	13.51
6/19	93.99	13.83	0.00	0.00
6/19	76.85	11.31	28.95	14.47
6/19	72.50	10.67	58.97	29.49
6/19	862.63	126.97	0.00	0.00
Mean	770.75	113.45	28.97	14.48
SD	2206.76	324.84	55.48	27.74

Table VIII. Exposures and Estimated Absorbed Dosages
During Application (ug)

Time	Dermal		Inhalation	
	Exposure	Absorbed Dose (14.7%)	Exposure	Absorbed Dose (50%)
6/10	1710.53	251.80	315.38	157.69
6/11	426.20	62.72	215.38	107.69
6/11	1591.42	234.25	0.00	0.00
6/12[1]	1038.44	152.85	133.33	66.67
6/12[1]	495.62	72.95	89.47	44.74
6/16	380.94	56.07	255.26	127.63
6/16	626.26	92.18	0.00	0.00
6/17	532.16	78.33	71.05	35.53
6/17	14.74	2.16	82.14	41.07
6/18	897.07	132.00	0.00	0.00
6/18	1436.50	211.45	618.42	309.21
6/19	271.04	39.89	160.53	80.26
6/19	71.00	10.45	0.00	0.00
6/19	228.00	33.56	51.35	25.68
6/19	2505.98	368.88	218.92	109.49
Mean	815.06	119.96	147.42	73.71
SD	712.08	104.82	165.05	82.53

[1] Applications were 13.8 lbs A.I. and 9.2 lbs A.I. for 6/11 and 6/12 respectively; otherwise, 23 lbs A.I. applications were made.

Table IX. Summary of Estimated Absorbed Dosages (Total)
During Mixing and Application (ug)

Date	Mixer/Loading	Applicator	Applied 23 lbs.	Applied 1.0 lbs.
6/10	–	409.49	–	–
6/11	1234.69	170.42	1405.11	61.09
6/11	13.76	234.25	413.30	17.97
6/12[1]		219.52		–
6/12[1]	11.89	117.69	129.58	5.63
6/16	7.55	183.70	191.25	8.31
6/16	18.61	92.18	110.79	4.82
6/17	10.15	113.86	124.01	5.39
6/17	3.23	43.23	46.46	2.20
6/17	29.55	–	–	–
6/18	–	132.00	–	–
6/18	125.00	520.66	645.90	28.00
6/18	111.39	120.15	231.54	10.06
6/19	13.83	10.45	24.28	1.05
6/19	25.78	59.24	85.02	3.69
6/19	40.16	478.37	518.50	22.50
6/19	126.97	–	–	–
Mean	126.61	193.68	327.14	14.23
SD	322.06	156.62	392.14	17.03

[1]　Applications were 13.8 lbs. A.I. and 9.2 lbs. A.I. for 6/11 and 6/12 respectively; otherwise, 23 lbs. A.I. applications were made.

was selected for further study. The aliquot was submitted to GC-mass spectral analysis and using this technique, the presence of S-(N,N-dipropyl carbamoyl)-N-acetylmethyl cysteine was confirmed.

The exposures that resulted in detectable levels of urinary metabolites occurred on 6/10, 6/11, and 6/17. No urinary metabolites were found on 6/13, 6/14, and 6/15 when there was not exposure and on 6/16, 6/18, and 6/19 when there was considerable exposure based on patch and inhalation monitoring data.

Table XI gives the daily exposure for a worker mixing/loading and applying EPTC to 120 acres of soil in mg/person/day and in mg/kg/day along with their mean and standard deviation. The average lifetime exposure expressed in mg/kg/day is also given in Table XI along with the mean value and standard deviation. A margin of safety of 68 was determined for the mixer/loader-applicator by dividing the rat chronic NOEL of 5.0 mg/kg/day by the exposure level of 0.074 mg/kg/day determined in this study from patch and inhalation data. A much wider margin of safety of 340 was calculated using the NOEL of 5.0 mg/kg/day and the daily exposure value of 0.0147 mg/kg/day determined from urinary values. A margin of safety of 2940.0 was determined using the lifetime average estimate of exposure of 0.0017 mg/kg/day determined from patch and inhalation data.

Discussion

The adsorptive nature of EPTC made it difficult to determine the fate of a topically applied dose in glass metabolism cages normally used by investigators to collect respiratory volatiles. Topically applied ^{14}C-EPTC, which volatilized, was not quantitatively collected on the XAD-2 resin as glass surfaces retained approximately 30% of this material. This necessitated the use of a skin-depot as described by Susten et al. (3) for

Table X. Total Metabolite Found in Urine
During Mixing/Loading and Application

Time Collected		Urine Volume (ml)	ug of Metabolites	Corrected Absorbed[1,2] Dose in ug/23 lbs of Applied EPTC (n=7)
Day	Time			
6/10	16:33	286	0.00	0.00
6/10	22:15	146	12.56	87.10
6/11	4:30	186	0.00	0.00
6/11	19:00	275	24.38	302.89[3]
6/12	5:10	258	13.29	0.00
6/17	18:30	262	0.00	0.00
6/17	22:40	170	9.53	60.42
6/18	5:00	244	0.00	0.00
Mean				64.34[4]
SD				111.05

1/ Twenty-one urine samples were collected 6/9 to 6/19. Metabolites were found in samples collected on 6/10, 6/11, and 6/17.

2/ Urine values corrected to 1200 ml and urinary metabolites to S-(N,N-dipropyl-carbamoyl)-N-acetylcysteine. Metabolite assumed to be 28% of absorbed dose (40% of absorbed dose eliminated in urine over a 24 hr period and 70% of the urinary metabolites as the cysteine or N-acetyl derivatives).

3/ Value obtained for 6/11 and 6/12.

4/ Absorbed dose in ug/kg/d = 0.0147.

Calculations: 2.8 ug/lb of applied EPTC;
3.3 lb/A x 120 A/d = 396 lbs EPTC applied/d;
2.8 ug/lb x 396 lbs/d = 1.1 mg/75 Kg worker/d.

Table XI. Daily and Average Lifetime Absorbed Dose From
Mixing/Loading and Application

Time	Daily Absorbed[1] Dose (120 acres/day) Per Person		Average[2] Lifetime Absorbed Dose (mg/kg/day) Commercial Worker
	(mg/day)	(mg/kg/day)	
6/11	24.19	0.320	73.60—04
6/11	7.12	0.090	20.70—04
6/12	—	—	—
6/12	2.23	0.029	6.67—04
6/16	3.29	0.043	9.89—04
6/16	1.78	0.024	5.52—04
6/17	2.13	0.028	6.44—04
6/17	0.87	0.012	2.76—04
6/17	—	—	—
6/18	—	—	—
6/18	11.09	0.147	33.80—04
6/18	3.95	0.053	12.19—04
6/19	0.42	0.006	1.38—04
6/19	1.46	0.019	4.37—04
6/19	8.90	0.119	27.37—04
6/19	—	—	—
Mean	5.62	0.074	17.05—04
SD	6.75	0.089	20.53—04

[1]   Daily Absorbed Dose = 120 acres x 3.3 lbs/A x ug absorbed dose/A (from Table IX).
[2]   Average Lifetime Absorbed Dose = Daily Absorbed Dose x 0.023
15d/365d x 40 yr/70yr = 0.023.

the mouse and modified in this study to fit the rat. The removable XAD-2 resin adsorption column facilitated the topical application and trapping of volatilized ^{14}C-EPTC.

EPTC was retained by cloth patches long enough to enable us to collect and estimate the amount of EPTC deposited on clothing. EPTC did not appear to be retained by the skin of the worker long enough to be absorbed into the body as indicated by the small number of urine samples having detectable levels of EPTC metabolite. The use of gloves during mixing/loading and nozzle cleaning may have actually enhanced the absorption of EPTC through the skin of the hands. Studies by Lavy et al. (12) indicate that workers exposed to 2,4-D and picloram on a daily basis excrete these pesticides in urine shortly after exposure and during the period of exposure. If the EPTC was being absorbed, daily exposure of the worker to EPTC should have resulted in EPTC metabolites in all urines collected. Evaporative losses of EPTC from skin most likely occurred reducing the amount of EPTC available for absorption.

A better estimate of actual exposure/absorption to EPTC may be obtained from urinary metabolites than from cloth patches. This estimate reduces the daily absorbed dose from 0.074 to 0.0147 mg/kg/day for a 75 kg man and increases the margin of safety from 68 to 340. Lifetime absorbed dosages are 1/5 of the absorbed dose estimated from cloth patches when urinary values are used.

Acknowledgments

We wish to thank Fiorella Gielow and Scott Folwarkow for their expert technical assistance in carrying out the analyses required in the rat percutaneous absorption study.

Literature Cited

1. Knaak, J. B.; Yee, Karin; Ackermann, C. R.; Zweig, G.; Wilson, B. W. Toxicol. Appl. Pharmacol. 1984, 72, 406–416.
2. Medinsky, M. A. J. Anal. Toxicol. 1986, 10, 24–27.
3. Susten, A. S.; Dames, B. L.; Burge, J. R.; Niemeier, R. W. Am. J. Ind. Med. 1985, 7, 323–335.
4. Popendorf, W. J. Ph.D. Thesis, University of California, Berkeley, CA, 1976.
5. Guyton, A. C. W. B. Saunders Co., Philadelphia, PA, 1966, 552.
6. Hubbell, J. P.; Casida, J. C. J. Agric. Food Chem. 1977, 25(2), 404–413.
7. Knowles, D. PPG Industries, Inc. Report, Br-24055, 1986.
8. Mull, R.; McCarthy, J. F. Vet. Hum. Toxicol. 1986, 28, 328–336.
9. Raabe, O. University of California, Davis; Contract No. A3-132-33 with California Air Resources Board.
10. Ross, J. H.; Leber, A. P.; Lucas, F. D.; Chun, S. A. PPG Industries, Inc. Report, Br-24060.
11. Hazelton Laboratories American, Inc., Final Report. Two-Year EPTC Dietary Study in Rats, 1987.
12. Lavy, T. L.; Norris, L. A.; Mattice, J. D.; and Marx, O. B. Environ. Toxicol. and Chem. 1987, 6, 209–224.

RECEIVED January 28, 1988

Chapter 23

Assessing Risk for Humans on the Basis of Animal Toxicology Data

Use of Dermal Absorption Data for Animal Studies

E. J. Hixon

Data Evaluation Department, Health, Environment and Safety, Mobay Corporation, Stilwell, KS 66085

A method is presented for predicting dermal absorption of a chemical by man based on data collected in animal studies. The data from dermal absorption studies in animals can be fit to the most appropriate equation based on statistical tests. Once the equation has been fit, the coefficients for the parameters of the equation can be estimated. These parameters can then be used to estimate the amount of applied material that is absorbed. After field exposure studies have determined the amount of material contacting the skin and the time of exposure for the workers, the parameter estimates can be used to estimate the amount of the material that will be absorbed. The absorbed dose can then be compared to available toxicology data for hazard determination.

One of the most difficult aspects of risk assessment is estimating the risk of chemical exposure for humans based on animal toxicity data. This estimation is even more difficult when the animal study data are collected using a different route of exposure than that expected for humans. A case in point is estimating the risk for pesticide applicators. The animal toxicity database for a pesticide consists largely of data collected in feeding studies. The only studies available to address the routes of exposure appropriate for applicators are typically a single subacute dermal study and (sometimes) a subacute inhalation study. These studies are often conducted using treatment five days per week, whereas the exposure to the applicator may be daily for an extended period. Subacute studies rarely last longer than three weeks, whereas the applicators' exposure may be longer. These discrepancies can make it difficult to compare the exposure situation to the animal data.

0097–6156/89/0382–0304$06.00/0
© 1989 American Chemical Society

In the past few years it has become common to perform a dermal absorption study to determine the extent to which a material in contact with the skin is absorbed into the general circulation. The intent has been to use the dermal absorption study as a basis for calculation of the dose to which an individual is exposed. Once the dose "delivered" has been determined, animal studies using any route of administration could theoretically be used to estimate the likelihood of toxicity.

Several protocols have been used to determine dermal absorption of a chemical (pesticide). All the protocols have at least one major difference from the way dermal exposure actually occurs in the field. In the animal studies a measured amount of material is applied to the treated skin area and left in contact with the skin for a specified period of time. In contrast, an individual working in the field has a graded exposure to a slowly but steadily increasing amount of material. The "dose" starts out relatively small and increases steadily throughout the exposure period.

In studies conducted to measure the exposure of workers under field conditions, it is standard to measure the total amount of material on the skin at the end of the exposure period and divide by the number of hours (or minutes) of exposure to express the exposure as mass of material deposited per unit time. This measure has been referred to in some cases as the "rate" of dermal exposure. In contrast, animal studies may determine the amount of material absorbed (usually as the amount appearing in the urine) per unit time, and refer to this as the "rate" of dermal absorption. Clearly these two "rates" do not refer to the same phenomenon, and should not be considered comparable.

Despite this key difference in the way the data are collected, it is possible to use the animal dermal absorption data to estimate the amount of applied material absorbed by an exposed individual. The purpose of this paper is to present a method for making this determination.

Dermal Absorption Processes

Studies conducted in animals (1) and with human volunteers (2) have clearly demonstrated that the amount of material absorbed tends to increase as the amount applied increases. Several studies have demonstrated that the percent absorbed decreases with increasing dose; however the absolute mass absorbed tends to increase (1). This may not be, and in fact usually is not, a linear process. Similar results have been observed with respect to time. The amount of material absorbed across the skin generally increases with increasing time of contact with the skin (3-4). It is not uncommon for the amount of absorption to plateau after a time.

Clearly it is necessary for dermal absorption studies in animals to take into account both dose and time. It is not practical in the laboratory setting to apply increasing doses to experimental animals, particularly when the study is being done with radio-labeled material. It is practical, however, to use more than one dose, and to look at more than one time point after application. The protocol outlined by R. P. Zendzian addresses both of these needs (5). Briefly, groups of animals are treated with one of at least three doses of material with the doses spaced at log intervals. The application areas are covered and the animals are placed in metabolism cages for collection of urine and feces. At intervals of 0.5, 1, 2, 4, 10 and 24 hours after application subgroups of animals from each treated group are sacrificed for determination of radioactivity remaining in skin and carcass. The amount of material absorbed is determined based on the amounts of radioactivity excreted and that remaining in the carcass.

Mathematical Treatment of Results

All analyses were done using software of SAS Institute Inc., Cary, NC. Table I presents data collected in a study using the Zendzian protocol with four logarithmically spaced doses and time points up to 24 hours. The data from a dermal absorption study conducted according to the Zendzian protocol will contain two independent variables, dose and time, as well as the dependent variable, the amount absorbed. The first test to be done on the data is to determine whether linear or quadratic regression is most appropriate. Since we know from separate experiments that the amount absorbed increases with both time of exposure and dose, we might expect to find an interaction of these two factors when effects of both are investigated simultaneously. Thus it is important that the data from each experiment be tested for quadratic response.

Table I. Dermal Absorption Test Data

(Time)	Dose (mg/kg)			
	0.04	0.4	4.0	40
0.5	.00348[a]	.0267	.312	4.77
1.0	.00277	.0319	.303	4.56
2.0	.00378	.0319	.308	5.05
4.0	.00428	.0323	.348	4.44
10	.00498	.0452	.402	5.20
24	.00519	.0440	.449	5.06

[a]Amount absorbed in mg equivalents

This test can be done easily using the SAS procedure RSREG. This procedure fits the parameters of a quadratic response surface (6). The equation describing the response surface is shown here:

$$y = B_0 + B_1 x_1 + B_2 x_2 + B_3 x_1^2 + B_4 x_2^2 + B_5 x_1 x_2$$

where x_1 is the dose applied, x_2 is the time of exposure, B_0 is the intercept and B_1, B_2 etc. are the coefficients of each term. The RSREG procedure will perform a test to determine how much of the residual error is due to lack of fit. This fit test can be used to determine whether a quadratic response best describes the results.

These data were tested using the RSREG procedure, and the results are shown in Table II. The procedure applies first a linear regression, then adds the quadratic terms (x_1^2 and x_2^2), then adds the cross product ($x_1 x_2$). In testing for lack of fit, the procedure RSREG partitions the total error into lack of fit and pure error. When lack of fit is significantly different from pure error, then there is variation in the model not accounted for by random error. As can be seen from Table II, lack of fit is significantly different from pure error for the test data set. This indicates that a quadratic response model does not fit the data, despite the apparently favorable R^2 values.

Now we are free to perform a simple linear regression on the data. The best way to approach the data next is to determine whether either or both of the independent variables (dose and time) have an effect on the dependent variable (amount absorbed). Examining the data in Table I shows that, while there appears to be a reasonable relationship between dose and amount absorbed, the relationship between time and amount absorbed is not so clear. We can test this using the SAS procedure RSQUARE. This procedure finds the subset of independent variables that best predicts the amount absorbed based on the optimum value of R^2, the coefficient of determination (7).

The results obtained when the data in Table I were tested using the RSQUARE procedure are shown in Table III. Clearly using time as the sole regressor resulted in a poor fit of the data; in other words, the amount absorbed did not correlate very well with time alone. In contrast, a good fit was achieved using dose as the sole regressor. However, the statistics for the regression analysis using both dose and time is slightly better than that using dose alone. Therefore, although the effect of time is small it does appear to improve the fit of the curve to the data, so we are better off including the time factor in our analysis.

Now that we have learned that a regression using both dose and time results in a curve that best fits the amount absorbed, we are free to perform a simple linear regression using these two independent variables. This was done using the SAS procedure REG. The REG procedure fits least-squares estimates to linear regression models (8). For our data with two independent variables, the equation that is fitted to the data is represented by:

$$y = B_0 + B_1 x_1 + B_2 x_2$$

The procedure REG will estimate the values of B_0, B_1 and B_2 and will compare the actual data to the responses predicted by the model. By comparing the predicted values to those actually obtained we can examine the fit of the curve to the data obtained. This comparison is shown in Table IV.

From examining Table IV it is clear that for this test data set the fit of the predicted values to the actual values is not good at very low dose/short time combinations. At these points the predicted values are negative numbers, which cannot occur in the real world. Actual exposure doses in mg/kg/day can easily be in the range of these low doses, however, so it is important to find a way

Table II. RESULTS OF THE RSREG PROCEDURE

REGRESSION	DF	TYPE I SS	R-SQUARE	F-RATIO	PROB
Linear	2	100.506	0.9952	2733.72	0.0001
Quadratic	2	0.0804	0.0008	2.19	0.1412
Crossproduct	1	0.0747	0.0007	4.07	0.0589
Total Regress	5	100.660	0.9967	1095.18	0.0001

RESIDUAL	DF	SS	MEAN SQUARE	F-RATIO	PROB
Lack of Fit	18	0.331	0.0184	9999.990	1.0000
Pure Error	0	0	0		
Total Error	18	0.331	0.0184		

Table III. RESULTS OF THE RSQUARE PROCEDURE

NUMBER IN MODEL	R-SQUARE	INTERCEPT	PARAMETER ESTIMATES	
			X1	X2
1	0.0006	1.2674		0.0061
1	0.9946	-0.0469	0.12	
2	0.9952	-0.0894	0.12	0.0061

Table IV. Comparison of Actual vs Predicted Values

Time of Exposure (Hours)	Dosage Applied (mg/kg)							
	0.04		.4		4		40	
	Actual	Predicted[a]	Actual	Predicted[a]	Actual	Predicted[a]	Actual	Predicted[a]
0.5	.00348	-.0814	.0267	-.0375	.312	.402	4.77	4.80
1.0	.00277	-.0784	.0319	-.0344	.303	.405	4.56	4.80
2	.00378	-.0722	.0319	-.0282	.308	.411	5.04	4.81
4	.00428	-.0599	.0323	-.0160	.348	.424	4.44	4.82
10	.00498	-.0230	.0452	.0209	.402	.461	5.20	4.86
24	.00519	.0630	.0440	.107	.449	.547	5.06	4.94

[a] Actual or predicted amount absorbed in mg equivalents

to predict the amount absorbed at these low doses. One possibility
is to do the statistics on the data from just the two lower doses.
The results of the RSREG procedure again showed that the quadratic
model does not fit the data well (data not shown). The RSQUARE
procedure indicated again that time alone does not fit the data well
but does improve slightly the fit of the data compared to using dose
as the sole regressor (data not shown). In Table V the REG results
are shown using only the two lowest dosages of 0.04 and 0.4 mg/kg.
This time the predicted values agree very well with the actual
values.

Table V. Comparison of Actual vs Predicted Values
Using the Two Lowest Dosages

Time of Exposure (Hours)	Dosage Applied (mg/kg)			
	0.04		0.4	
	Actual	Predicted[a]	Actual	Predicted[a]
0.5	.00348	.00162	.0267	.0329
1.0	.00277	.00181	.0319	.0331
2	.00378	.00220	.0319	.0335
4	.00428	.00296	.0323	.0342
10	.00498	.00526	.0452	.0365
24	.00519	.0106	.0440	.0419

[a]Actual or predicted amount absorbed in mg equivalents

REG Statistics
Intercept: −0.0020
    B_1:   0.08
    B_2:   0.0004
    R^2:   0.95

The same procedures were done using the data from only the two
middle dosages of 0.4 and 4 mg/kg. As expected, the RSREG procedure
indicated that the quadratic model does not fit the data well (data
not shown). The RSQUARE procedure showed again that regression
based on time of exposure alone does not fit the data well, but that
time and dose together provide a slightly better fit than using dose
alone (data not shown). The results of the REG procedure are shown
in Table VI: again the predicted values agree reasonably well with
the actual values. Finally, the data from the highest two dosages
were tested. The quadratic model did not fit the data, and in this
case time provided only a miniscule effect on the regression results
(data not shown). Table VII presents the results of the REG
procedure, and again it can be seen that the predicted values agree
with the actual values.

Discussion

The statistics from the three sets of data are summarized in Table
VIII. Several interesting observations can be made from these data.

First, the intercept (or B_0) appears to be a constant distance from the lowest dosage considered in the calculations. Second, the effect of time (B_2) appears to increase with increasing dosage.

Table VI.   Comparison of Actual vs Predicted Values Using the Two Middle Dosages

| Time of Exposure (Hours) | Dosage Applied (mg/kg) | | | |
| | 0.4 | | 4 | |
	Actual	Predicted[a]	Actual	Predicted[a]
0.5	.0267	.0129	.312	.331
1.0	.0319	.0146	.303	.333
2	.0319	.0181	.308	.337
4	.0323	.0251	.348	.344
10	.0452	.0461	.402	.365
24	.0440	.0952	.449	.414

[a]Actual or predicted amount absorbed in mg equivalents

REG Statistics
Intercept: −0.02
B_1: 0.09
B_2: 0.003
R^2: 0.97

Table VII.   Comparison of Actual vs Predicted Values Using the Two Highest Dosages

| Time of Exposure (Hours) | Dosage Applied (mg/kg) | | | |
| | 4 | | 40 | |
	Actual	Predicted[a]	Actual	Predicted[a]
0.5	.312	.277	4.77	4.77
1.0	.303	.283	4.56	4.78
2	.308	.295	5.05	4.79
4	.348	.319	4.44	4.81
10	.402	.390	5.20	4.88
24	.449	.557	5.06	5.05

[a]Actual or predicted amount absorbed in mg equivalents

REG Statistics
Intercept: −0.23
B_1: 0.12
B_2: 0.012
R^2: 0.99

Third, the effect of dose (B_1) appears to be relatively constant, although it may increase very slightly with increasing time.

Thus for this particular data set the effect of time appears to be extremely small until the dosages get fairly large. A dosage of 4 mg/kg for a 60 kg individual represents a total exposure of 240 mg, while at 40 mg/kg the total exposure would be 2400 mg. These are probably larger than most of the actual exposures under normal conditions of use. Thus for average exposure conditions this analysis of these data indicates that we can virtually ignore the duration of exposure and merely consider the total dose of material applied to the skin. Under these circumstances it might be appropriate to use the estimated value of B_1 as a measure of the fraction of the applied dose that we would expect to be absorbed. In other words, using the results from the two lowest dosages as an example (Table VIII), we might expect that 0.08, or 8%, of the applied dose would be absorbed regardless of time of exposure. This approach can only be used when the effect of time is miniscule, as is the case at these low dosages for this data set.

Table VIII. Summary of Statistics for Three Data Sets
Model: $Y = B_0 + B_1$ (Dose) $+ B_2$ (Time)

	Lowest Dosages	Middle Dosages	Highest Dosages
Intercept	−0.002	−0.02	−0.23
B_1	0.08	0.09	0.12
B_2	0.0004	0.003	0.012
R	0.95	0.97	0.99

Given that these data can be fit to a model better when not all the dosages are used at once, it clearly becomes extremely important that the dosages used in the animal study bracket as closely as possible the anticipated range of exposures in the field. The data might be easier to fit to a model if the dosages used were spaced more closely than one log apart. For example, dosages spaced at half log intervals might give us a better fit, although the results in Table VIII showed only small differences in the B_1 and B_2 values between the three sets of regression data.

It is obvious from the results presented that the pesticide used to produce these data is not particularly well absorbed regardless of applied dose or time of exposure. Another compound that is better absorbed might produce a completely different set of statistics. For example, one might find that the quadratic model fit a data set quite well. In either case, by substituting the estimates of B_0, B_1, B_2 etc. into the model equation one can determine the actual amount absorbed using the amount of dermal exposure measured in a field study as the dose (x_1) and the time over which the exposure was measured as the time (x_2). In this way we can take advantage of the dose and time effects noted in our animal studies and apply these effects to human exposure. An example of such calculations is shown in Table IX. Here the estimates of B_1 and B_2 from the regression using the two lowest dosages are used because the amount of material applied to the skin is in the range of these dosages. By substituting the amount applied and the time of exposure into the model equation, the amount absorbed is predicted to be 0.009 mg equivalents of material. Thus it can be easy to predict the amount absorbed once we have the correct regression parameter estimates. The calculations would be done in a similar fashion if the quadratic model were found to fit the data best, although it would be slightly more complicated.

Table IX. Estimating Human Exposure
Using Animal Study Data

Human Data		
Total Dermal Exposure:	6	mg
Body Weight of Subject:	60	kg
Dosage Applied:	0.1	mg/kg
Time of Exposure:	8	hours

Study Data	
Intercept:	−0.002
B_1:	0.08
B_2:	0.0004

$$\text{Amount Absorbed} = (0.8)(0.1) + (.0004)(8) - .002$$

$$= .009 \text{ mg equivalents}$$

This presentation has centered around a single data set, and certain procedures were followed based on the characteristics of these data. The important thing to remember is that each data set should be considered unique, and the tests should be applied to each sequentially to determine how best to proceed. To summarize these steps:

1. Because there will always be two independent variables, the data should always be tested using quadratic and cross-product models. Simple linear regression should not be attempted until you are satisfied that a more complex equation will not fit the data.

2. Regardless of the type of regression, whether quadratic or linear, predicted values should be compared to actual values to be sure the equation works in the real world.

3. It may be necessary to perform regressions on only part of your data set to give a good fit that works in the real world. You can only justify omitting part of your data if the parameters of the exposure situation fit within the range of the data you use.

In conclusion, the availability of dermal absorption study data greatly enhances our ability to perform proper and reasonable hazard assessments for fieldworker exposure. The flowscheme for data analysis proposed here is intended to standardize our approach to these data, to minimize improper use of the data and to provide a more effective tool for human hazard assessment.

Nontechnical Summary

Dermal absorption studies conducted in animals using the Zendzian protocol provide large sets of data. These data must be analyzed carefully for proper use in predicting the amount of material an exposed worker might absorb across the skin. The data must first be tested against a quadratic model to determine the effect of dose, time and dose plus time. If the quadratic model does not fit, a simple linear regression can be performed. Regardless of the type of regression, the model can be used to estimate the coefficient of dose and time. These coefficients can then be used to calculate the predicted amount of material absorbed after a given exposure.

Literature Cited

1. Shah, P. V.; Fisher, H.; Sumler, M.; Monroe, R.; Chernoff, N.; Hall, L. J. Toxicol. Env. Health 1987, 21, 353-366.
2. Wester, R. C.; Maibach, H. J. Toxicol. Env Health 1985, 16, 25-37.
3. Burka, L. T.; Sanders, J.; Kool, C.; Kim, Y.; Matthews, H. Toxicol. Appl. Pharmacol. 1987, 87, 121-126.
4. Feldmann, R. J.; Maibach, H. Toxicol. Appl. Pharmacol., 1974, 28, 126-132.
5. Zendzian, R. P. Procedure for Studying Dermal Absorption; Third edition revised June 14, 1985; California Modifications, October 9, 1985.
6. SAS Institute Inc. SAS User's Guide: Statistics, Version 5 Edition. SAS Institute Inc.: Cary, 1985; Chapter 33.
7. SAS Institute Inc. SAS User's Guide: Statistics, Version 5 Edition. SAS Institute Inc.: Cary, 1985; Chapter 32.
8. SAS Institute Inc. SAS User's Guide: Statistics, Version 5 Edition. SAS Institute Inc.: Cary, 1985; Chapter 31

RECEIVED March 23, 1988

Chapter 24

Insecticide Absorption from Indoor Surfaces

Hazard Assessment and Regulatory Requirements

Peter E. Berteau[1], James B. Knaak[1], Donald C. Mengle[1], and Jay B. Schreider[2]

[1]Hazard Evaluation Section, California Department of Health Services, Berkeley, CA 94704
[2]Medical Toxicology Branch, California Department of Food and Agriculture, Sacramento, CA 95814

Insecticides are often applied indoors where dermal absorption from surfaces as well as inhalation exposure may occur. Children may also have oral exposure due to hand-to-mouth activities. Poison control centers frequently receive complaints of illness following such applications. These complaints may be coincidental due to odors or to a systemic toxic action from an ingredient. Using an appropriate algorithm, surface exposure and total absorption was calculated for chlorpyrifos, dichlorvos and propoxur. With each of these insecticides, the dose calculated might provide a toxic dose, particularly to an infant. More data are, therefore, needed for these and other insecticides to ensure that the levels in the air and on treated surfaces will not be injurious to health. Such data will include bioavailability of surface residues, rate of transfer from surfaces and dose-response data. Pending such data, risk assessments based upon health-protective assumptions should be used to decide the safety of various components.

Pesticides, particularly those containing cholinesterase inhibitors, are often applied to combat insect infestations in indoor environments. The treated sites may include room air, closets, storage areas, baseboards, window sills, cracks, crevices, inaccessible areas, house plants, pets, pet beds, beds, upholstery, carpets and smooth floor areas. Respirable droplets or vapor may be inhaled during or after pesticide spraying and fogging operations. Human exposure may also occur as a result of dermal contact with treated or exposed surfaces followed by percutaneous absorption of the chemicals. In small children, there is also oral exposure through hand-to-mouth transfer. Thus, the cholinesterase-inhibiting pesticides represent a potential acute human health hazard when used indoors, particularly for small children.

An appreciable number of persons in California require poison center and medical attention each year following exposure subsequent to treatment of homes, apartments, and offices by structural pest control operators, landlords, or employers as well as by adult household members.

In Table I some of the California Department of Food and Agriculture's (CDFA) priority cases for 1984 which involved structural treatment are indicated.

In 1984 the San Francisco Poison Control Center and its Toxic Information Center received 1,180 calls on pesticides. Of these calls, 340 involved insecticides and children under the age of 6. The symptoms and history of exposure were in agreement in 41 percent of the cases involving illnesses. The place where the exposure

0097–6156/89/0382–0315$06.00/0
○ 1989 American Chemical Society

occurred, indoors or outdoors, was not recorded. The most common symptom was nausea.

Large numbers of poisoning cases due to cholinesterase inhibitors are handled each year by the Los Angeles Poison Control Center and the San Diego Poison Information Center. The great majority of the exposures to these pesticides occur in the home.

Young children clad in little more than diapers are at risk playing on previously sprayed surfaces such as floors, carpets, furniture, and bedding. The higher body surface area to volume ratios of children compared to adults increases the likelihood that children will receive a toxic dose. Mild cholinergic symptoms are difficult to identify from normal childhood functions such as drooling, diarrhea, or excessive urination. In this connection, it should be noted that not all the subjects exposed are sick from symptoms of cholinesterase depression; many reports of illness may be coincidental due to the unpleasant odor of some of the pesticide chemicals and adjuvants used, resulting in a nauseous response. However, as will be shown, these concerns necessitate an assessment of the potential adverse health effects from the indoor use of these types of pesticides.

The use of non-volatile pesticides for crack and crevice treatment is not expected to be hazardous to human health, because dermal contact is minimal and inhalation is not a significant route of exposure. Volatile pesticides such as dichlorvos are especially hazardous if the enclosed area is not adequately ventilated prior to reentry.

TABLE I. EXAMPLES OF REPORTED PESTICIDE ILLNESSES FROM STRUCTURAL APPLICATION

Applicator	Number Sick	Circumstances	Pesticide
Landlord	5	Two residents and three visitors to an apartment house.	Chlorpyrifos
Employer	13	County office building. Building evacuated.	Chlorpyrifos
Structural Pest Control Operator	10	Hospital employees.	Chlorpyrifos, bendiocarb, and diazinon
Structural Pest Control Operator	1	Four-month-old child.	Chlorpyrifos
Structural Pest Control Operator	5	All five family members.	Methyl bromide
Employer	15	School district office workers.	Propoxur

Mobay Chemical Company submitted two reports to the California Department of Food and Agriculture concerning the use of propoxur for flea control indoors. According to the reports, infant children are expected to be at risk when they come in contact with propoxur-treated floors and carpets. On the basis of these studies, Mobay made a label amendment on their indoor use product containing propoxur that explicitly limited indoor applications to surfaces along baseboards and inaccessible areas and recommended against the use of propoxur on large floor areas or floor coverings or as a space spray.

In Table II an outline of a worst case situation where a scantily clad infant is playing in a room is given. Many of the parameters stated are measured values which can be located in various textbooks. Others are assumptions or "educated guesses" based upon little or no supporting data.

TABLE II. WORST CASE ASSUMPTIONS FOR AN INFANT PLAYING IN A ROOM

The 50th percentile body weight of a 6—9 month old child is approximately 7.5 kg (1).

The body surface area of a 6—9 month old child is approximately 0.45 m² (4.8 ft²) (2).

An infant's hands account for approximately 4.8 percent of the total body surface area (2).

Contact with the carpet will remove the total dislodgeable pesticide (12.9 mg/m²).

A child will play on approximately 18.6 m² (200 ft²) of treated carpet.

A child is in contact with a maximum of 25 percent of the available floor space (4.6 m²) and dermal contact takes place in four hours or less.

Dermal exposure is uniformly distributed over 50 percent of the body surface area.

It is assumed that all pesticide on the hands is subsequently ingested (approximately 9.6 percent of dermal exposure).

It is assumed that airborne exposure is continuous for 24 hours per day.

It is assumed that both the inhalation and oral doses are 100 percent absorbed.

The three pesticide chemicals which were initially considered by us were propoxur (Baygon), dichlorvos (DDVP), and chlorpyvifos (Dursban). The calculations which were used in developing an exposure dose are outlined in the forthcoming tables.

Propoxur
Propoxur, a carbamate insecticide the structure of which is shown below, was

introduced in 1971 as a low hazard vector control agent to replace DDT in developing countries. Its low dermal toxicity, > 2400 mg/kg, in the rat and reversible inhibitory action on acetylcholinesterase make it a reasonably safe material to use for mosquito control in and around the home. Its high oral toxicity (LD 50, 83 to 86 mg/kg in the rat), however, should be recognized when handling this material indoors. Propoxur is utilized for its rapid knockdown properties due to its vapor toxicity and its long-term residual properties. Villages in developing countries sprayed with propoxur were protected from mosquitoes for as long as 30 weeks after spraying (3). Propoxur is often used in combination with dichlorvos in pesticide foggers to provide residual insecticidal properties to the registered product. This residual property is the subject of concern as a possible hazard in dwelling places when propoxur is used alone or in combination with dichlorvos in foggers that deposit residues on furniture and carpets.

Acceptable levels for propoxur on surfaces that persons might have dermal contact with have not been established by regulatory agencies. A recent risk assessment made by Hackathorn and Eberhart (4), which is summarized in Table III, involved the use of propoxur on carpets for flea control. It indicated that an adequate safety factor does not exist for infants playing on carpets after treatment. If the child spends four hours on the floor, this time would be considered short-term exposure.

TABLE III. CALCULATION OF A WORST CASE EXPOSURE DOSE FOR AN INFANT EXPOSED TO PROPOXUR

Total dose	$= \dfrac{100\% \text{ inh. exp.} + 20\% \text{ dermal exp.} + 100\% \text{ oral exp.}}{\text{body weight}}$
	$= \dfrac{0.26 \text{ mg} + 0.2 \ (53.6 \text{ mg}) + 5.7 \text{ mg}}{7.5 \text{ kg}}$
	$= 2.2$ mg/kg
Inhalation exposure	$=$ max. air conc. x resp. min. vol. x exp. period
	$= 0.022 \text{ mg/m}^3 \times 0.5 \text{ m}^3/\text{hr} \times 24 \text{ hr}$
	$= 0.26$ mg
Dermal exposure	$=$ (carpet area contacted) x (propoxur residue available) − amount of propoxur ingested
	$= 4.6 \text{ m}^2 \times 12.9 \text{ mg/m}^2 - 5.7 \text{ mg}$
	$= 59.3 - 5.7$ mg
	$= 53.6$ mg
Oral exposure	$=$ (carpet area contacted) x (propoxur residue available) x (0.096)
	$= 59.3 \text{ mg} \times 0.096$
	$= 5.7$ mg

Thus, the worst case exposure value is 2.2 mg/kg.

Based on human exposure, the lowest effect level for a single dose is 0.36 mg/kg which produced mild cholinergic symptoms, stomach discomforts, blurred vision, facial redness, and sweating. In repeated applications 0.15 to 0.20 mg/kg of propoxur was administered orally five times in 30 minutes resulting in 60 percent cholinesterase depression but no symptoms (5). Thus, there is a definite possibility for an adverse reaction in a very young child who plays on a treated carpet.

Similar calculations were performed for a 12-year-old child (total dose = 0.04–0.31 mg/kg) and for an adult (total dose = 0.03–0.11 mg/kg). In these cases the likelihood of a toxic reaction appears to be considerably less. Even less safety would apply to applications to smooth floor surfaces. In the assessment, a number of assumptions were made that may result in estimating more exposure than actually occurs. For instance, studies conducted on the dog by Raabe (6) demonstrated that the lung may absorb only 50 percent of an inhaled air pollutant and not 100 percent. Studies by Knaak and Wilson (7) showed that the rate of absorption of pesticides through skin decreases exponentially as the concentration decreases on the skin. Pesticide concentrations amounting to 1.0 $\mu g/cm^2$ of skin are absorbed at rates amounting to 0.01 $\mu g/hr/cm^2$ (1.0 percent per hour or less). At this rate, 100 hours is required to absorb 1.0 μg of propoxur. Feldman and Maibach (8) used a dose of 4.0 $\mu g/cm^2$ on skin in their studies with propoxur. Approximately 20 percent of the topically applied dose was absorbed and eliminated over the study period of five days. Based upon these figures, the average rate of absorption over the five-day period was 0.007 $\mu g/hr/cm^2$. The relationship between the dermal dose of propoxur and its effect (dermal dose cholinesterase response) is not known. Gaines (9) reported a dermal LD50 in the rat of greater than 2400 mg/kg. This work suggests that propoxur is not readily absorbed or the inhibitor-acetylcholinesterase complex is short lived. In any case, data on the relationship of exposure and dermal dose cholinesterase response do not appear to be adequate to assure safe use in households, especially if carpets, open floor areas, furniture, or bedding are treated.

Dichlorvos

Dichlorvos (2,2-dichlorovinyl dimethyl phosphate, DDVP) the structure of which is shown below was one of the first of the vinyl phosphate insecticides to be discovered.

$$CH_3O \diagdown \underset{CH_3O \diagup}{\overset{O}{\overset{\|}{P}}} - O - CH = CCl_2$$

These compounds are formed by the Perkow rearrangement when a dihaloaldehyde or a dihaloketone is allowed to react with a trialkyl phosphite (10). The high vapor pressure of dichlorvos allows the material to penetrate spaces and kill insects.

A concentration of 0.015 mg/m³ (16 m³/day) for several hours is sufficient to control flies and mosquitoes in the home. The rapid disappearance of dichlorvos from air and surfaces in the home makes it ideally suited for treating insect infestations. An airborne exposure level of 30 mg/m³ is capable of killing rats within a four-hour period. Industrial hygiene guides limit workplaces concentrations to 1.0 mg/m³. A safety factor therefore exists for this chemical between the concentration required to control insects and those well-tolerated by adult healthy persons in the workplace. For safe use in the home, it would be desirable not to exceed a level of 0.01 mg/m³ in the room air for long-term exposure.

Maddy et al. (11) monitored dichlorvos residues in a home after fogging. In one or two hours after fogging, airborne residues were below 1.0 mg/m³. Wipe samples taken from smooth surfaces during this study indicated that levels as high as 0.8 mg/100 cm² were present on smooth surfaces after fogging.

These surface residues persisted over a period of seven hours. According to the monitoring and efficacy data on hand, the amount of dichlorvos initially released into the rooms, 2.8 to 5.7 mg/m^3, exceeded the amount, 0.015 mg/m^3, needed to control insects and might well be hazardous for some persons. A level of 0.015 mg/m^3 was finally reached in one room 24 hours after the aerosol was released into the room. By using the same values as were used for propoxur, a calculation of a worst case exposure for an infant was made and is shown in Table IV.

TABLE IV. CALCULATION OF A WORST CASE EXPOSURE DOSE FOR AN INFANT EXPOSED TO DICHLORVOS

Using the same assumptions as were used for propoxur but assuming 100 percent absorption from the skin.

Maximum air concentration after 30 minutes aeration = 0.75 mg/m^3.

Maximum surface concentration after 30 minutes aeration = 0.8 mg/cm^2

Inhalation exposure	=	conc. x resp. min. vol. x exposure time
	=	0.75 mg/m^3 x 0.5 m^3/hr x 24 hr
	=	9 mg

For 4.6 m^2 (50 ft^2) of carpet contacted by the child

Dermal exposure	=	Surface area contacted x dichlorvos residue available
	=	4.6 m^2 x 0.8 mg/100 cm^2 x 100
	=	368 mg — oral exp.

Assume all dichlorvos on skin of the hands is licked off.

Oral exposure	=	Dermal exp. x fractional surface area absorbed
	=	368 x 0.096
	=	35 mg
Net dermal exposure	=	368 — 35 mg
	=	333 mg

Total dose = $\dfrac{9 + 333 + 55}{7.5}$ mg/kg

= 50 mg/kg

It should be noted, however, that this calculation does not take into consideration the rapid metabolic breakdown of dichlorvos; consequently, a value of 50 mg/kg following a day's play on a treated carpet will be unreasonably high. However, the differences in the concentration attained versus the concentration required for insecticidal purposes suggest that dichlorvos should be reevaluated for efficacy as well as safety.

Chlorpyrifos

Chlorpyrifos, an organic phosphorothioate insecticide, the structure of which is shown below,

was introduced into the marketplace by Dow Chemical Company in 1965 for the control of mosquitoes and other household pests. The dermal LD50 of this pesticide was determined to be 202 mg/kg in the rat (9) and the acute oral LD50 in the rat is 135 mg/kg (12). Studies with this cholinesterase inhibitor in several animal species, including man, indicate that plasma cholinesterase activity is depressed to a greater extent than red cell acetylcholinesterase. For example, workers applying chlorpyrifos were exposed to water suspensions (0.25 and 0.5 percent) of wettable powders while spraying mosquitoes. Plasma cholinesterase was reduced more than 50 percent with no commensurate reduction in red cell cholinesterase (13). A daily dose of 0.08 mg/kg for six months failed to depress red cell cholinesterase in the monkey, while levels of 0.4 and 2.0 mg/kg/day depressed plasma and red cell activity. Dogs wearing flea collars containing 8 percent chlorpyrifos lived without detectable clinical symptoms even though plasma cholinesterase was depressed 100 percent below that of preexposure values (14).

A dermal absorption study (15) in human volunteers using 0.5 and 5.0 mg/kg of chlorpyrifos indicated that less than 3 percent of the applied dose was absorbed. A treatment area of less than 100 cm^2 was used. The dose was left on the bare skin of the forearm for a period of 12 to 20 hours and then removed by showering. No changes in red cell acetylcholinesterase or plasma cholinesterase activity were seen. The half-life for the absorption into blood was 14 to 31 hours. The elimination half-life was determined from an oral study. The results of the dog flea collar and human volunteer studies need to be considered together. In the dog study the total body surface area was exposed to several milligrams of chlorpyrifos each day, while in the human study an area of only 100 cm^2 was exposed (100 cm^2 divided by 20,000 cm^2 x 100 = 0.5 percent of total surface) to a single dose of the pesticide. In addition, chlorpyrifos was left on the skin of the dog for an extended period of time, while in the human studies chlorpyrifos was washed off 12 to 20 hours after application. The total surface area involved, the concentration per unit of surface area, and the length of the exposure period are important factors that must be considered. A dermal dose cholinesterase-response study is needed to clarify this relationship.

In separate studies involving chlorpyrifos, the safe use of chlorpyrifos was investigated in the home environment. Naffziger et al. (16) monitored the application of chlorpyrifos to floor coverings. Standard air sampling/gas chromatograph analytical procedures were used for air residues. Wiping procedures were used for carpets and vinyl floor covers.

Table V gives the dose calculation for exposure of infants to chlorpyrifos using the same assumptions as were used for both propoxur and dichlorvos.

In a personal communication from Dow sent on June 17, 1985, a lower dose is reported based upon a number of factors including the statement that chlorpyrifos is only 3 percent absorbed through the skin. However, the possibility of a toxic dose being absorbed by an infant under the conditions of application exists for chlorpyrifos as it does for propoxur and dichlorvos. The acceptable daily intake established by the World Health Organization for chlorpyrifos is 0.0015 mg/kg/day, and the minimal human response level has been reported to be 0.03 mg/kg (17).

TABLE V. CALCULATION OF A WORSE CASE EXPOSURE DOSE
FOR AN INFANT EXPOSED TO CHLORPYRIFOS

Using the same assumptions as were used for propoxur, but assuming 100 percent absorption from the skin.

Assume that the 0.5 percent spray is applied undiluted and that one hour is allowed for drying (i.e., prior to contact with the surface).

Air concentration $\quad = \quad 0.015$ mg/m^3 (kitchen dinette)

Average surface concentration $= 0.0433$ mg/100 cm^2

Inhalation exposure	=	conc. x resp. min. vol. x exposure time
	=	0.015 mg/m^3 x 0.5 m^3/hr x 24 hour
	=	0.18 mg

For 4.6 m^2 (50 ft^2) of surface area contacted

Dermal exposure	=	Surface area contacted x chlorpyrifos res. available
	=	4.6 m^2 x 0.0433 mg/100 cm^2
	=	4.6 x 0.0433 x 100 mg
	=	19.9 mg

Assuming all chlorpyrifos on the skin of the hands is licked off

Oral exposure	=	Dermal exp. x fractional surface area absorbed
	=	19.9 x 0.096
	=	1.91 mg
Net dermal exposure	=	19.9 − 1.91
	=	18.0 mg

$$\text{Total dose} = \frac{0.18 + 18.0 + 1.91}{7.5}$$

$$= 2.68 \text{ mg/kg}$$

Limitations of the Dose Calculations

There are limitations in the validity of the doses calculated, which are mainly:
1. They do not consider metabolic breakdown (e.g., as with dichlorvos).
2. They do not consider cumulative effects.
3. The data are very limited (e.g., surface deposition data were located for only three pesticide chemicals).
4. Dermal absorption data are available for only a few pesticide chemicals.

It should be noted that more information on rate of metabolic breakdown and extent of dermal absorption would generally result in lower values for the doses. On the other hand, the calculations do not address the probability that a child will continue to play daily on a treated surface. Although it is recognized that with most pesticides the level of chemical on the surface under consideration will attenuate each day, the repeated exposure, albeit to a successively reduced dose, will contribute to the continued lowering of acetylcholinesterase in blood and other tissues and consequent possible development of toxic symptoms.

Data That Would Be Useful for Setting Safe Levels

Should a registrant wish to attempt to develop data which might indicate that a certain level of a cholinesterase inhibitor could be used indoors in room air or on open floor areas, carpets, furniture, or bedding, a considerable amount of new data would be needed. Examples of the kind of data that would be needed are safe indoor levels in the air and on treated surfaces such as smooth floors and carpets as well as furniture and bedding. To establish these levels for a pesticide, the following information would be required, using standardized methods:

1. Levels of pesticide residues in room air through time after application.
2. Bioavailability of residues on surfaces (smooth floors, carpets, furniture, and bedding) through time after application.
3. Rate of transfer from surfaces (smooth floors, carpets, furniture, and bedding) to the skin and clothing of individuals.
4. Animal dose-response data from dermal and respiratory absorption studies. It would be necessary to determine the dose of a pesticide or mixture of pesticides in a product required to inhibit 50 percent red cell cholinesterase activity. These data should be used to evaluate and establish safe levels based on the procedure used for dislodgeable field foliage residues (18).

Methods for Collecting Required Data

Methods for collecting required data involve extraction procedures and information on the rate of transfer to the subject, which are as follows:

1. Bioavailability
   a. Solvent wipes
   b. Solvent extraction procedures
2. Rate of transfer of dislodgeable pesticide residues
   a. Use of adults with pesticides
   b. Use of surrogate tracer materials (e.g., fluorescent clothing brighteners)
   c. Use of household pets such as small dogs

Techniques for measuring bioavailability are currently limited to solvent wipes and solvent extraction procedures. Wiping procedures are preferred when it is impossible to remove samples of carpet or fabric for extraction. Carpet with pile not exceeding 1 cm. in depth should be used. In order to minimize the variability inherent in the wipe procedure, it is recommended that samples of carpet (12 x 12 inches) and fabric be used to collect pesticide residues. These samples may be extracted by a continuous solvent (water-surfactant) extraction procedure similar to the one used for dislodgeable residues on foliage (19). This procedure would make it possible for registrants to develop consistent and reliable information on the amount of dislodgeable pesticide deposited on or remaining on smooth floor surfaces (such as vinyl), carpet, furniture fabrics, and bedding through time subsequent to applications.

Studies are needed to determine the rate of transfer (μg/hr) of the dislodgeable pesticide residue to the skin or clothing of individuals coming in contact with the treated surfaces. A study was conducted involving the transfer of the organophosphorus pesticide propetamphos (Safrotin) from a furniture fabric to clothing (20). The study involved a single individual repeatedly sitting and standing in order to simulate a typical home-type exposure. This procedure provided information on the rate of transfer of pesticide residues involving adults, but did not address the transfer of residues to young children playing on treated areas. This is a difficult problem, because studies involving the direct transfer of pesticides to the skin and/or clothing of young children are an unacceptable form of human experimentation. It may be quite possible to address this indirectly by using surrogate tracer materials such as nontoxic fluorescent clothing brighteners to quantify the transfer of residues from surfaces to skin or clothing. If this is possible, information on the relationship (ratio of brightener to pesticides) between the tracer and the pesticide under investigation will have to be independently developed.

Dogs might be used as animal models for developing such data in a household setting. Procedures already exist for determining the relationship between a dermal dose and cholinesterase inhibition (7). Those procedures could be extended to cover absorption via lungs and the respiratory tract. The data collected (rate of transfer, dislodgeable residue, and dermal dose response information) could be used to set safe levels in a manner described by Knaak and Iwata (21). The procedures of Knaak et al. (22) require that a safe level be known for some pesticides presently in use indoors. At the present time, the recommended use of propoxur and chlorpyrifos are being re-examined and therefore cannot be used as standards for setting acceptable levels indoors.

Conclusions and Recommendations

This chapter indicates that it might be possible for the various regulatory agencies to set acceptable levels for pesticide residues in room air and on treated surfaces subject to considerable skin contact in households. Information from studies performed by the registrants would be needed on household residues deposited from foggers, compressed air sprayers, and other application procedures to determine the amount of the residues remaining in air and on surfaces after each application. The levels should be compared against safe levels still to be established for residues in air and levels for surface residues for each pesticide.

Should a registrant wish to justify the use of a cholinesterase inhibitor in treatment of smooth floor surfaces, rugs, furniture, bedding, or entire rooms where people reside, it is recommended that the following data be submitted on each active ingredient such as propoxur, dichlorvos, and chlorpyrifos or any other cholinesterase inhibitor.

1. Information on room air levels of the pesticide and total dislodgeable residues on smooth floors, carpets, furniture, and bedding after application of the product containing the active ingredient of interest. The dissipation of these residues should be followed through time or until the residues completely dissipate (i.e., 2, 4, 8, and 24 hr; 3, 6, 9, 12, 21, 24, 27, and 30 days).
2. Dissipation data plotted in $\mu g/cm^2$ against time (semi-log paper) should be determined and therefore, if possible, the half-life in the room air and of the dislodgeable residue on the surface from which it was taken.
3. Rate of transfer ($\mu g/hr$) of the dislodgeable residue from smooth floors, carpet, furniture-fabric, and to the skin of surrogate animals. Five-month-old Beagle dogs should be used to study contact exposure in treated rooms. The same animals should be exposed sequentially to different levels of dislodgeable residues present in the house, starting with the level deposited at application of twice the recommended amount and then exposing the animals at the recommended amount. These exposures should begin just as soon as the application has been completed and any ventilation period on the label has expired. Separate exposure studies should begin when residues are found to be one-half those at the time of application and also when they reach one-fourth those found at the time of application. Dislodgeable residue in $\mu g/cm^2$ versus dose transferred to the animal in $\mu g/hr$ should be plotted. The slope of the line in cm^2/hr should be determined. To remove residues for measurement, the dogs can be washed with soap and water at sampling times.
4. Dermal dose-cholinesterase response data in the rat for the technical or active material can be determined using the method of Knaak et al. (22).

5. A table of safe levels should be calculated using acceptable daily exposure levels (use results of dermal dose cholinesterase response studies) as indicated by Iwata et al. (18).

In addition, for individual products formulated from these active ingredients, data should be required on air and surface residues resulting from the application of the products. Data is needed on the amount of dislodgeable residues that are deposited on smooth flooring, carpet, furniture, and bedding by applying the pesticide product in accordance with label-use instructions. In presenting the data, the registrant should use a dissipation curve developed with the technical material (active ingredient) to estimate when a safe level would be present from the use of a product in the room; the registrant should determine the level of dislodgeable residues at that time. If air and dislodgeable residues are at a safe level for infants to play in the room immediately at the end of a ventilation reentry period specified on the label, then the product should be considered safe to use as directed.

In the State of California, regulatory action has already been taken in the form of advice to the registrant of the data needed on insecticide chemicals in products used indoors if registration is to continue to be permitted (reevaluation). The manufacturers and others who sell chlorpyrifos, dichlorvos, and propoxur have been notified. In addition, similar action will probably be taken on indoor use products containing carbaryl (Sevin), propetamphos malathion, and diazinon.

Literature Cited

1. Pomerance, H. H., Growth Standards in Children, Harper and Row, Hagerstown, M D., 1979, 225 pages.
2. Vaughan, V. C., III; McKay, R. J.; Nelson, W. E.; Textbook of Pediatrics, 10th Edition, Saunders, Philadelphia, London, Toronto 1975, 1,876 pages.
3. Wright, J. W.; Fritz, R. F.; Hocking, K. S.; Babione, R.; Gratz, N. G.; Pal, R.; Stiles, A. R.; Vandekar, M. Bull. World Health Org., 1969, 46, 67–90.
4. Hackathorn, D. R.; Eberhart, D. C., 1983, Report No. 1-83-42, Mobay Chemical Corporation.
5. Vandekar, M.; Plestrina, R.; Wilhelm, K. Bull. World Health Org., 1971.
6. Raabe, O. 1985 personal communication.
7. Knaak, J. B.; Wilson, B. W., 1984, American Chemical Society, Symposium Series No. 273.
8. Feldman, R. J.; Maibach, H. I. Toxicol. Appl. Pharmacol., 1974, 28, 126–132.
9. Gaines, T. B., Toxicol. Appl. Pharmacol., 1969, 14, 515–534.
10. Perkow, W., Chem. Ber., 1954, 87, 755–758.
11. Maddy, K. T.; Edmiston, S.; Fredrickson, A. S., 1981, Calif. Dept. Food Agric. report number HS-897.
12. McCollister, S. B.; Kociba, R. J.; Humiston, C. G.; McCollister, D. D. Food Cosmet. Toxicol., 1974, 12, 45–61.
13. Eliason, D. A.; Cranmer, M. F.; von Windeguth, D. C.; Kilpatrick, J. W.; Suggs, J. E.; Schoof, H. F., Mosquitos News, 1969, 29, 591–595.
14. Boyd, J. Pat, P.A.C.E. International, Dallas, Texas, 1985.
15. Nolan, R. J.; Rick, D. L.; Freshour, N. L.; Sanders, J. H, Toxicol. Appl. Pharmacol., 1984, 73, 8–15.
16. Naffziger, D. H.; Sprenkel, R. J.; Mattler, M. P., Down to Earth, 1985, 41, 7–10.
17. 1972 Evaluations of Some Pesticide Residues in Food. The Monographs. World Health Organization, Geneva, 1973, 161–162.
18. Iwata, Y.; Knaak, J. B.; Carmen, G. E.; Dusch, M. E.; Gunther, F. A., J. Agr. Food Chem., 1982, 30, 215–222.
19. Iwata, Y.; Knaak, J. B.; Spear, R. C.; and Foster, R. J., Bull. Environ Contam. Toxicol., 1977, 18, 649–655.
20. Labriola-Tomkins, T.; Ranion, T., 1982, Safrotin EC Carpet Study, (A) Cholinesterase dose/response; (B) Dislodgeable Residues on Carpets, Sandoz, Inc., Crop Protection, East Hanover, New Jersey, 1977, 18, 649–655.

21. Knaak, J. B.; Iwata, Y. 1982 American Chemical Society, Symposium Series No. 182, 23.
22. Knaak, J. B.; Schlocker, P.; Ackerman, C. R.; Seiber, J. N., Bull. Environ. Contam. Toxicol., 1980, 24, 796–804.

RECEIVED February 10, 1988

Chapter 25

The Environmental Protection Agency's Use of Biological Monitoring Data for the Special Review of Alachlor

Curt Lunchick, Gary Burin, Joseph C. Reinert, and Karen E. Warkentien

Office of Pesticide Programs, Hazard Evaluation Division (TS–769C), Exposure Assessment Branch, Environmental Protection Agency, Washington, DC 20460

In conducting the Special Review of the herbicide alachlor, the U.S. Environmental Protection Agency (EPA) evaluated biological monitoring studies conducted by the Monsanto Chemical Company, the registrant of alachlor. The biological monitoring studies allowed the Agency to estimate the internal dosage of alachlor received by workers during mixing/ loading and ground boom application of alachlor from enclosed tractor cabs. The Monsanto study contained only four replicates per formulation, used Monsanto employees, and only used enclosed application vehicles. Because internal dosage estimates from bio- logical monitoring data are chemical-specific and, therefore, not amenable to the use of surrogate data, the Agency evaluated patch exposure studies to ensure representation of a wider range of potential exposure situ- ations. A Monsanto patch exposure study in which alachlor was applied similarly to the biological monitoring studies and six expo- sure studies from the published literature provided approximately 100 exposure repli- cates employing a variety of commonly used application equipment. The exposure studies established a two orders of magnitude range of exposure to which the Monsanto exposure estimates were at the low end. This range was transferred to the biological monitoring dosage establishing a dosage range of 0.0054 to 0.54 ug/kg body weight (bwt)/lb active ingredient (ai) when open pour mixing/loading occurs and a range of 0.0034 to 0.34 ug/kg bwt/lb ai when a mechanical transfer loading system is used.

This chapter not subject to U.S. copyright
Published 1989 American Chemical Society

In the United States, the Office of Pesticide Programs (OPP) of EPA has the responsibility of regulating the use of pesticides under the aegis of the Federal Insecticide, Fungicide, and Rodenticide Act (FIFRA). Under FIFRA, pesticide registrants have the responsibility of providing the health and safety data necessary to support the registration of their products. The Agency, in turn, is charged with evaluating these data and determining that the registered uses of the products do not produce an unreasonable adverse effect on the environment. To assist the registrants in providing data on the exposure to individuals handling pesticides, the Agency has published the Pesticide Assessment Guidelines, Subdivision U: Applicator Exposure Monitoring.

Subdivision U is intended to aid registrants in conducting field studies that estimate the level of exposure to individuals who are occupationally exposed to pesticides during application and related activities, such as mixing, loading, and flagging.

Historically, OPP has recommended that applicator exposure studies be carried out using passive dosimetry. This technique measures the amount of chemical impinging on the surface of the skin or the amount of chemical available for inhalation as determined through the use of appropriate trapping devices. Patches of various construction are used to trap residues which could result in dermal exposure to various body parts. Potential inhalation exposure is generally measured using a personal sampling pump with an intake placed close to the worker's breathing zone.

Another type of monitoring that may be used to estimate human internal dosage to pesticides is biological monitoring. This method estimates the level of internal dosage from either a measurement of body burden in selected tissues or fluids, or from the amount of pesticide or metabolite excreted from the body. Most studies using biological monitoring methods have involved the collection of blood, urine, or both. Prior to designing a biological monitoring study, the pharmacokinetics (including metabolism and excretion) of the pesticide must be known so that the appropriate tissue or fluid, as well as time periods for monitoring, can be chosen. Without this information, extrapolation back to dose is not possible.

Estimating occupational exposure by passive dosimetry or biological monitoring offers distinct advantages and disadvantages (see Table I). A major advantage of biological monitoring is that, when the pharmacokinetics of a pesticide are understood sufficiently, the actual absorbed dose may be calculated. With passive dosimetry, only the amount of chemical potentially available for absorption or inhalation is measured. This amount of chemical is the exposure. Unlike biological monitoring, passive dosimetry requires independent estimates of dermal and lung absorption to

Table I.   THE PERCEIVED ADVANTAGES AND DISADVANTAGES OF ESTIMATING OCCUPATIONAL
EXPOSURE WITH PASSIVE DOSIMETRY AND BIOLOGICAL MONITORING

	Advantages	Disadvantages
Passive dosimetry	Routes and areas of exposure are known.[a] Routine experimental design and execution. Participant under supervision of investigator. Generic databases may be created.	Dermal and respiratory absorption must be estimated.[a] Extrapolation from patch to body surface area must be made. Not all exposure scenarios are amenable.
Biological monitoring	Actual dose may be measured.[a] Unnecessary to adjust for value of garment/protective clothing. Effects of complacency factor overcome.	Pharmacokinetics must be known.[a] Routes of exposure cannot be distinguished. Difficult to ensure participant cooperation. Potential problems when using invasive techniques.

[a]Considered most important.

estimate dosage. These absorption estimates are generally
very difficult to derive and interpret using available data
from in vivo and in vitro systems. In addition, when using
passive dosimetry, some assumptions concerning the value of
normal clothes or protective clothing in intercepting
residues must also be used to attempt to estimate actual
dose.

The major advantage with passive dosimetry is that the
relative contributions of the inhalation and dermal routes
and of the different body areas to total dermal exposure can
be readily established. This is extremely important for
evaluating and recommending exposure mitigation measures.
For example, if it can be demonstrated that a substantial
fraction of total exposure for a work day occurs to the
hands, forearms, and face during the ten minutes a farmer
pours the concentrated solution of a pesticide formulation
into the mix tank, total risk may be minimized by requiring
chemical-resistant gloves, a face shield, and/or a closed
mixing system for this short duration/high exposure period.
A biological monitoring study, which provides a composite
picture of dosage, would not distinguish the various routes
of exposure. In addition, since biological monitoring is
typically carried out after a complete work day, the relative
contributions of the different work activities to total
internal dose could not be distinguished, assuming the
individual had engaged in more than one work activity.

Registrants have extensive experience with carrying out
passive dosimetry studies where the study participants are
typically under the supervision of the investigator during
the entire monitoring period. This is generally not the case
in biological monitoring studies, for example, when 24-hour
urine voids are collected. Many passive dosimetry techniques
require extrapolation from the residues on the small surface
area of the trapping devices to entire body surface areas, a
process which introduces an error factor. Crucial areas of
exposure may also be missed. It should be recognized that
not all exposure scenarios are amenable to passive dosimetry
techniques. Examples include measuring exposure to
pesticides in swimming pools, in dishwashing detergents, or
measuring dermal exposure to volatile organic chemicals. On
the other hand, there are potential legal and ethical
problems associated with the use of invasive techniques in
field studies.

Biological monitoring may hold some promise for dealing
with what has been called the "complacency factor." It is
widely recognized that when workers are handling pesticides
that are known to be highly acutely toxic, e.g., parathion,
extra care is exercised. It is thought that the results of
passive dosimetry studies may not entirely capture this extra
care, and therefore may overestimate exposure for these
pesticides. For example, if during the course of a routine
work cycle a worker's clothing becomes contaminated, this
individual is likely to change clothes prompted by his

awareness of the highly toxic nature of the pesticide being handled. Conversely, if during a work activity designed to monitor exposure, some pesticide impinges on a trapping device, which in principle does not allow penetration to the clothing, work is likely to continue uninterrupted to the conclusion of the monitoring period.

A related advantage of passive dosimetry is the ability to create large generic databases. In this context, "surrogate" or "generic" data are defined as exposure monitoring data collected for other pesticide chemicals applied using comparable application methods and under similar conditions as for the pesticide under assessment. The mechanics of the use of surrogate data have been discussed in public fora and in the published scientific literature in recent years [1-4]. A basic assumption in the creation of generic databases is that in many application scenarios, the physical parameters of application, and not the chemical properties of the pesticide, are most important in determining the level of exposure. Note that, when using passive dosimetry methods, what is measured is the amount of chemical impinging on the skin surface, or available for inhalation, not the actual dose received. Factors such as dermal and lung penetration influence the latter, and are, of course, expected to be highly chemical-dependent. A review of all available information on pesticide exposure during application activities supports the use of surrogate data for exposure assessments.

Alachlor Studies

In November 1984, EPA issued the Guidance for the Reregistration of Pesticide Products Containing Alachlor as the Active Ingredient. In that document, the Agency stated its determination that alachlor met one of the risk criteria (oncogenic potential) used to determine whether it causes unreasonable adverse effects [40 CFR 162.11(a)(3)(ii)(A)]. In response to that determination, a Special Review, in which the risks and benefits of continued use of a pesticide are intensively examined, was initiated for alachlor in December 1984. Alachlor is an acetanilide herbicide that has been produced in the United States by Monsanto Chemical Company since 1969. Almost all of the alachlor used in the United States is applied by tractor-drawn ground boom sprayers.

Monsanto submitted three biological monitoring studies to EPA to support the continued registration of alachlor. In addition, supporting pharmacokinetic studies were evaluated. These studies indicated that an average of 87 percent of alachlor in laboratory primates is excreted in the urine as metabolites in two chemical classes. Using only these data, EPA was able to calculate the internal dosage of alachlor, based on the total quantity of the two metabolite classes, expressed as alachlor, measured in the participant's urine.

In the first of the three studies [5], eight applicators

were studied by Monsanto, four using the Lasso EC formulation
and four with the Lasso MT formulation. The alachlor was
incorporated into corn fields at 4 lb ai per acre (lb ai/A).
The subjects were Monsanto employees who wore goggles and
elbow-length rubber gloves during mixing and loading, and
boots, trousers, long-sleeved shirt, and a cap during the
entire operation. The mixing and loading involved open
pouring from the pesticide containers. The application was
conducted from enclosed cab tractors and 20 acres were
treated by each study participant. Urine was collected prior
to use of alachlor and for five days thereafter. The mean
internal dosage for Lasso EC was estimated to be 0.0066 ug/kg
bwt/lb ai.

The second study [6] monitored the internal dosage
received during mixing, loading, and applying Lasso Micro-
Tech and Lasso WDG. Four replicates were monitored for each
formulation and all study participants were Monsanto
employees. As in the first study, the alachlor was incorporated into corn fields at 4 lb ai/A. Each individual
treated 20 acres and applied the alachlor from enclosed
tractor cabs. The study participants wore long-sleeved
shirts and long pants at all times and wore goggles, rubber
gloves, and rubber overshoes during the mixing and loading.
Urine was collected prior to use of alachlor and for five
days thereafter. The mean internal dosage of alachlor was
estimated to be 0.0038 ug/kg bwt/lb ai for Lasso Micro-Tech
and 0.0059 ug/kg bwt/lb ai for Lasso WDG.

The third study [7] monitored the internal dosage of
alachlor received when a closed loading system was employed
during mixing and loading and an enclosed tractor cab was
used to incorporate alachlor at 4 lb ai/A. Lasso EC was the
formulation used and the four study participants were Monsanto employees. The Lasso EC was transferred from a 100-
gallon bulk tank to the spray tanks using a Scienco pump.
The workers wore long-sleeved shirts, long pants, goggles,
rubber gloves, and rubber overshoes during the mixing and
loading routine. Alachlor was incorporated into corn fields
at 4 lb ai/A. Each participant treated 20 acres from an
enclosed tractor cab while wearing long-sleeved shirts and
long pants. Urine was collected prior to using alachlor and
for five days after use. The Agency estimated the internal
dosage of alachlor to be 0.0034 ug/kg bwt/lb ai. It should
be noted that most of the urine samples contained nondetectable levels of alachlor metabolites and the Agency's dosage
estimate predominantly reflects 50 percent of the detection
limit of the analytical method. The Monsanto dosage estimate, which was less than the Agency's, reflected Monsanto's
use of "0" for samples containing nondetectable levels of
alachlor metabolites.

Several factors prevented EPA from estimating the risk to
users of alachlor based solely on these biological monitoring
studies. The studies were conducted with only four replicates per formulation. Subdivision U of the Pesticide

Assessment Guidelines recommends that 15 replicates of each work function be monitored. The study participants in all three Monsanto studies were employees of Monsanto. EPA prefers that participants in exposure studies be experienced individuals who are being monitored while performing their normal work functions to more accurately assess worker exposure. As previously discussed, the lack of control over study participants in collecting urine voids is a perceived disadvantage of biological monitoring. Monsanto believed the benefits of better control over urine collection outweighed the benefits of using actual farmers and, therefore, elected to use its own employees to maintain control over urine collection. Finally, all replications involved the use of enclosed tractor cabs during spraying. Enclosed tractor cabs, when properly used, provide an efficient physical barrier between the applicator and the pesticide spray which will reduce contact with the pesticide. Because the use of enclosed tractor cabs is not a requirement for the use of alachlor, EPA concluded that the dosage of alachlor received by individuals on tractors without cab enclosures would be greater than that received by the individuals in the three submitted Monsanto studies.

The concerns stated above lead EPA to conclude that the dosages estimated from the Monsanto biological monitoring studies would not accurately reflect the range of dosages received by all users of alachlor in the United States. A large range would be expected because of differences in spray equipment, individual work habits, and variations in environmental conditions at the time of alachlor use. In order to estimate the range of exposure likely to occur during the ground boom application of alachlor, EPA evaluated a Monsanto applicator exposure study and other exposure studies available in the published literature which employed passive dosimetry.

EPA evaluated a total of six studies [8-13] available in the published literature that contained sufficient information to conduct an exposure assessment for ground boom applicator exposure. The six studies contained 101 replicates. The exposure estimates were calculated assuming that the applicator wore "normal" work attire consisting of long pants and a shirt. Because of variations in how the data were reported and in placement of the patches, the use of a long-sleeved or short-sleeved shirt and the degree of protection afforded by the shirt varied. Table II provides the mean exposures with specific clothing assumptions used for each study. In addition to the six published studies that were reviewed, a seventh study that was conducted by Monsanto with alachlor was also evaluated [14]. In all cases, the exposure estimates were normalized to an application rate of 1.0 lb ai/acre to permit comparison of exposure without the application rate as variable.

The exposure estimates for the seven ground boom applicator studies varied over a range of greater than two orders

Table II.   DERMAL EXPOSURE DURING GROUND BOOM APPLICATION

Study Author	Number of Replicates	Mean Exposure (mg/hr)	Clothing Assumptions
Abbott	18	40.0	Long-sleeved shirt, long pants, 50% protection
Dubelman	12	0.93	Long-sleeved shirt, 50% protection Long pants, 100% protection
Maitlen	21	0.70	Short-sleeved shirt, long pants, 100% protection
Staiff	20	0.40	Short-sleeved shirt, long pants, 100% protection
Wojeck	23	72.0	Long-sleeved shirt, long pants, 100% protection
Wolfe	7	9.4	Short-sleeved shirt, long pants, 100% protection
Monsanto	2	0.15	Potential dermal exposure reduced by 80%

All exposure estimates are based on an application rate of 1.0 lb ai/A.

of magnitude from 0.15 mg/hr in the Monsanto study to 72 mg/hr in the Wojeck study. This variability was not unexpected and resulted from differences in equipment, weather, individual work habits, and study methodologies. The Monsanto and Dubelman studies involved application from enclosed tractor cabs. The Abbott study used enclosed tractor cabs with the rear window open. Open tractors, enclosed tractor cabs, high clearance tractors, and booms with shielded nozzles were all used in the Wojeck study. Maitlen, Staiff, and Wolfe did not describe the tractors used; however, Staiff did state that low pressure sprayers were partially responsible for the low exposure potential observed in that study.

EPA also estimated the exposure received during mixing/loading when the pesticide is poured from the pesticide container. The Abbott [8] and Monsanto [14] studies provided a total of 20 replicates in which mixer/loader exposure could be expressed in terms of the amount of ai handled. The mean dermal exposure for the 18 Abbott replicates was 0.93 mg/lb ai. The two Monsanto replicates had an estimated exposure of 0.077 mg/lb ai. All estimates assumed that the mixer/loaders wore protective gloves.

Conclusions

In evaluating the exposure data from the published literature, EPA concluded that dermal exposure could vary over approximately one order of magnitude during mixing/loading and over two orders of magnitude during ground boom application. Based on these ranges, it was assumed that the combined exposure for mixing/loading and application would reasonably be expected to vary over two orders of magnitude.

The Monsanto passive dosimetry study [14] provided the lowest estimates for both mixer/loader and ground boom applicator exposures. Because the Monsanto biological monitoring studies were conducted in a similar manner to the Monsanto patch study, EPA concluded that the dosage estimates derived from the biological monitoring studies represented the lowest point of a range of dosages likely to occur during the use of alachlor. It was further assumed that the range of dosage received during mixing/loading and ground boom application would also vary over two orders of magnitude depending on equipment used, conditions of the protective clothing, weather conditions, and individual work habits.

As previously discussed, EPA concluded that the dosages received in the Monsanto biological monitoring studies during open pour mixing/loading and enclosed cab ground boom application were 0.0066 ug/kg bwt/lb ai for Lasso EC, 0.0038 ug/kg bwt/lb ai for Lasso Micro-Tech, and 0.0059 ug/kg bwt/lb ai for Lasso WDG. EPA further concluded that the different formulations had no appreciable effect on the dosage received. Therefore, the mean dosage of the Lasso EC, Lasso Micro-Tech, and Lasso WDG formulations was calculated to be 0.0054 ug/kg bwt/lb ai for the Monsanto study participants.

EPA concluded that 0.0054 ug/kg bwt/lb ai represented the low
end of the range of likely alachlor dosages and that the
range of likely internal dosage would be 0.0054 to 0.54 ug/
kg bwt/lb ai for open pour mixing/loading and ground boom
application. Based on the dosage estimate of 0.0034 ug/kg
bwt/lb ai from the Monsanto biological monitoring study
employing closed loading systems and enclosed tractor cabs,
EPA concluded that the internal dosage of alachlor received
using closed loading systems and ground boom application
would range from 0.0034 to 0.34 ug/kg/lb ai. This closed
loading dosage may be an overestimate of actual dosage,
because it reflects the use of 50 percent of the detection
limit for the nondetectable urine samples. The Agency's
review of mixer/loader exposure data indicates that closed
loading systems produce more than a two-fold reduction in
total exposure.

Nontechnical Summary

Subdivision U of the Pesticide Assessment Guidelines permits
the use of either passive dosimetry studies to estimate
worker exposure to pesticides or biological monitoring
studies to estimate internal dosage of a pesticide in workers. During the Special Review of Alachlor, Monsanto submitted three biological monitoring studies which permitted
EPA to estimate the dosage of alachlor received during
mixing/loading and ground boom application of alachlor. EPA
did not believe that the estimates from the study would
predict the actual range of dosage received during use of
alachlor by U.S. farmers because of the limited number of
replicates, use of Monsanto employees, and use of only enclosed tractor cabs. EPA evaluated passive dosimetry studies
in which alachlor and other pesticides were applied by ground
boom to establish a range of exposures likely to occur during
alachlor use. This range was transferred to the biological
monitoring study dosage estimates to establish a range of
internal dosage likely to occur during alachlor use. This
range of internal dosage was used in EPA's risk assessment
for occupational risk from alachlor use.

Literature Cited

1.   Severn, D.J. In Genetic Toxicology. An Agricultural
      Perspective; Fleck, R.A.; Hollaender, A., Eds.; Plenum:
      New York, 1982; pp 235-242.

2.   Hackathorn, D.R.; Eberhart, D.C. In Dermal Exposure
      Related to Pesticide Use - Discussion of Risk Assess-
      ment; Honeycutt, R.C.; Zweig, G.; Ragsdale, N.N., Eds.;
      American Chemical Society: Washington, DC, 1985; pp
      341-355.

3.   Honeycutt, R.C. In Dermal Exposure Related to Pesticide
     Use - Discussion of Risk Assessment; Honeycutt, R.C.;
     Zweig, G.; Ragsdale, N.N., Eds.; American Chemical
     Society: Washington, DC, 1985; pp 369-375.

4.   Reinert, J.C.; Severn, D.J. In Dermal Exposure Related
     to Pesticide Use - Discussion of Risk Assessment;
     Honeycutt, R.C.; Zweig, G.; Ragsdale, N.N., Eds.;
     American Chemical Society: Washington, DC, 1985; pp
     357-368.

5.   Klein, J.J., et al. Urinary Excretion of Alachlor
     Residue Following Normal Application of Lasso or Lasso
     Micro-Tech Herbicide Under Commercial Conditions in
     Indiana; Report No. MSL-4207; Monsanto Chemical Company,
     1984.

6.   Danhous, R.G., et al. Operator Exposure from Open-Pour
     Transfer and Application of Lasso EC, Lasso MT and Lasso
     WDG; Report No. MSL-5398; Monsanto Chemical Company;
     1984.

7.   Danhous, R.G., et al. Operator Exposure from Closed
     System Transfer and Application of Lasso EC and Lasso MT
     Herbicides; Report No. MSL-5320; Monsanto Chemical
     Company; 1986.

8.   Abbott, I.M., et al. Am. Ind. Hyg. Assoc. J. 1987,
     48(2), 167-175.

9.   Dubelman, S., et al. J. Ag. Food Chem. 1982, 30, 528-
     532.

10. Maitlen, J.C., et al. In Pesticide Residues and Expo-
     sure; Plimmer, J., Ed.; American Chemical Society:
     Washington, DC, 1982; pp 83-103.

11. Staiff, D.C., et al. Bull. Environ. Contam. Toxicol.
     1975, 14, 334-340.

12. Wojeck, G.A., et al. Arch. Environ. Contam. Toxicol.
     1983, 12, 65-70.

13. Wolfe, H.R.; Durham, W.F.; Armstrong, J.F. Arch.
     Environ. Hlth. 1967, 14, 622-633.

14. Lauer, R.; Arras, D.D. Aerial and Ground Applicator
     Exposure Studies with Lasso Herbicide Under Actual Field
     Conditions; Report No. MSL-1889; Monsanto Chemical
     Company; 1981.

RECEIVED January 28, 1988

Chapter 26

Use of Biological Monitoring Data from Pesticide Users in Making Pesticide Regulatory Decisions in California

Study of Captan Exposure of Strawberry Pickers

Keith T. Maddy[1], R. I. Krieger[1], Linda O'Connell[1], M. Bisbiglia[1], and S. Margetich[2]

[1]California Department of Food and Agriculture, 1220 N Street, Sacramento, CA 95814
[2]California Department of Food and Agriculture, 3292 Meadowview Road, Sacramento, CA 95832

Exposure of users of pesticides containing active ingredients which have the potential of causing adverse effects, especially those of subchronic and chronic types, has to be accurately measured in order to make meaningful risk mitigation determinations. Acceptable methodology is usually available to measure inhalation exposure, however, most pesticide exposure is dermal. Analysis of residues on cloth pads that had been on various parts of the body during exposure may provide an overestimate of dermal exposure. Availability of dermal absorption-rate data in rodents is useful, but at least on some chemicals it is more likely to overestimate exposure than such studies done on humans or other primates. The most useful data results from development of metabolism data in humans or a suitable test animal with appropriate pharmacokinetics, including excretory data, and then biologically monitoring blood, urine, saliva or feces of persons being exposed to the chemical under normal use conditions. As an example results of recent measurements of mixer/loader/applicator and hand harvest worker exposures to captan in strawberry fields included dislodgeable residues, dermal dosimetry, and urine monitoring. Calculation of the urinary levels resulted in substantially reduced estimates of human exposure. Such data are used to reach safety and regulatory decisions. The goal is to avoid an inaccurate estimate of exposure that can result from less direct methods of exposure assessment.

The kinds of worker exposure data needed by California have been described in two previous reports: "Pesticide Safety Program of The California Department of Food and Agriculture Based Upon Measurements of Potential Workplace Exposure and the Elimination of Excess Exposures"([1]), and "Risk Assessment of Excess Pesticide Exposure to Workers in California" ([2]). California in its Department of Food and Agriculture (CDFA) has a more restrictive pesticide regulatory program than the U.S. Government or of any

0097–6156/89/0382–0338$06.00/0
© 1989 American Chemical Society

other state in the United States. California also requires more basic toxicology data and exposure data than the U.S. E.P.A.in order to meet recently imposed toxicology test standards , both on new requests for registration as well as for an extensive reregistration and reevaluation program which is now underway. In California more than 13,000 products are currently registered on an annual basis which contain more than 700 active pesticide ingredients and almost 1000 chemicals which are "inert" as pesticides but which may be quite toxic to man.

Since 1971, new California laws have emphasized requirements for assessing workplace hazards for pesticide users (including long-term exposure hazards) and ways of mitigating these hazards. This has resulted in specific California requirements for data which may be used to estimate the extent of such hazards.

The pesticide safety program of CDFA requires the presentation and consideration of data on : 1) pesticide vapors, mists, or dusts in the breathing zone of exposed persons; 2) pesticide dusts, powders or liquids on the skin of persons mixing, loading, and/or applying pesticides; 3) pesticide residues, including the more toxic breakdown products, on foliage and in soil of fields where work is to take place which may later contact skin; and, 4) residues in the air, on floors, counters, furniture etc., following application of pesticides indoors.

These measurements are of value in designing methods to reduce exposure to persons agriculturally exposed, such as commercial agricultural applicators, but also to persons who use pesticides in non-agricultural settings. CDFA evaluates basic toxicology data, exposure measurements and the manner in which the pesticide product is to be used. By modifying the way the pesticide is to be used, establishing reentry intervals, or suggesting changes to EPA of precautionary statements on pesticide labels (which they then agree to make), the risk of exposure to a potentially hazardous pesticide may be greatly reduced.

In the past, a major difficulty in conducting hazard assessments for any persons who might be exposed before, during, and after a pesticide application was the lack of information on the amount of pesticide that might be inhaled or might reach the skin, the rate and amount of dermal absorption, the rate and pathway of biotransformation, and the route and rate of elimination from the body.

Some of the specific data that may be required by CDFA to assist in making exposure estimates of persons in various activities involving the use of pesticides include: indoor exposure; field reentry exposure; mixer, loader, and applicator exposure, metabolism, dermal absorption rate, dermal dose response data and biological monitoring data.

TYPES OF EXPOSURE DATA

Indoor Exposure. Pesticide products to be used indoors such as in houses, apartments, offices, other institutions, and greenhouses may have exposure (inhalation, dermal, and ingestion) hazards both during the application and upon reentry. Apart from protective measures for applicators, an appropriate ventilation period may be needed to protect residents, inhabitants, or workers in the treated area from inhalation of hazardous chemicals in addition to mitigation measures such as reentry periods directed at reducing dermal contact of excess residues on carpets, furniture and countertops.

Field Reentry. Certain pesticides pose a potential hazard to persons if they enter a treated area and have significant contact with treated plants or soil. A waiting period long enough to mitigate exposure is called a reentry interval.

The following is a guide used by CDFA in deciding if reentry data is needed.

Such data will be needed if the product is to be applied to a commercially grown crop, particularly to its foliage or the soil, and cultural practices (such as pruning or harvesting) of that particular crop involving substantial body contact with the foliage, bark, or soil, or exposure to pesticide residues shaken from the foliage or bark, and the product contains: (a) a cholinesterase inhibitor; or (b) a significantly toxic principle that can cause a detrimental acute systemic toxic reaction or is suspected of causing a chronic effect, and may be readily absorbed through the skin or inhaled following exposure to pesticide residues contacted while conducting usual cultural practices; or (c) a chemical which causes a significant primary skin irritant reaction in appropriate test animals or man; or (d) a chemical which is a significant skin sensitizer in appropriate test animals or man.

Reentry (safe waiting period) intervals are now established on the basis of: (1) data on dermal absorption rates or dermal dose response rates; (2) inhalation and dermal acute toxicity studies in animal models; (3) foliar and soil residue and dissipation rate data; and, (4) available human exposure data.

In the past, acute toxicity was the major reentry regulatory concern; more recently subacute and chronic toxicity has also become a major concern.

Mixer, Loader, Applicator Exposure. Unless the acute and chronic toxicology data on the formulated product indicates negligible toxicity; mixer, loader and applicator exposure data is needed, at least on the use most reasonably expected to give the most risk.

In order to make an appropriate hazard assessment, information is needed on the amount of pesticide that may be inhaled and/or reach the skin, or more importantly absorbed during and subsequent to a "typical" application.

Metabolism Data. Complete metabolism data in mammals is needed in order to understand the distribution and excretion of the pesticide and its breakdown products. Usually radiotracer studies in rodents are provided to define metabolic pathways. Greater attention needs to be given to defining pathways in accidentally exposed humans. Such data would establish a better experimental basis for biological monitoring.

Dermal Absorption Rate Or Dermal Dose Response Rate. Dermal absorption data which is usually developed in rats or monkeys, is needed in conducting the risk assessment for field workers, mixers/loaders, applicators, flaggers, other pesticide users as well as for bystanders; these data may also be used in the development of reentry intervals. The data provides information to calculate how much of the chemical enters the body after it comes into contact with the skin. Data on monkeys is considered the most likely to approximate human exposure; often the absorption by monkey skin appears to be slower than it is in rodents.

Biological Monitoring. Data collected on dermal deposition with current methods, when used along with the animal dermal absorption rate or dermal-dose-response data is often assumed to overestimate actual exposure. Metabolism data is used to determine pharmacokinetic and excretion parameters and can form the basis for biological monitoring. For example, if a parent chemical or a urinary metabolite can be fully characterized and tested for, then the amount of the chemical in the urine of users can be monitored as a measure of internal dose. At the same time, the amount of chemical that might be inhaled and the amount that falls on the skin can also be measured. With such data a much more objective assessment can be made of the actual exposure. Use of such data may indicate safe use even though dermal deposition data and the animal study dermal absorption rate data alone might signal an unacceptable risk. We have previously summarized biological monitoring data on about 50 pesticide active ingredients (3).

HAZARD EVALUATION PROCESS, HAZARD IDENTIFICATION, EXPOSURE ASSESSMENT RISK CHARACTERIZATION

The CDFA conducts its hazard evaluation process based on the consideration of the following factors:

1. Review of the basic toxicology data submitted by the registrant;

2. Review of other toxicology data available to CDFA (journal articles, CDFA studies, computerized national data banks, texts, etc.);

3. Human illness information developed by CDFA or others involving the pesticide under consideration or similar pesticides;

4. Available exposure data on this pesticide or this class of pesticides developed by CDFA or any other group; and,

5. Work practices known about or expected in California for the proposed use.

A hazard evaluation is much more than a basic toxicology review. For example, a specific pesticide can be found in the toxicology review to be extremely toxic; however, in the hazard evaluation process, it may be determined that the product is to be used in such small quantities with such specialized equipment that a person could only be overexposed in the unusual case of equipment failure. On the other hand, a product could be found to be of low toxicity; but, the most common use might involve long hours of exposure to many workers in orchards while using hand-held spray wands spraying the pesticide above their heads with no protective clothing, due to lack of specification in the precautionary label statements. In another example, the basic toxicology data for a product may only indicate a moderate toxicity; however, in assessing the proposed use of the product mid-summer in a citrus grove in the San Joaquin Valley, there could be substantial conversion of the active ingredient to a highly toxic degradation product in the duff under trees under actual field conditions which would be hazardous to field workers.

As well as a toxicology assessment, the CDFA evaluation may include:

1. Determining the use pattern (geographic, climate, season, equipment-type etc.) of the proposed product;

2. Determining significant possible human exposure hazards;

3. Evaluating the adequacy of use instructions and/or regulations that are in place to inform users of the possible use hazards and how to avoid excess exposure.

4. Evaluating the adequacy of information provided to recognize illness due to exposure if it occurs;

5. Determining the adequacy of first aid information; and,

6. Examining the availability of data to support medical management.

Data from the toxicology base, plus those from the additional health and safety studies, including exposure, that are sometimes required, allow for the estimation and calculation of potential exposure hazards. For some products, experience already gained allows for a quick determination that adherence to the proposed or existing use instructions should result in a low hazard use situation. On the other hand, a number of the pesticides considered for registration have significant hazards from either a short-term or long-term exposure standpoint. These hazards are estimated and/or calculated to determine if a favorable recommendation on the proposed registration can be given, and if not, whether additional restrictions would be expected to acceptably reduce the hazards of use.

For example, a particular product might be a highly dusty wettable powder with only moderate acute toxicity but with demonstrated potential for producing chronic effects. The calculations for the hazard evaluation are based upon the total workday measurement of the skin and inhalation exposure to this pesticide when it is used in accord with the label instructions. The potential daily dermal dose is then adjusted by the estimated 24-hour dermal absorption rate. This figure is then added to the inhalation exposure value and the sum is compared to animal test data for the dose expected to produce a specific adverse effect. The safety factor for this specific effect will then be calculated to determine if it is adequate to protect the workers. In some cases, the exposure assessment might not lead to an acceptable safety factor for a mixer/loader; but, if this product were repackaged in water-soluble packets formulated as a dry flowable or if it were reformulated to be used as a liquid product and then required to be transferred through a closed system, the hazard might be acceptably reduced.

Of particular concern are potential adverse effects such as carcinogenicity and developmental toxicity (primarily those which occur prior to birth).

Adequacy Of Mitigation Measures. After all relevant data are fully evaluated, an assessment is made regarding the adequacy of the possible mitigation measures to protect workers from hazards of use. The label with its use instructions may be accepted and the product may be registered without further concern. On the other hand, one or more of the following conditions may be required before the product is considered for registration by the CDFA: (1) the EPA may be advised of the desirability of requiring a label change giving more specific use instructions, or the registrant may recognize the need to ask EPA for such a label change; (2) a California regulation on the use may be enacted (which will have the same effect as a label change, but this can take several months to accomplish); (3) the product may be made a California restricted or regulated material which will allow imposition of specific permit requirements or regulations (this process can also take a number of months); (4) closed system transfer of liquid pesticides may be required, (this is currently required for all toxicity Category I liquids, when specified on labels regardless of the toxicity category and when specifically required by regulations); (5) change in the product's formulation may be required to reduce excess hazards (e.g., reduce dustiness); (6) water-soluble packaging of the more toxic powders may be required; (7) minimum field reentry intervals may be set by regulation (a several-month process unless they are adequately specified on the label); (8) medical supervision may be required by regulation; and/or (9) detailed safety training may be required for specific pesticides.

EXAMPLE OF VALUE OF BIOLOGIC MONITORING DATA

The current common methods for measuring worker exposure to pesticides involve measurement of dislodgeable foliar residues or residues in the breathing zone and/or on the skin. The dermal deposition data is then used with dermal absorption rate data collected in rodents or monkeys to calculate probable human exposure. Uncertainties about the bioavailability and transfer of residues in work environments may result in overestimated exposures. Below we have summarized our recent study of captan exposures of strawberry harvest workers to illustrate some of these considerations.

Introduction. Studies of the dermal pesticide exposures of strawberry harvesters have been reported by Popendorf et al. (4), Everhart and Holt (5), Zweig et al. (6), Winterlin et al. (7) and Ritcey et al. (8). Some of the data accumulated from studies of strawberry harvesters figured prominently in the development of the empirical transfer coefficient (commonly called the Zweig-Popendorf factor) of 5000 cm^2/h which can be used to relate dislodgeable foliar pesticide residues to hourly dermal pesticide exposures of fieldworkers (Zweig et al. (9)). The transfer coefficient seems to be a helpful tool to provide a first estimate of the dermal exposure of fieldworkers engaged in work tasks such as harvesting fruits and vegetables or picking flowers in a greenhouse. The transfer coefficient will vary depending on the task and use scenario (protective clothing etc.) although specific data about factors influencing it are very limited.

We developed three estimates of strawberry harvester exposure to captan based upon dislodgeable foliar residues, dermal dosimetry, and biological monitoring. We were particularly interested in the quantitative relationship between the estimates due to their critical importance in the risk assessment process. Additionally, we sought to measure the degree of mitigation of the captan exposure provided by the use of chemically-resistant gloves.

METHODS: Setting. In June 1987, we obtained the cooperation of the California Strawberry Advisory Board and Mr. Larry Galper, Watsonville, California. The Board provided financial support to compensate the producer for any lost time and productivity when we stopped work to put on measurement devices or to collect samples. We had complete access to a 72 acre strawberry farm which was considered by all concerned to be representative of the approximately 16,000 acres of California strawberry production.

The strawberry beds were planted with 18,500 plants/acre of either the Pajaro and Selva varieties. The plants were grown on elevated beds (14") with 52" centers. The plants were well past their peak production, e.g. 10-12 crates per row at peak versus 2-3 crates per row in July. This provided maximal seasonal worker contact with treated foliage. Production data were recorded (crate = 10 pounds).

Two crews of workers (approximately 35-50 workers/crew) pick the fields twice in each 6-day week (8 hour days) of the picking season which extends from April to October. The crews consisted of men and women in apparent good health (85 percent were below age 35) with up to a maximum of 20 years experience as strawberry pickers. They usually wear long pants and long-sleeved shirts to protect themselves from the generally cool weather of the area where strawberries grow well. Some of the men wear short-sleeved shirts, and others roll up their sleeves as the mornings warm. Women additionally wear scarves which cover most of their face. All of the women and less than 5 percent of the men normally wear chemically resistant gloves to protect their hands from dirt and strawberry juice.

For this study, a crew of 40 male volunteers was assembled by the foreman and the ranch manager. Males were selected to provide sufficient numbers of workers of one sex to meet experimental objectives. Additionally, because men did not usually wear gloves they permitted establishment of glove/no glove groups without reducing any worker's normal protection. The gloves were 13", chemically resistant, and made from Long Service^{tm} rubber. Exposure data were collected during three consecutive days. The assistance provided by the foreman was critical to obtaining the enthusiastic cooperation of the pickers. Throughout the study, the ranch management served as an effective liaison between CDFA staff and the fieldworkers.

Captan Application. Four days before harvest, each part of the field was treated with Captan 50 WP (4 lbs. a.i./acre) tank mixed with Benlate 50 WP (1 lb a.i./acre) and Vendex (2 lbs. a.i./acre). Captan had not been previously used during 1987. Two hundred gallons of spray mix were applied to each acre using a fixed-boom sprayer. Samples of tank mix were collected for captan and tetrahydrophthalimide (THPI), a metabolite of captan, analysis.

Foliar Residue Monitoring. Prior to the captan application and during each day of the three-day study, foliage samples were collected. Each sample consisted of forty 2.54 cm diameter leaf discs (Birkestrand punch) replicated three times before and after harvest. Samples were taken along a diagonal line from 10 rows of strawberries in a given section of the field. Eleven sections of the field were sampled. The sample jars were sealed with aluminum foil, capped, and kept on wet ice until they were transported to the laboratory for captan residue analysis.

Dermal Dosimetry. Measurements of dermal exposure and evaluation of the protection provided by gloves were made on days 2 and 3 of the study. In order to have minimal effects on normal work practices and to assure that CDFA staff could adequately assist each worker, the crew was randomly divided into two groups of 20 that were monitored for one day each. On a given day each group of 20 was provided with a set of 100% cotton, tight fitting long underwear to be worn for four hours beneath normal workclothes and which served as dermal dosimeters. Each worker was given the underwear the day before their scheduled monitoring. The group was further divided into "glove" and "no glove" subgroups.

Dermal exposure was monitored during a 4-hour, morning work period. The workers carefully removed the dosimeters in temporary change rooms constructed in the back of two rental trucks using sheets and plastic pipe. The garments were placed into Zip-lock bags and stored on dry ice until processing. At that time arm and leg dosimeter samples were prepared, iced, and transported to the laboratory.

Concurrently, handwashes were done on each subject using 400 ml of 1% Surten solution contained in a one gallon Zip-lock bag. Each person washed their hands for two one-minute periods. Handwashes (800 ml) were subsampled (500 ml) and stored on dry ice for transport to the laboratory.

During the three day study the work period was approximately divided into three 7-hour segments. During a 4-hour segment of either day two or three of the study, each worker wore gloves and long underwear as a dermal dosimeter. Thus, exposure potentials might be reduced by a factor of 21 - 4/21. No direct estimates of the amount of exposure occurring during the period of passive dosimetry are available and no corrections were used to make exposure estimates.

Urine. Pickers were provided three or four polyethylene urine collection bottles for daily 24-hour collections. The bottles were held in insulated boxes in the field during the work day and two unused bottles were taken home each night. Creatinine levels were measured in each 24-hour void at a local clinical laboratory as an indicator of compliance.

Extraction, Clean-up and Analysis. Dislodgeable captan residues on leaf samples were prepared according to Gunther et al. (10). Samples were shaken three times with Surten solution and extracted three times with ethyl acetate after addition of Na_2SO_4. After volume reduction the samples were analyzed by gas chromatography.

Captan was analyzed on the dermal dosimeters in a similar fashion. The initial extract was prepared by separately tumbling individual sets of underwear arms and legs with ethyl acetate.

Urinary THPI (cis-1,2-dicarboximido-4-cyclohexene) was determined as reported by Winterlin et al. (7). Twenty-five ml aliquots were extracted with methylene chloride, filtered, dried, and taken up in benzene. The extract was analyzed using Hewlett-Packard 5880A gas chromatograph with a N/P ionization detector. The minimum detectable level of THPI in urine was 0.03 ug/ml and recoveries ranged from 80 to 89 percent.

Subsequently a set of 10 urine samples from high exposure workers were further analyzed by Morse Laboratory, Sacramento, CA. A pH 11 clean-up and nitrogen specific electrolytic conductivity detector were used to achieve a minimum 0.005 ppm sensitivity. At 0.02 and 0.01 ppm sensitivity the recoveries of THPI were 75 and 67 percent respectively.

Statistics. The differences between means (3 replicates) pre- and post-harvest dislodgeable foliage residues were compared using paired t-tests. A randomized block design was used to investigate potential mitigating effects of gloves on dermal captan exposure. Factors included in the linear model for analysis included glove assignment, day, and a glove interacting with day term. If no glove assignment by day interaction was determined (P<0.10), then we made comparisons for the two remaining effects. All analyses were made using Type III Sums of Squares in the SAS General Linear Model Procedure.

Since the exposure data were skewed, the variable itself, a natural logarithmic transformation, and rank transformed data were analyzed.

RESULTS: Production. The 40-man crew picked 12, 12.2, and 11 acres of strawberries on the three days of the study (Table I). The number of crates picked was 916, 1413, and 1239, respectively. The work period was approximately seven hours each day. The high yield of strawberries on day two was made up of 832 crates of Selvas and 581 crates of Pajaros.

It was the subjective observation of the foreman and ranch manager that the use of gloves slowed some pickers on the first day of the study. They reported normal picking rates for the following two days of the study. They additionally noted that after the study had ended only a few of the men continued to wear their gloves.

Dislodgeable Residues. Eleven separate large beds of the ranch were sampled for pre- and post-harvest dislodgeable captan residues. The pre-harvest sample mean $\pm$ S.D. was 2.4 ± 0.6 ug/cm^2, and the post-harvest mean was 2.1 ± 0.5 ug/cm^2. These measurements provided direct evidence that the spray mix was uniformly applied to the areas under study. Additionally, the post-harvest samples contained 0.3 ug/cm^2 less dislodgeable residue (P=0.024) as evidence of the substantial contact by the picking crew.

Dermal Dosimetry and Handwashes. Fieldworker work practices were carefully observed prior to our selecting cotton long underwear as a whole body dosimeter. We monitored only hands, arms, and legs since those were the body parts that had substantial contact with treated foliage. A similar strategy was used by Ritcey et al. (8) who assessed exposure using oversleeves and leggings. Table II shows exposure data for days two and three of the study. Table III shows the range of exposures found. Recoveries from dermal dosimeters were about 90-95 percent.

Gloves very effectively reduced hand exposure as indicated by the captan and THPI in handwashes. Approximately 50 percent of the captan was recovered as THPI in the handwashes. No other samples contained more than trace amounts of THPI. As expected due to limited worker contact during picking, low amounts (<15 percent) of captan exposure were the result of leg contact. Since the gloves covered more than half of the forearm, the apparent mitigating effect of gloves may be overestimated to a small extent by the simple calculation of percent of total captan recovered on the arm dosimeter.

Urinalysis. In animals captan is rapidly absorbed through the skin (2 percent of applied dose per hour) and urine is the primary route of excretion. These factors contribute to the feasibility of using biological monitoring to gauge captan exposure. Our study began on Monday (no Sunday picking) and no captan had been used previously during 1987. No preexposure urine samples were collected.

There are numerous metabolic studies of the fate of captan in rats, but unfortunately none are available for humans. ^{14}C-Carbonyl has been used to study the THPI moiety of captan by Hoffman et al. (11). When ^{14}C-captan was orally administered, 85 percent of the radioactivity was recovered in urine within 96 hours. The metabolic scheme includes hydrolytic cleavage of captan

Table I: WATSONVILLE STRAWBERRY FIELDWORKER STUDY

DATE	DAY	ACRES	CRATES	STRAWBERRY
7/20	1	12	916	PAJARO
7/21	2	12.2	1413	SELVA; PAJARO
				(832) (581)
7/22	3	11	1239	PAJARO

Table II: DERMAL CAPTAN EXPOSURE OF
STRAWBERRY PICKERS (MILLIGRAMS)

DAY 2	ARMS	LEGS	HANDWASH	TOTAL
NO GLOVES	9.2	1.2	11.4	21.8
GLOVES	3.6	0.7	0.3	4.6

DAY 3	ARMS	LEGS	HANDWASH	TOTAL
NO GLOVES	27.4	0.8	14.4	42.6
GLOVES	10.9	1.3	0.2	12.4

Table III: RANGE OF DERMAL CAPTAN EXPOSURES OF
STRAWBERRY PICKERS (MILLIGRAMS)

Estimates

DAY 2	MEAN	$^{+}$S.D.	MEDIAN	MINIMUM	MAXIMUM
NO GLOVES	22	6	22	10	30
GLOVES	5	5	3	1	17

DAY 3	MEAN	$^{+}$S.D.	MEDIAN	MINIMUM	MAXIMUM
NO GLOVES	43	32	31	17	117
GLOVES	12	10	10	1	29

to yield THPI which constituted 15 percent of the urinary radioactivity. Subsequently four additional metabolites are produced by hydroxylation, epoxidation, hydrolysis, and hydroxylation-rearrangement. Human exposures were estimated assuming that THPI was a captan metabolite, and that it constituted 15 percent of the urinary metabolites which were 85 percent of the dose. No corrections were made for the fact that each worker wore a full body dosimeter for four hours of the approximately 21 hours worked during the three days of the study.

The samples analyzed by electrolytic conductivity were 72-hour composites and they were estimated to contain about 200 ug captan equivalents (48 percent absorption; 15/85 metabolism). The actual values are shown in Table IV. The median was 0.005 ppm and the range was <0.005 to 0.014 ppm.

Estimates of Exposure. Estimates of fieldworker exposure based upon dislodgeable foliar residues, dermal dosimetry, and biological monitoring differ markedly. From the 2.4 ug/cm^2 dislodgeable residue level on foliage, a daily dermal exposure of 96 mg/day was calculated (5000 cm^2/h; 8 h). Based upon dermal absorption studies in the rat, the absorbed dose (24 h) was assumed to be 48 percent (2%/h; 24 h) resulting in an effective dose of 46 mg/captan/day. Based upon the rat metabolic work, 85 percent of an oral dose of captan would be eliminated in 96 hours and 15 percent of that would be the metabolite, THPI. If anything, larger amounts of THPI in urine might be expected following dermal exposure since the metabolic (especially hydrolysis) contribution of gastrointestinal tract would be minimized (or totally eliminated) following dermal exposure. As a result, daily urine would be expected to contain about 3 mg THPI or 2.5 ppm THPI. This level of THPI is approximately 500-times the minimum detectable level (0.005 ppm). Apparently, the approach of using the dislodgeable residue and the rat dermal absorption rate data for estimating dermal captan exposure is of limited usefulness since it predicts much higher exposure than occurs based upon urinalysis of the workers. Due to the lack of specific human absorption and metabolic data and our poor understanding of the foliage-worker transfer process, the basis for the overestimate can not be identified.

Dermal dosimetry also apparently overestimates dermal captan exposure. Following careful preliminary observations of strawberry pickers, we measured arm, leg, and hand exposures using tight-fitting, long underwear to capture captan which contacted the extremities. Handwashes were analyzed to estimate hand exposure. Workers without gloves had three to four times greater exposure than gloved workers (P<0.05). In Table II gloved worker exposure is assumed to be 10 mg captan/day. On this basis the potential THPI excretion would be 0.3 mg THPI/day. The captan exposure (10 mg/day) was about one-ninth of that estimated using dislodgeable residues. The hypothetical level of THPI was approximately 60-times the minimum detectable limit. Both dislodgeable residue and dermal dosimeter based exposures are higher than exposure estimates based on urinary excretion under the assumptions given in the preceding paragraph.

DISCUSSION

This study demonstrates the magnitude of fieldworker exposure
generated using dislodgeable foliar residues, dermal dosimetry, and
urine monitoring (Figure 1). The quantitative differences are
striking and would ultimately result in substantially different
risk assessments and mitigation measures. The dislodgeable foliar
residue approach gives investigators an estimate of exposure, but
it probably should be made more work task specific to reflect major
differences in foliage contact between strawberry pickers and
lettuce cutters on one hand and peach thinners and grape pickers on
the other. At this time we are trying to construct a set of
transfer coefficients to represent high, medium, and low contact
work tasks. The possible influence of the physical and chemical
nature of the deposit of the applied pesticide may also be
considered. Furthermore, additional data will be gathered in a
long term evaluation of the regulatory usefulness of the transfer
coefficient to estimate dermal exposure.

In the specific example presented here the apparent transfer
coefficient was 250-650 cm^2/h for gloved fieldworkers as compared
to the generic 5000 cm^2/h coefficient (9). Gloves and long sleeved
shirts may be necessary to maintain low fieldworker exposures in
crops containing high (>0.5 ug/cm^2) dislodgeable foliage residues.
This is especially important for chemicals such as captan that have
significant chronic toxicity and potentially long periods of
exposure.

In a more general vein, it is clear that biological monitoring
yields more direct estimates of pesticide exposures than passive
dosimetry or the dislodgeable residue approach. However, analysis
is currently severely limited by inadequate absorption and
metabolism data. This limitation will not disappear and exposures
will continue.

If improved exposure assessments are to be obtained, perhaps
procedures to index worker exposures using key metabolites can be
developed. Metabolic indices seem to have a place in exposure
assessments since it is extremely unlikely that complete human
metabolic and pharmacokinetic data bases will become available for
most pesticides. A pesticide metabolic index would be specific to
a particular active ingredient and would include factors known to
influence excretion of the parent chemical or its derivatives.

In the case of captan a relatively simple model has been
suggested. It assumes measurement of THPI as a principal, stable
captan metabolite. At this time only data from single dose, oral
gavage studies in rats are available. Urine and feces respectively
contained 85 percent and 15 percent of the administered dose (over
97 percent accounted for in 96 hours). The dosage was 77-92 mg/kg.
This is considerably more than the 0.1 - 0.2 mg/kg that we predict
for gloved field workers based upon passive dosimetry. The dosage
consideration would tend to inflate our exposure estimate. The rat
studies additionally revealed that THPI accounted for 15 percent of
the total urinary radioactivity. For the present we propose to
relate urinary THPI (ppb x volume) to exposure using an index which
includes a stoichiometric factor (0.5), metabolism factor
(0.15/0.85), and a dermal absorption factor (0.5). As a result if

Table IV: TETRAHYDROPHTHALIMIDE IN
THREE-DAY COMPOSITE URINE SAMPLES

FIELDWORKER	THPI(PPM)
1	0.006
2	0.005
3	<0.005
4	<0.005
5	0.005
6	0.010
7	<0.005
8	0.014
9	ND
10	0.005

MLD = 0.005 PPM; if a response less than MDL but greater than 0 was
observed the amount of THPI was listed as <0.005.

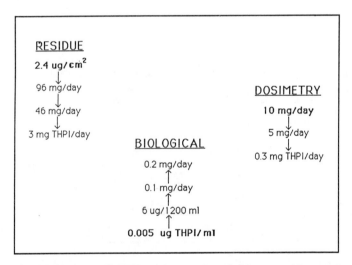

Figure 1. Estimates of THPI urine using foliar residue and passive
dosimetry data. Same assumptions about absorption, metabolism, and
excretion were used in each case. Measured values are in bold
type. The estimated captan exposure ranges from 96 mg/day (foliar
residue) to 0.2 mg/day (biological monitoring).

the amount (ug) of THPI excreted is multiplied by 30, the dermal captan dose can be estimated.

We have limited data to validate this model. Ample data are available to establish that THPI is a human captan metabolite. Unpublished data (Krieger and Thongsinthusak) show that low percentages of THPI are excreted following single oral dosages (0.1 and 1.0 mg/kg). If this is generally true, the metabolic index overestimates the available captan dose. This factor requires further evaluation as does the potential role of route and rate of exposure. At this time no additional data are available. Present data make it possible to estimate exposure with fewer assumptions than required when either dislodgeable residue or passive dosimetry is used as the basis of an exposure estimate.

There is a need to be much more aggressive in evaluating human pesticide exposures. Such estimates will meet a growing need for better human data on the fate and disposition of pesticides in humans. This is not a call for experimental pesticide disposition studies in humans. Sensitive and specific analytical procedures used to measure vanishingly small amounts of chemical residue on treated crops must be adapted to the trace analysis of pesticide metabolites in urine and other samples from humans. Fieldworkers, producers, registrants, regulators, and the general public will benefit from the significantly more reliable assessments of risk which will result.

LITERATURE CITED

1. Maddy, K.T., Edmiston, S.C. Pesticide Safety Program of the California Department of Food and Agriculture Based Upon Measurements of Potential Workplace Exposure and the Elimination of Excess Exposures; American Chemical Society Symposium Series No. 182, Pesticide Residue and Exposure, 1982, pp. 75-81.
2. Maddy, K.T., Wang, R.G., Knaak, J.B., Liao, C.L., Edmiston, S.C., Winter, C.K. in Risk Assessment of Excess Pesticide Exposure to Workers in California; American Chemical Society Symposium Series, 272, Dermal Exposure Related to Pesticide Use, 1985, pp. 445-465.
3. Coye, M.J., Lowe, J.A. and Maddy, K.T., Biological Monitoring of Agricultural Workers Exposed to Pesticides: II Monitoring Intact Pesticides and Their Metabolites; Journal of Occupational Medicine, 28:628-636, 1986.
4. Popendorf, W.J.; Leffingwell, J.T. Residue Rev. 1978, 82, 125.
5. Everhart, L.P.; Holt, R.F. J. Agric. Food. Chem 1982, 30, 222.
6. Zweig, G.; Gao, R.; Popendorf, W.J. J. Agric. Food Chem. 1983, 31, 1109-1115.
7. Winterlin, W.L.; Kilgore, W.W.; Mourer, C.; Schoen, S.R. J. Agric. Food Chem. 1984, 32, 664-672.
8. Ritcey, G; Frank, R.; McEwen, F.L; Braun, H.E. Bull. Environ. Contam. Toxicol. 1987, 38, 840-846.
9. Zweig, G.; Gao, R.; Witt, J.M.; Popendorf, W.; Bogen, K. J. Agric. Food Chem. 1984, 32, 1232-1236.

10. Gunther, F.A.; Westlake, W.E.; Barkley, J.H.; Winterlin, W.; Langbehn, L. <u>Bull. Environ. Contam. Toxicol.</u> 1973, <u>9</u>, 243-249.

11. Hoffman, L.J.; DeBaun, J.R.; Knarr, J.; Mann, J.J. <u>Metabolism of N-(Trichloromethylthio)-1,2-dicarboximido-^{14}C-4-cyclohexene (Captan) in the Rat and Goat,</u> 1973, Western Research Center, Stauffer Chemical Company.

RECEIVED March 29, 1988

Chapter 27

Use of Biological Monitoring in the Regulatory Process

Leonard Ritter and Claire A. Franklin

Environmental and Occupational Toxicology Division, Environmental Health Directorate, Tunney's Pasture, Ottawa, Ontario K1A 0L2, Canada

Occupational risks associated with pesticide use can only be estimated if exposure can be quantified. Dermal exposure has historically been estimated from patches placed on the worker or his clothing while more recent advances have focused on the use of biological monitoring. Biological monitoring of pesticides can be carried out in a variety of body fluids including blood, urine, sweat, saliva, adipose tissue and exhaled breath; indeed, urinary concentration of the chemical or its metabolites has become one of the most frequently reported biological measures of exposure. For pesticides such as 2,4-D, which is excreted largely unmetabolized, urinary concentrations may be quantitatively related to exposure. Similarly, for organophosphorus compounds, data are presently available which establish the relationship between dermal dose and urinary metabolites. It has been postulated that this standard curve approach could then be utilized to estimate exposure in workers based on the metabolite excretion. There are many products, however, for which the metabolite excretion pattern is not known, thus severely limiting the usefulness of the biological monitoring approach as a measure of exposure to such products.

Occupational exposure to pesticides may present health risks to both applicators and agricultural workers. In order to properly assess this exposure and estimate risk, accurate data on exposure and absorption are necessary. In addition to quantifying exposure, precise information should be available on the dose levels for biological endpoints established through experimental toxicity studies.

This chapter not subject to U.S. copyright
Published 1989 American Chemical Society

Historically, risk from pesticide residues in food has been estimated by comparing the theoretical daily intake of the pesticide residue to the acceptable daily intake. The acceptable effect level seen in experimental animal studies and utilization of an appropriate safety factor for the toxicologic end-point being considered. If the theoretical daily intake is determined to be less than the acceptable daily intake, the pesticide is generally considered safe for use on food. Similarly, risk to agricultural workers can be estimated by comparing the theoretical daily exposure to a pesticide and the acceptable daily exposure. As is the case with food residues, if the theoretical daily exposure is estimated to be less than the acceptable daily exposure, the pesticide may be considered safe for use by agricultural workers. These comparisons are summarized in Figure 1. From the figure it can be seen that for the determination of agricultural worker safety there is a need to obtain reliable and accurate estimates of worker exposure.

The majority of exposure in pesticide workers has been shown to take place via the dermal route (1- 3) and this exposure was often estimated by the use of adsorbent patches located at various sites on the workers' bodies or clothing. Classical patch techniques may overestimate exposure (4) leading to exaggerated risk estimates and improper restriction on registration and use of the pesticide. More recently, considerable interest has developed in the technique of human biological monitoring to supplement or indeed replace many of these older patch techniques for estimating dermal exposure (5). Biological monitoring, a specific form of monitoring of human exposure, can be used to determine if an agricultural worker has been exposed to a chemical and, in selected cases, the extent to which exposure may have taken place. Measurements can be made in a variety of biological fluids including urine and blood. The advantages of biological monitoring, when compared to classical patch technique, lie in the ability of this approach to more accurately estimate body burden of the chemical from all routes of exposure. Limitations of this technique include individual pharmacokinetic variability (6) and a requirement for extensive knowledge on metabolism and disposition of the chemical. The reliability of this technique is therefore limited by the general unavailability of such extensive data for the majority of pesticides in use today. Low concentrations of a metabolite in urine could be the result of any one or combination of the following: (i) the chemical is not well absorbed; (ii) the chemical is absorbed but is sequestered in the body; (iii) the chemical is metabolized into a number of different metabolites all of which are excreted at low levels. If the kinetics and metabolism of the chemical are not well understood it would be possible to incorrectly conclude that low levels of the measured metabolite in urine indicate that only a small amount of the chemical was absorbed. This in turn would result in an underestimate of risk.

In this paper we will focus on the use of biological monitoring for quantifying exposure and will discuss these cases which show how prior knowledge of the metabolism of the chemical can influence the suitability of biological monitoring to predict exposure.

1. CHEMICALS WHICH ARE RAPIDLY ABSORBED, NOT SEQUESTERED, AND
EXCRETED IN URINE LARGELY UNMETABOLIZED ARE GOOD CANDIDATES FOR
ESTIMATING EXPOSURE (2,4-D).
        An example of a chemical that is a good candidate for
estimating exposure from biological monitoring is 2,4-D. It is a
broad spectrum agricultural herbicide widely used throughout the
world. Its absorption, distribution and metabolism in animals have
been studied by several authors and reported in the literature
(7-14).
        The absorption and excretion of 2,4-D in humans via the oral
route have been investigated in a controlled laboratory situation.
The first of these studies (9) involved a single oral dose of 5 mg
2,4-D acid/kg body weight to each of 5 volunteers. Urine was
collected over a period of 144 hours following ingestion and the
percentage of the oral dose of 2,4-D excreted was then calculated.
It was shown that 2,4-D was excreted unmetabolized as free or
glucuronide conjugated 2,4-D (9). As can be seen from Table I,
complete recovery of the initial dose was possible in the first 96
hours. In addition, 70 to 83% of the ingested 2,4-D was recovered
in the free form. Although two subjects excreted up to 26% as the
conjugated form, two other subjects excreted no more than 10% of the
conjugate and the remaining subject excreted only free 2,4-D. This
study in man shows that 2,4-D is absorbed following oral
administration and eliminated largely as unchanged parent compound.
It has also been shown in man that 6% of a dermally applied dose of
2,4-D acid is absorbed (15).
        Results from our own laboratory (unpublished) have also shown
that 15% of a dermally applied dose of 2,4-D acid is absorbed from
rhesus monkey forearm and that 29% of the applied dose is absorbed
from the forehand (Figure 2). It was also shown that 100% of an
intravenous dose was excreted indicating that the compound was not
sequestered (15).
        The results reported above show that 2,4-D is a compound which
is absorbed by the oral and dermal routes, is excreted largely as
unchanged parent compound and is not sequestered. Although a
defined relationship between the amount of 2,4-D applied dermally
and the concentration of urinary metabolite has not been
established, the type of information described above gives one some
confidence in concluding that low urinary metabolite levels in
workers reflect low absorbed doses.
        The relationship between dermal exposure and urinary metabolite
excretion under normal use conditions has been investigated by
Grover and his co-workers (16). In this study, a total of 9
farmers who repeatedly sprayed 2,4-D were monitored during normal
spray applications. In all cases the total amount of 2,4-D
available for absorption was estimated utilizing a standard patch
technique, while absorption was estimated by measuring 2,4-D in
urine collected for 96 hours following the last exposure to the
chemical. The results are summarized in Table II. As can be seen
from the table there was a very wide range of calculated dermal
deposition in workers applying 2,4-D (75 to 13,286 ug 2,4-D/kg
sprayed) while there was a much narrower range of urinary excretion
of 2,4-D in these same workers. It is noteworthy that deposition

Table I. Percentages of 2,4-D (Free and Conjugate) Excreted in Urine Following A Single Oral Dose of 5 mg/kg 2,4-D*

SUBJECT	1		2		3		4		5	
	Free	Conjugate	Free	Conjugate	Free	Conjugate	Free	Conjugate	Free	Conjugate
0 – 96 hrs	82	21	88	–	70	26	87	5	83	10
Total	103		88		96		92		93	

* adapted from (9)

Food $\dfrac{\text{NOEL}}{\text{Safety Factor}}$ = Acceptable Daily Intake

- animal toxicity data generated using oral route of
  exposure

- oral route of exposure to humans through food and water

- if Theoretical Daily Intake (TDI) is less than Acceptable
  Daily Intake (ADI), pesticide may be safe for use on food

Workers $\dfrac{\text{NOEL}}{\text{Safety Factor}}$ = Acceptable Daily Exposure

- animal toxicity data generated using oral route of
  exposure

- dermal route of exposure generally the greatest for
  workers and bystanders

- if Theoretical Daily Exposure (TDE) is less than
  Acceptable Daily Exposure (ADE), pesticide may be safe
  for use by agricultural workers.

Figure 1. Risk Estimation

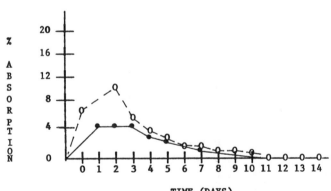

TIME (DAYS)

O = FOREHEAD
● = FOREARM

Figure 2. 2,4-D Acid - % Recovery in Monkeys

Table II. Cumulative Estimates of Dermal 2,4-Da.e.* Deposition and Urinary 2,4-Da.e. Excretion for Farmers Involved in Spraying of 2,4-D BY Ground Rig.•

SUBJECT	AMOUNT SPRAYED (kg a.e.)	CALCULATED DERMAL DEPOSITION OF ug 2,4-Da.e/Kg sprayed	CUMULATIVE URINARY EXCRETION OF ug 2,4-Da.e.a/kg sprayed
B	24	75	11
B	35	391	6
B	49	1,529	14
F	127	13,286	3
D	89	1,339	17
A	102	444	17
G	186	1,572	33
E	71	951	17

a Total amount excreted during exposure period and for 4 days after last exposure.

* Acid equivalent

• adapted from (16)

levels were not necessarily correlated with the amount of 2,4-D sprayed.

These data suggest that compounds that are rapidly absorbed, not sequestered and excreted in an unchanged form are well suited to the principle of biological monitoring and that urinary metabolite levels may more accurately reflect both exposure and body burden than would be estimated by more classical patch techniques.

2. CHEMICALS FOR WHICH URINARY METABOLITES ARE QUANTITATIVELY RELATED TO DERMAL DOSE. (AZINPHOS-METHYL)

Azinphos-methyl is an insecticide widely used for the control of a variety of orchard insects. Early work with organophosphorus insecticides has demonstrated that in humans (17-20) and in rats (21-22) a relationship exists between exposure to organophosphorus pesticides and excretion of alkyl phosphate metabolites. Specifically, it has been shown (23) that azinphos-methyl is degraded primarily in microsomal and soluble fractions to dimethyl thiophosphate (DMTP), dimethyl phosphate (DMP) and the oxygen analog. The structure of azinphos-methyl and the site of hydrolysis are shown in Figure 3. Studies undertaken in our laboratory have examined the relationship between increasing doses of topically applied azinphos-methyl and the urinary excretion of this dose as DMTP (metabolite) in rats (24) and in man (25). As can be seen from Table III, dermally applied doses of between 100 and 800 microgram per rat resulted in approximately 10% of the applied dose being excreted as DMTP metabolite. Following our initial observations that approximately 10% of a topically applied azinphos-methyl dose in rats could be recovered as urinary DMTP, a similar investigation was undertaken in man (Table IV). It was shown that a similar 10:1 proportion of the dermally applied dose in humans could be recovered as urinary DMTP metabolite. Further, as can be seen from Table V, the relationship between dermally applied dose and the amount of DMTP metabolite excreted was relatively linear over a dermal dosage range of 500 to 6000 micrograms per person. The results obtained from both the rat and human investigations have suggested that there is a quantitative relationship between dermal dose and the proportion of this dose that can be recovered in urine as a DMTP metabolite. Specifically, these results suggest that there is approximately a 10 to 1 relationship between the dose that is applied and the concentration of urinary metabolites (Table V). This relationship can be very useful in field monitoring of agricultural workers in that it allows estimation of dermal exposure simply by the determination of levels of urinary metabolites. It should, however, be noted that while this method may be useful for estimation of dermal exposure levels, urinary metabolites may not be useful for purposes of estimating risk. DMTP represents only one of several metabolites formed on exposure to azinphos-methyl and may not reflect relative concentrations of other biologically important metabolites in various species.

3. CHEMICALS WHICH UNDERGO COMPLEX METABOLISM AND WHERE DOSE AND ROUTE OF ADMINISTRATION MAY QUALITATIVELY QUANTITATIVELY AFFECT METABOLISM AND BIOLOGICAL OUTCOME (METHYLENE CHLORIDE). Mice exposed to 3500 and 7000 mg/kg/6 hr day methylene chloride (MC) by

Table III. Excretion of DMTP Following Dermal Application of Azinphos-methyl in Male Rats*

| Dose (μg/rat) | N | Route | Cumulative Total (μg DMTP) % Dose | | | | | | % Dose Excreted As DMTP |
			24 hours	48 hours	72 hours	96 hours	120 hours	
100	8	Dermal	6.9	8.3	8.8			9
200	5	Dermal	12.2	15.5	16.0			8
400	5	Dermal	23.0	34.8	36.4	37.3		9
800	3	Dermal	18.9	73.6	81.7	86.1	91.2	11

* Adapted from (24)

Table IV. Excretion of DMTP Following Dermal Application of Azinphos-methyl to the Forearm of Human Volunteers*

Dose (ug/person)	Cumulative Total (ug DMTP)			Average Total	% dose excreted as DMTP
	24 hours	48 hours	72 hours		
500	82	110	123	85	17
	25	41	41		
1,000	52	80	92	152	15
	140	180	212		
2,000	36	104	148	119	6
	76	76	90		
4,000	188	264	454	404	10
	120	270	354		
6,000	122	246	278	323	5
	184	322	368		

* adapted from (24)

Azinphos-methyl: s-(3,4-dihydro-4-oxobenzo [d]- [123]-triazin-3-yl
methyl)-0,0-dimethyl phosphorodithioate

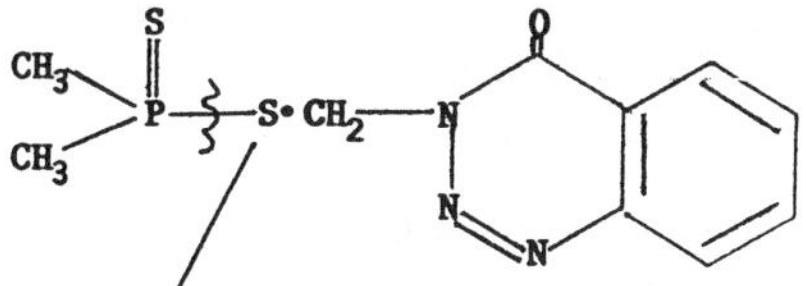

hydrolysis

Metabolite: DMTP

Analysis: Azinphos-methyl by HPLC

:   Metabolite by a modified shafik method to
derivatize alkyl phosphates followed by G.C.
analysis

Figure 3   Analysis of Azinphos-methyl by HPLC

Table V. Relationship Between Amount of DMTP Excreted and the
Amount of Azinphos-methyl (A.M.) Applied*

	Dermal Dose Range	Metabolite Excretion/ Amount A.M. Applied
Rat	100 - 800 ug	1 ug DMTP/10 ug A.M.
Human	500 - 6000 ug	1 ug DMTP/10 ug A.M.

* adapted from (25)

inhalation for 5 days/week demonstrated an excess of hepatocellular
adenomas/carcinomas as compared to unexposed controls (26). These
results contrasted with an earlier study conducted by the National
Coffee Association (27) in which mice exposed to MC in drinking
water at concentrations leading to exposure of 250 mg/kg/day showed
no increase in the incidence of liver tumours. There are two
pathways involved in the metabolism of MC. Relative tumour response
associated with these two pathways is shown in Figure 4. The two
pathways involved include the saturable mixed function oxidase (MFO)
pathway and the glutathione -s-transferase (GST) pathway. Estimates
of the concentration of MC and the rates of each of the two
metabolic pathways have been examined (28). The results of these
studies are given in Table VI and have shown that while the rate of
the MFO pathway is comparable in the two studies, the delivered dose
by the GST pathway and parent compound concentrations differ
substantially. This would tend to imply that the MFO pathway is not
responsible for the tumour induction seen. Furthermore, in view of
the fact that the rate of the MFO pathway is comparable in both the
drinking water and inhalation studies, utilization of this metabolic
pathway alone for the purpose of assessment of potential risk would
lead to erroneous conclusions; it could not be utilized to explain
the biological response seen in the inhalation study but absent in
the drinking water study. Clearly, in this case, the examination of
the GST pathway is of paramount importance in assessing the overall
risk associated with exposure to MC. The case of methylene
chloride, demonstrates rather elegantly the need for a thorough
understanding of metabolism prior to utilizing metabolite levels as
an indication of exposure for the purpose of estimating risk.

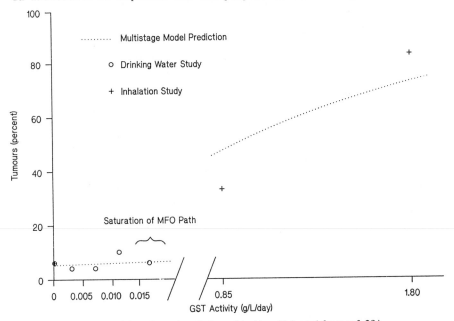

Figure 4. Metabolism of methylene chloride. (Adapted from ref. 28.)

Table VI. Metabolism of Methylene Chloride in Female Mice*

Route of Administration (dose units)	Administered Dose	Delivered Dose		
		MFO Path (g/L/day)	GST Path (g/L/day)	Parent Compound (mg hr/L)
Drinking water (mg/kg/day)	0	0.0	0	0
	60	1.3	0.003	1.3
	125	2.8	0.007	2.9
	185	4.0	0.011	4.6
	250	5.4	0.016	6.4
Inhalation (mg/kg/6 hr day)	0	0.0	0.00	0
	3500	3.6	0.85	360
	7000	3.7	1.80	770

*adapted from (28)

SUMMARY We believe that biological monitoring, specifically
urinary metabolite levels, can be used to estimate exposure if the
absorption, distribution, metabolism and excretion are known for the
chemical. The relationship between exposure and urinary metabolite
levels are more easily understood for chemicals that are absorbed,
not sequestered and excreted virtually unmetabolized. Selection of
a few such chemicals for in depth evaluation could lead to a better
estimation of dermal exposure than that presently obtainable from
patches. This in turn would assist in the eventual validation of
the concept of a generic approach to estimates of exposure.

It must be emphasized that measurement of urinary metabolite
levels following exposure, in the absence of adequate information on
absorption, distribution, metabolism and excretion, is useless.
Under such circumstances, it could not be determined whether a low
concentration of metabolite in urine was due to poor absorption (and
therefore low risk), whether it was well absorbed and sequestered
within the body or whether the chemical was well absorbed and
excreted as many metabolites, not all of which were known or
measured. Another possibility would be that excretion had taken
place via other routes.

Acknowledgments:

The authors gratefully acknowledge the typing of this
manuscript by Wendy Milks.

Literature Cited

1.   Wolfe, H.R.; Durham, W.F.; Armstrong, J.F. Arch. Environ.
     Health, 1967, 14, 622-633.
2.   Wolfe, H.R.; Armstrong, J.F.; Staiff D.C.; Comer, S.W. Arch.
     Environ. Health, 1972, 25, 29-31.
3.   Durham, W.F.; Wolfe H.R.; Elliott, J.W. Arch. Environ. Health,
     1972, 24, 381-287.
4.   Nigg, H.N.; Stamper, J.H. In Dermal Exposure Related to
     Pesticide Use; Honeycutt, R.C.; Zweig, G.; Ragsdale, N.N.,
     Eds.; ACS Symposium Series No. 273; American Chemical Society:
     Washington, DC, 1985; pp 95-108.
5.   Ashford, N.A.; Spadafor C.J.; Caldart, C.C. Harvard
     Environmental Law Review, 1984, 8, 263-363.
6.   Gompertz Ann. Occup. Hygiene, 1980, 23, 405-410.
7.   Erne, K. Acta Vet. Scand. 1966, 7, 264-271.
8.   Kolmodin-Hedman, B.; Hoglund, S.; Akerblom, M. Arch Toxicol
     1983, 54, 257-265.
9.   Sauerhoff, M.W.; Braun, W.H.; Blau, G.E.; Gehring, P.J.
     Toxicology, 1977, 8, 3-11.
10. Gutenmann, W.H.; Lisk, D.J. NY Fish Game J., 1965, 12(1),
     108-111.
11. Erne, K.; Sperber, I. Acta Pharmacol. Toxicol., 1974, 35,
     233-241.
12. Guarino, A.M.; Arnold, S.T. In Pesticide and Xenobiotic
     Metabolism in Aquatic Organisms; Khan, M.A.Q., Lech, J.F.,
     Menn, J.J., Eds.; ACS Symposium Series; American Chemical
     Society: Washington, DC, 1979; pp 250-258.
13. James, W.H. Lancet, 1977, 1, 603.

14. Pritchard, J.B.; Miller, D.S. Fed. Proc., 1980, 39(14), 3207-3212.
15. Feldman, R.J.; Maibach, H.I. Toxicol. Appl. Pharmacol., 1974, 28, 126-132.
16. Grover, R., Franklin, C.A.; Muir, N.I.; Cessna, A.J.; Riedel, D. Toxicology Letters, 1986, 33, 73-83.
17. Kraus, J.F.; Mull, R.; Kurtz, P.; Winterlin, W.; Franti, C.E.; Borhani, N.; Kilgore, W. J. Toxicol. Environm. Hlth. 1981, 8, 169-184.
18. Wojeck, G.A.; Nigg, H.N.; Stamper, J.H.; Bradway, D.E. Arch. Environm. Contam. Toxicol., 1981, 10, 725-735.
19. Knaak, J.B.; Maddy, K.T.; Khalifa, S. Bull. Environm. Contam. Toxicol. 1979, 21, 375-380.
20. Lores, E.M.; Bradway, D.E.; Moseman, R.F. Arch. Environm. Hlth. 1978, 33, 270-276.
21. Bradway, D.E.; Shafik, T.M.; Lores, E.M. J. Agric. Food Chem. 1977, 25, 1353-1358.
22. Bradway, D.E.; Shafik, T.M. J. Agric. Food Chem. 1977, 25, 1342-1344.
23. Motoyama, N.; Dauterman, W.C. Pest. Biochem. Physiol. 1972, 2, 170-177.
24. Franklin, C.A.; Greenhalgh, R.; Maibach, H.I. In IUPAC Pesticide Chemistry, Human Welfare and the Environment; J. Miyamoto et al Eds.; Perg Press. 1983; pp 221-26.
25. Franklin, C.A.; Muir, N.I.; Moody, R. Toxicology Letters, 1986, 33, 127-136.
26. NTP: National Toxicology Program, CAS No. 75-09-2. National Institute of Health, 1986.
27. EPA/600/8-82/004F. Final Report. United States Environmental Protection Agency, 1985.
28. Krewski, D.; Murdoch, D.J.; Withey, J.R. Drinking Water and Health 1987, 8, 441-448.

RECEIVED February 23, 1988

Chapter 28

National Agricultural Chemicals Association Overview on Assessment of Mixer–Loader–Applicator Exposure to Pesticides

Biological Monitoring

Richard C. Honeycutt

National Agricultural Chemicals Association, 1155 15th Street, NW, Washington, DC 20005

Agricultural worker exposure to pesticides is rapidly becoming a major issue in occupational health. With this in mind, the National Agricultural Chemical Association (NACA) along with member companies has over the past few years begun to throughly address this issue. The objective of this paper is to present an overview of how NACA regards mixer-loader-applicator exposure assessment. This paper will briefly consider a historical perspective on the NACA viewpoint on worker exposure and discuss the development of the NACA protocol for worker exposure as well as the development of the NACA - EPA - public worker exposure data base to be used for surrogate or generic estimation of mixer-loader-applicator exposure. This paper will also deal with specific field methods of measuring mixer-loader-applicator exposure including biological monitoring that are commonly used by U.S. companies and supported in the published NACA protocol. Finally, directions for future research in field worker exposure technology will be considered.

A Historical Perspective of NACA Involvement in Field Worker Exposure Research

In September 1983, NACA formed an ad hoc subcommittee on worker exposure assessment. The goal of this subcommittee was to bring together technical level experts from several member companies involved directly in performing field worker exposure studies to assess and advance the state of the art in mixer-loader-applicator exposure to pesticides. This subcommittee (part of the NACA Public Health and Toxicology Committee) has accomplished the following objectives:

0097–6156/89/0382–0368$06.00/0
© 1989 American Chemical Society

1. Developed a NACA protocol for performing field worker exposure
    studies. This protocol was published in 1985.
2. Supported and assisted EPA in the development of a joint NACA -
    EPA - public generic data base.
3. Developed and coordinated research to improve exposure moni-
    toring technology (e.g., R. Fenske's research on Fluorescent
    Tracer Technology).
4. Interacted with state and federal regulatory agencies to resolve
    issues of mutual interest on mixer-loader-applicator exposure
    assessment.

The communication with EPA in the development of the worker-exposure
protocol and the generic data base have been timely and have had
some impact on regulatory policy at EPA in recent months. This is
reflected in the fact that the NACA protocol and EPA Subpart U
guidelines are quite similar. In addition the EPA-NACA - public
data base will save industry considerable resources in time and
money on future exposure studies.

Development of the NACA Protocol for Conducting Mixer-Loader-Applicator Exposure Studies

The NACA protocol on worker exposure was developed between 1983-1985
by the NACA submcommittee. The objectives of the protocol were to
standardize the methodology for field exposure studies within industry and give direction to new researchers in this field.
        The NACA protocol is consistent with the WHO protocol on worker
exposure. Comments on the NACA protocol were also solicited from
EPA and it is generally felt among the subcommittee members that the
Applicator Exposure Monitoring Guidelines (Subpart U) published by
EPA in 1987 (1) reflect many methods similar to those in the NACA
protocol.

A listing of the general contents of the NACA protocol follows:

1. Evaluation of the need for a field study.
2. Procedures for administration of a field exposure study, e.g.,
    selection of the work crew.
3. While the general nature of the protocol is standardization,
    exposure assessment techniques are flexible giving the
    researcher some latitude in methodology.
4. Field data collection forms are presented in order to standard-
    ize reporting and add quality assurance. Calculation methods
    are also included.
5. Appendices are attached which provide detailed methodology for
    researchers with little experience in this field.

These NACA guidelines point out that the existing patch method of
exposure assessment, while theoretically not the most reliable method, is the method of choice in the U.S. The NACA protocol recog-
nizes the short comings of such an empirical method. However, the
only current alternative, Biological Monitoring, while theoretically
the superior method, has not been developed to a point of general
implementation or to a point of regulatory impact. This indirect

method requires considerable support studies to make the data inter-
pretable. Such studies are discussed below and as you will see are
complex and expensive.

A Discussion of Specific Field Methods as Recommended by the NACA
Protocol for Mixer-Loader-Applicator Exposure Assessment

Measuring Inhalation Exposure: Currently in the U.S. industry it is
recognized that inhalation exposure to pesticides is only a small
fraction (1%) of dermal exposure. There are, however, a few instances when inhalation exposure can be critical such as a Category
I pesticide that may be highly volatile. In this case respirator
protection will be required.
     Inhalation exposure is somewhat difficult to measure in a field
study. The NACA protocol preferred method is to use personal sampling devices which are calibrated to an airflow of 4 liters/minute.
Appropriate calibration and retention controls are necessary to
validate this method. Modified Respirators utilizing gauze pads as
described by Duhram and Wolf are acceptable but have some disadvantages, such as ease of contamination and inconvenience to the test
subject.

Measuring Dermal Exposure: The NACA protocol calls for use of the
classical patch method to measure dermal exposure. Gauze pads or
-cellulose pads are commonly used with a backing material such as
aluminum foil or a plastic film. Patches are generally placed inside or outside the clothing. Recent advances in technology have
shown that patches can be covered with a chambray or denim cover to
simulate inside patches. These "inside" patches as well as
uncovered patches can all be worn on the outside of work clothing
for convenience.
     It is now recognized that hand exposure is the major component
of total exposure for mixer-loaders and is far greater than for any
other type of exposure involving pesticides. Hand wash procedures
for measuring hand exposure are commonly used in the industry. Hand
exposure can also be measured by using adsorbent cotton gloves,
although this technique may overestimate exposure.

Calculating Total Dermal Exposure from Patch Data: Total dermal
exposure is generally calculated using individual patch data. The
amount of pesticide per cm^2 on a patch is multiplied by the specific
body area in question (e.g., chest, neck, arm, leg, etc.). This
procedure may lead to considerable error if patches are small.
Thus, it is desirable to maximize the size of the patches used.
These elemental exposures are then summed to give total body exposure. It is preferable to express results in terms of amount of
exposure per pound ai handled or per load handled. Maximum exposure
values are calculated by determining the total pounds handled/day or
the number of loads/day.

Measuring Exposure Using Biological Monitoring: The term biological
monitoring refers to any method which derives exposure from measuring parent or metabolites in body fluids. The use of biological
monitoring is the most effective means for measuring total dose or

body burden. Use of this technique resolves many problems associated with the patch technique including overestimation of dermal
exposure. The NACA protocol considers Biological Monitoring to be
an indirect method and must be accompanied by adequate supporting
studies to define the absorption, metabolism, pharmacokinetics and
excretion of the parent/metabolites in humans or an appropriate
surrogate animal. These studies define the quantitative relationship between dose and excretion of the pesticide and its metabolites. I will briefly describe these requirements below:

Criteria for Utilization of Biological Monitoring

A. Dermal Absorption - Dermal absorption studies should be per-
    formed on appropriate species (the use of rats, monkeys or pigs
    are common). In vitro dermal absorption studies are gaining in
    popularity. The pesticide in question must be absorbed to an
    appropriate extent over an 8-hour work day before biological
    monitoring can be used as an effective tool.

B. Pharmacokinetics - Pharmacokinetic and excretion kinetics in
    appropriate surrogate animals or man must be understood. Multi-
    ple species should be tested since the chance of one species
    excretion pattern being different from the other is consider-
    able. Ideally, excretion of parent/metabolites should occur
    over the first 24 hours after oral dosing and within a few days
    after dermal dosing. In addition, a large percentage of the
    dose should be excreted into urine.

C. Analytical Method - The analytical method must measure excreted
    parent and metabolites and account for a large percentage of the
    excreted compounds. The sensitivity of the analytical method
    must be enough to detect exposure at and below the toxicological
    end point concentration. Extensive metabolism makes biological
    monitoring extremely difficult and makes it expensive to develop
    supporting pharmacokinetic and analytical methods.

D. Convenience to and Cooperation of Field Workers - Urine moni-
    toring of agricultural workers is difficult. Collecting 24-hour
    urines carries with it considerable loss of control of the
    experiment since workers generally take a casual attitude toward
    their responsibility. Activity patterns may also appreciably
    change urinary output by altering perspiration rates. Also,
    liquid intake can alter urine output. Measurement of creatinine
    (WHO protocol) can overcome some of these potential problems
    since creatinine excretion is constant over time and measurement
    allows one to estimate total excretion volume.

    Additional problems may arise if urine samples are to be taken
    on a long-term basis. Of course, Biological Monitoring of body
    tissues such as blood is an intrusive method and should always
    be accompanied by medical surveillance and supervision to avoid
    potential problems.

Costs for Biological Monitoring:

1. Dermal Absorption Studies

   Rat Model   - $70,000
   Monkey Model   - $100,000
   In Vitro Models - $25,000

2. Pharmacokinetic Excretion Studies

   Rat Model   - $65,000
   Monkey Model   - $20,000

3. Analytical Method Development

   Metabolism Studies (2 species) - $200,000
   Method Development
     2 Major Metabolites   - $40,000
     Multiple Metabolites - $100,000
   Method Validation   - $10,000

Examples of Uses of Biological Monitoring of Pesticides by Industry:
There are a few companies which have developed biological monitoring
for specific pesticides and for specific purposes.

Dow Chemical - Scientists at Dow Chemical were some of the first to
develop urine monitoring as a tool for exposure assessment. In a
1982 review article by Leng, Levy and others (2), it was shown that
exposure to 2.4,5T could be measured reliably and in fact urinary
excretion provided a more reliable measure of dose than analysis of
patch data.

Monsanto - Scientists at Monsanto have recently performed supporting
studies for biological monitoring of Lasso® for mixer-loader applicators. These supporting studies meet many of the criteria listed
above. Researchers at Monsanto point out that multiple species
studies are of great importance in their experience and that when
appropriate supporting studies are performed, patch and urine data
are quite compatible.

CIBA-GEIGY - Scientists at CIBA-GEIGY have utilized biological monitoring in a highly practical manner. Over the past seven years,
some 50,000 urine samples from aerial applicators/mixer-loaders have
been analyzed to determine chlordimeform exposure. A discussion of
the results of these monitoring studies are beyond the scope of this
presentation. However, the supporting studies which were used to
develop the biological monitoring system meet many of the criteria
listed above and the program is one of the few that has been used to
study an entire population of workers using biological monitoring.
This extensive program has overcome one serious problem of the patch
method, i.e., doing enough replications to achieve a representative
portion of the population of workers and their work habits.

Development of a Generic Data Base to Estimate Mixer-Loader-Applicator Exposure

Development of a generic exposure data base is one of the major projects which the NACA subcommittee on exposure assessment has been working on for 2 years. This data base was first proposed during a NACA subcommittee meeting and put forth at a pesticide division symposium at the ACS meeting in St. Louis, Missouri in 1983 (3). Later, NACA and EPA agreed to jointly develop this data base. Public groups were invited to participate in this project.

The purpose of the generic data base is to provide equivalent mixer-loader-applicator exposure data to EPA, industry and the public in order to standardize exposure estimates. It is well recognized that mixer-loader-applicator exposure is a function of formulation and type of applicator equipment and that a data base could be developed to coordinate all available exposure data for worker exposure and risk assessment. This would add statistical credibility to small pockets of data which in themselves were weak in credibility mainly due to the number of replicates performed.

Ground rules for development of the data base have been laid out over the past year in several meetings between EPA and NACA representatives. EPA has contributed $145,000 and Canada regulatory officials $40,000 (Canadian). EPA is committed to the data base development and will regulate with the data. Criteria have been selected to evaluate all studies for acceptability into the data base. Both industry and academic studies will be evaluated. Data will be entered and retrieved on a patch by patch basis. The user can build a "Body Parts" surrogate model for any scenario desired (e.g., protected vs. nonprotected).

There are several advantages for EPA, the public and industry to have this data base in place.

1. Data at EPA on which regulatory decisions are based will be expanded and its credibility strengthened. Also, the reliability and statistical power of the Agency's risk assessments for workers will be improved.
2. Industry will incur cost savings of $200,000–$500,000 per year since EPA will not require field studies where sufficient data exists to perform a surrogate estimate.
3. Use of a mutually agreed upon data base will reduce contention in the exposure of the risk assessment process.
4. Public use of the data base will result in a better understanding of the risk assessment process for agricultural chemicals.

The NACA - EPA joint committee has made significant progress over the past few months in implementation of the data base. VERSAR, Inc. has agreed to review studies with developed criteria of validity and to input the data into storage. Retrieval by industry will be through computer hookup. Retrieval by EPA and the public will be through the NTIS.

Future Research Issues for the NACA Subcommittee

The NACA subcommittee on exposure will continue to monitor the progress of the data base as well as look at other exposure issues;
areas such as Biological Monitoring will be high on our list of
activities. Other activities will be to address reentry research as
well as research in dermal penetration, improvement in exposure
assessment technology (Fenske) and research in exposure reduction
technology.

Conclusions:

1. NACA ad hoc subcommittee on pesticide worker exposure is and
    will continue to address procedures for measuring worker expo-
    sure.
2. NACA guidelines for exposure assessment have been developed and
    agree in principle with EPA Subpart U.
3. A generic exposure data base is being developed and should be in
    place by mid 1988.
4. In the future the NACA subcommittee will address; reentry; Bio-
    logical Monitoring; improved exposure assessment technology and
    exposure reduction technology.

REFERENCES

1. Reinert, J. C. et. al., Pesticide Assessment Guidelines, Sub-
    division U, Applicator Exposure Monitoring, U.S. Environmental
    Protection Agency, October 1986.

2. Leng, M. L., Ramsey, J. C., Braun, W. H., Lavy, T. L. "Review
    of Studies with 2,4,5-Trichlorophenoxyacetic acid in Humans
    Including Applicators under Field Conditions," American Chemical
    Symposium Series 182, p. 133-156, Editor: J. Plimmer, American
    Chemical Society, Washington, D.C. (1982).

3. Hackathorn, D. R., Eberhart, D. C., "Data Base Proposal for Use
    in Predicting Mixer-Loader-Applicator Exposure," American
    Chemical Society Symposium Series 273, p. 341-351, Editors:
    Honeycutt, R. C., Zweig, G., Ragsdale, N. N., American Chemical
    Society, Washington, D.C. (1985).

RECEIVED June 7, 1988

Author Index

Affiliation Index

Subject Index

Production and Indexing by Colleen P. Stamm
Jacket design by Alan Kahan

Elements typeset by Hot Type Ltd., Washington, DC
Printed and bound by Maple Press, York, PA

Recent ACS Books

Biotechnology and Materials Science: Chemistry for the Future
Edited by Mary L. Good
160 pp; clothbound; ISBN 0–8412–1472–7

Chemical Demonstrations: A Sourcebook for Teachers
Volume 1, Second Edition by Lee R. Summerlin and James L. Ealy, Jr.
192 pp; spiral bound; ISBN 0–8412–1481–6
Volume 2, Second Edition by Lee R. Summerlin, Christie L. Borgford, and Julie B. Ealy
229 pp; spiral bound; ISBN 0 8412 1535 9

The Language of Biotechnology: A Dictionary of Terms
By John M. Walker and Michael Cox
ACS Professional Reference Book; 256 pp;
clothbound, ISBN 0–8412–1489–1; paperback, ISBN 0–8412–1490–5

Cancer: The Outlaw Cell, Second Edition
Edited by Richard E. LaFond
274 pp; clothbound, ISBN 0–8412–1419–0; paperback, ISBN 0–8412–1420–4

Chemical Structure Software for Personal Computers
Edited by Daniel E. Meyer, Wendy A. Warr, and Richard A. Love
ACS Professional Reference Book; 107 pp;
clothbound, ISBN 0–8412–1538–3; paperback, ISBN 0–8412–1539–1

Practical Statistics for the Physical Sciences
By Larry L. Havlicek
ACS Professional Reference Book; 198 pp; clothbound; ISBN 0–8412–1453–0

The Basics of Technical Communicating
By B. Edward Cain
ACS Professional Reference Book; 198 pp; clothbound; ISBN 0–8412–1451–4

The ACS Style Guide: A Manual for Authors and Editors
Edited by Janet S. Dodd
264 pp; clothbound; ISBN 0–8412–0917–0

Personal Computers for Scientists: A Byte at a Time
By Glenn I. Ouchi
276 pp; clothbound; ISBN 0–8412–1000–4

Chemistry and Crime: From Sherlock Holmes to Today's Courtroom
Edited by Samuel M. Gerber
135 pp; clothbound; ISBN 0–8412–0784–4

For further information and a free catalog of ACS books, contact:
American Chemical Society
Distribution Office, Department 225
1155 16th Street, NW, Washington, DC 20036
Telephone 800–227–5558

R A
12 70
P 4
B531
19 89

CHEMISTRY
LIBRARY

RETURN TO: CHEMISTRY LIBRARY
Hildebrand Hall

DEC 18